TURF MANAGEMENT

TURF MANAGEMENT

A Publication of

The United States  *Golf Association*

by H. BURTON MUSSER
Professor Emeritus of Agronomy, The College of Agriculture
Pennsylvania State University

McGRAW-HILL BOOK COMPANY, INC.
New York Toronto London

TURF MANAGEMENT

REVISED EDITION

Library of Congress Catalog Card Number: 61-17144

VI

44134

Preface

Many valuable additions have been made to our knowledge of the turf grasses and their management during the past two decades. A principal source of information has been the experimental work of the United States Golf Association Green Section. This has been supplemented by research on turf problems at many state agricultural experiment stations and other research institutions and by careful study of practical phases of turf management by experienced observers. Unfortunately, much of this information is widely scattered in various publications of the Green Section, in technical journals, in trade magazines, and in the publications of other organizations interested in turf problems. Many of these do not have general distribution and are not readily available.

The United States Golf Association, recognizing the need for a comprehensive and easily accessible source of information on turf-management problems, has sponsored the preparation of *Turf Management.* It is hoped that the book may be a useful guide and practical reference for growing turf that will meet the requirements of the game.

Editorial boards appointed by the Association have reviewed and approved the subject matter of all chapters in both the first edition and this revision. The author is deeply indebted to each member of the boards, and particularly to O. J. Noer, for the many helpful suggestions and constructive criticisms made during the preparation of the manuscript.

Sincere thanks are due, also, to the many writers on turf problems whose published material has appeared in various scientific and popular journals. The following publications have been the most prolific sources of information:

Bulletin, United States Golf Association Green Section
Turf Culture, United States Golf Association Green Section

Timely Turf Topics, United States Golf Association Green Section
Journal, United States Golf Association
Journal, American Society of Agronomy
The Golf Course Reporter
Golfdom

Marshall E. Farnham, golf-course superintendent at the Philadelphia Country Club and past president of the National Greenkeeping Superintendents Association, prepared Chap. 11, Golf-course Operation, in collaboration with superintendents T. M. Baumgartner, The Sea Island Company; Ray Gerber, Glen Oaks Country Club; W. H. Glover, Fairfax Golf Club; and E. W. Van Gorder, Stanford University golf course. The editorial board recognized that practical day-to-day operations on the golf course could be discussed best by the individuals responsible for this phase of management. The above-named superintendents were invited to write the chapter because of their recognized professional ability and their knowledge of conditions in their respective localities. They are to be congratulated upon their broad approach to this difficult subject and their clear and concise presentation of sound and efficient operating procedures.

H. B. MUSSER

Contents

Foreword

The idea of creating the United States Golf Association Green Section was conceived by E. J. Marshall, an attorney of Toledo, Ohio, in September, 1920. Mr. Marshall was chairman of the Green Committee of the Inverness Club, where the Open Championship had been held in August, 1920, and no doubt his work in preparing Inverness for the Open stimulated him to envision a turf research and advisory agency of national scope—an impartial agency which could speak with authority. Marshall first discussed the idea with Hugh Wilson, a member of the Executive Committee of the United States Golf Association from Philadelphia, and his brother, Alan D. Wilson, at a meeting attended also by Dr. C. V. Piper and Dr. R. A. Oakley of the United States Department of Agriculture. As a result of this conference, Drs. Piper and Oakley were requested to take up the proposition with the United States Department of Agriculture and Hugh Wilson to present it to the United States Golf Association Executive Committee. Both missions were successful. The creation of the present Green Section of the USGA was authorized by its Executive Committee on November 30, 1920. Its formation was announced and the first bulletin appeared on February 10, 1921. Hugh Wilson had been succeeded on the USGA Executive Committee in January, 1921, by Alan Wilson, who thus became the first Chairman of the Green Section.

Over the years the cooperative arrangement between the United States Department of Agriculture and the United States Golf Association resulted in many experiments, first at the government test plots at Arlington, Virginia, and later at Beltsville, Maryland, which have resulted in finer turf for golf courses and better and more economical management by greenkeepers. Hundreds of thousands of dollars have been expended by the United States Golf Association in the work. In later years the Green Section helped to bring about expansion of experimental work on turf problems at many leading colleges and other research institutions, and has been active in assembling and coordinating experimental results.

This book was conceived by the late Fielding Wallace, Chairman of the Green Section Committee for many years and later President of the United States Golf Association, and H. Alfred Langben, when a member of the Green Section Committee and Chairman of the Turf Management Committee. Its function is to interpret the results of the experimental work on special-purpose turf conducted by the Green Section and other research agencies and to explain modern turf-propagation and maintenance practices. Great credit for the manuscript is due the author and editor, Prof. H. B. Musser, Professor Emeritus of Agronomy at the Pennsylvania State University, and to the editorial board for the first edition, consisting of Dr. Fred V. Grau, then Director of the Green Section; Herb Graffis, editor of the magazine *Golfdom;* O. J. Noer, agronomist for the Sewerage Commission, City of Milwaukee; and Marshall E. Farnham, formerly President of the National Greenkeeping Superintendents Association. The editorial board for this revised edition comprised William C. Chapin, Chairman of the USGA Green Section Committee; Agronomist-Directors of the USGA Green Section, William H. Bengeyfield, Marvin H. Ferguson, Charles K. Hallowell, A. M. Radko, and Joseph C. Dey, Jr., USGA Executive Director.

It is the hope of the United States Golf Association Green Section that this presentation will be of assistance to green committee chairmen, golf course superintendents, and others interested in the development of turf and that it will prove of value in a field where, heretofore, no comparable textbook has existed.

THE UNITED STATES GOLF ASSOCIATION

TURF MANAGEMENT

1

Broad Relationships in the Production of Special-purpose Turf

Three major factors control the production of good turf on the golf course. These are climate, soil, and management. Each is responsible for a whole series of direct effects upon the growth and quality of grass. Any one of them may be modified extensively by the others. This interdependence is of great practical importance in turf culture since adjustments in one set of conditions may compensate for deficiencies in the others. Even unfavorable climatic effects may be softened materially in this way. While it is true that not much can be done about the weather, it also follows that the response of turf to temperature and moisture depends directly upon a wide variety of soil conditions and management practices. An understanding of the influence of the major factors of climate, soil, and management upon turf production and an appreciation of the modifying effects of these upon each other are the first essentials for successful turf culture.

Growing good turf on the golf course implies not only a thorough knowledge of the relationship and response of grass to its environment and the way in which it is handled, but also an ability to adjust these to the demands of play. Unfortunately, there are many points at which the demands of the game and the results of play are directly contrary to what is best for the grass. Close clipping, for example, of such grasses as Kentucky blue and fescues adversely affects their persistence and ability to produce a satisfactory turf. Soil compaction, resulting from equipment operation and play under unfavorable conditions, may necessitate wide modifications of maintenance practices to compensate for their injurious effects. Tees are a particularly good illustration of how heavy use may affect turf quality and require adjustment of normal operations. The damage caused by constant abrasion from spikes on players' shoes, plus divot scars which are concentrated on limited areas, requires both the choice of grasses which will heal rapidly and a nice adjustment of maintenance to obtain quick renovation.

Because of the special requirements involved, the details of producing turf on the golf course are much more intensive and complex than those acceptable for home lawns, cemeteries, parks, and similar general turf areas. Successful management not only must adjust operations and practices to take full advantage of the normal responses of grass to soil and climatic environment, it must also employ a wide variety of techniques designed to correct or to modify environmental deficiencies created by the use to which the turf is subjected.

Finally, modern turf management on the golf course is concerned with the economics of growing grass. With the expansion of the game of golf into a national sport, cost considerations have become increasingly important. Good management requires an ability to make accurate budget estimates and to operate on a business basis. This involves all the details of labor supervision as well as efficient equipment operation. It also requires the keeping of detailed time and cost records so that accurate accountings may be made periodically.

Climatic Relationships

Based on the broad general climatic adaptations of the turf grasses, the United States may be divided into four regions. These are the Northern Cool Humid, the Southern Warm Humid, the Southwest Irrigated, and the West Central Areas of Limited Rainfall. In each region there are groups of grasses that are particularly adapted to the prevailing climatic conditions. Regional boundaries, however, are not absolute. Some grasses can be used far beyond the normal regional limits of adaptation because of a tolerance to temperature and moisture extremes greater than the average for the species.

The approximate regional boundaries of climatic adaptation of the turf grasses are outlined in the accompanying map (Fig. 1). In general the bluegrasses, fescues, and bents are the best adapted perennial grasses for the Northern Cool Humid region. Bermuda,

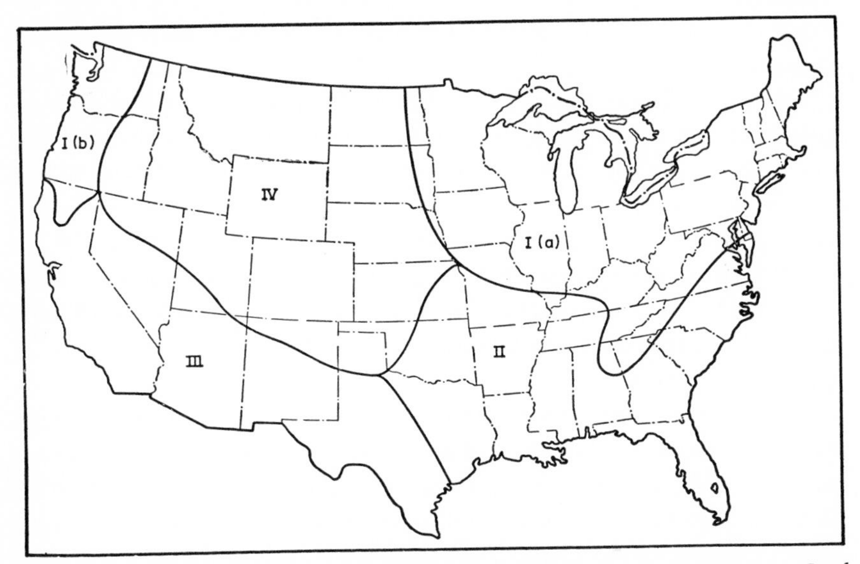

FIG. 1. General regions of grass adaptation. I(*a*) and I(*b*): Northern Cool Humid. II: Southern Warm Humid. III: Southwest Irrigated. IV: West Central.

carpet, centipede, St. Augustine, and the zoysia grasses are the most important species in the Warm Humid and Irrigated regions. In the West Central region of limited rainfall a group of species consisting of western wheatgrass, crested wheatgrass, buffalograss, and the grama grasses are of the greatest value under natural conditions.

In all three regions temperature and moisture are the major climatic factors controlling species adaptation. Temperature is by far the more important of these because in the large majority of cases sufficient moisture can be supplied through irrigation to maintain a satisfactory turf even in the driest areas. Thus Bermuda, zoysia, and the other grasses of the Warm Humid region will produce excellent turf under irrigation in the Southwest. Similarly, the bents, fescues, and bluegrasses will do well in the West Central region if sufficient water is supplied. On the other hand, grasses adapted to regions of limited rainfall may be questionable for turf production under humid conditions. In the few instances where critical observations have been made on the performance of these species in humid areas, results have not been very satisfactory. It is possible that factors not as yet thoroughly understood, such as disease susceptibility and soil-fertility levels, are the controlling influences in their apparent inability to adapt themselves readily to conditions outside their normal climatic range.

Soil Relationships

Since it is possible to control climatic conditions only to a limited extent, a consideration of the relationships of soil to the growing of grass assumes major importance. The principle that the more unfavorable one set of cultural conditions is, the more favorable all others must be is particularly applicable to turf production. Soil conditions may be modified to compensate for unfavorable climate. Although many soil characteristics are the result of climatic conditions, they may be altered to an extent that will adapt them to satisfactory turf production. Thus, acidity may be corrected by the use of lime, available nutrients may be maintained at a high level by fertilizer applications, and physical conditions may be improved by drainage, cultivation, and the use of organic materials. On the limited areas of greens and tees, soil texture may be extensively modified by additions of sand to heavy soils, and silt or clay to light soils. Aeration may be improved by various mechanical methods, and soil moisture may be increased by irrigation. It is practicable on small areas materially to reduce the effects of excess moisture by providing for increased permeability and complete underdrainage.

There are relatively narrow differences among the various species of special-purpose grasses in their adaptation to soil conditions. The bentgrasses, for example, will survive longer on more acid soils than will Kentucky bluegrass. It is significant, however, that the soil-reaction range that is most desirable for Kentucky bluegrass also is favorable to the bents. Similarly, the fescues have comparatively low moisture requirements in contrast with other species in their region of adaptation, but they will make their best growth where available moisture supplies are good. Broadly speaking, fertile soils that are permeable and yet of good water-holding capacity in the root-zone area, with relatively rapid subsoil drainage, are the most satisfactory for all the important species of turf grasses. Some soils possess an especially wide range of grass adaptation because they closely approach these requirements, and it is desirable to select such types for turf use whenever possible. It should be emphasized, however, that excellent turf can be maintained on soils that are far from ideal, especially where climatic conditions are favorable, where one makes a wise choice of grasses, and where it is practicable to correct existing deficiencies by adequate treatment.

Importance of Management

Management, the third major factor in the production of special-purpose turf, covers the complete series of techniques involved in grass establishment, maintenance, and renovation. As previously noted, it is particularly important on the golf course, because of the complex relationship between the normal influences of soil and climate and the demands of the game. Good management fits the very specialized problems of turf production to the basic and fundamental facts of grass adaptations and requirements. It consists, first, of a thorough understanding and application of the relatively simple operations of planting, clipping, fertilizing, watering, and similar normal practices. It also demands a high level of ability to apply and adapt these practices to conditions which frequently are very poor for normal turf development.

Further than this, management has the problem of adjusting labor and equipment to meet budget requirements. Establishment and maintenance costs of the high-quality turf demanded by modern golf admittedly are great. Where budgets are limited, it happens frequently that they will not cover the costs of all the items necessary to the development of first-class playing conditions.

Good management will recognize the relative importance of all these items and concentrate upon those which will achieve the greatest results for each dollar available.

The Basis of a Management Program

On the golf course, turf management begins with the start of construction operations and progresses through all the processes of soil preparation, seeding, and the recurring items of day-to-day care. The part which construction plays is perhaps worthy of particular note at this point. Those experienced in turf-maintenance problems fully appreciate that many of these can be entirely eliminated, or at least materially reduced, if construction details are adjusted to turf requirements.

The development of a sound management program rests on two bases: (1) knowing how to do the job, and (2) knowing the "why" of it. The first of these is the art of greenkeeping. It is founded upon experience and requires a knowledge of the mechanics of all the operations concerned with the growing of grass and an ability to perform them efficiently and in a timely manner. The second is the science of turf production. It is based on the fundamental principles of plant growth and development and is concerned chiefly with the underlying reasons back of the practices which constitute the art of successful turf building and maintenance.

Both the art and science of turf management have developed rapidly during the last three decades. Among the factors primarily responsible for this development are an increased interest in the broad uses of special-purpose turf and the beginnings of a realization of the magnitude of the services which it involves. The art of growing grass has made particularly rapid strides. This is perhaps best evidenced in the field of laborsaving equipment. The power shovel and bulldozer have replaced the horse-drawn scoop and pick and shovel in construction operations. The nine-gang tractor-drawn mower, cutting a swath of approximately 20 ft. at a speed of 6 to 8 miles per hour, has solved the clipping problem. Pop-up irrigation systems which will water large areas of the course by the turn of a single valve are becoming increasingly common, and high-pressure sprayers have completely replaced the sprinkling can and gravity-flow barrel. These, and similar developments in many other fields, emphasize the progress which has been made.

Notable gains also have been made in the development of a sound body of facts to serve as a basis for practical operations. The background of these has been an intelligent analysis of existing conditions on many golf courses in widely separated areas and an ever-growing number of carefully controlled experiments at research institutions. Here are some of the more important items which can be included in the record of progress. Organized breeding programs for the production of better strains of the most useful species of grasses are underway and have resulted in improved types of bent, bluegrass, fescue, Bermudagrass, and the zoysia grasses. By using information available from fertilizer experiments on pastures and other agricultural crops, supplemented with a limited number of controlled tests on turf, progress has been made in developing sound feeding practices. This applies particularly to such items as fertilizer quality and the time and rate of treatment. The value of lime for correcting soil acidity, the use of materials such as peat for improving poor physical condition, and the need for good drainage to grow healthy turf are becoming generally recognized. In the field of pest control, successful methods have been developed for eliminating or materially reducing the damage caused by disease, insects, and weeds.

In spite of the progress that has been made much remains to be done. Better types of tee and fairway grasses are needed which can stand abuse and resist attacks of diseases and pests for which there are no good methods of control. Disease resistance in putting-green grasses also is needed. This not only would greatly simplify maintenance but also would reduce the danger of turf injury from poor-quality or insufficiently tested fungicidal materials. In this latter connection a new problem has arisen. An almost endless stream of new chemicals for pest control is being offered for use on turf. In many cases there are no satisfactory performance records available to guide prospective users. A standardized testing and screening program for such products is a necessity.

More and better information also is needed on methods and materials for improving soil aeration and permeability. Some of the major problems here include conditioning materials, effects of subgrade construction, methods and results of turf tillage, and equipment modifications to reduce compaction. Closely allied to these is the problem of the use of water for irrigation. This is particularly troublesome in those sections of the country having the heavier types of soils. It will not be possible to water without danger of injury until more is known about the effects of soil saturation on the various grasses under the wide range of environmental and use conditions to which they are subjected. We should know more, also, about the relative effects of watering in stimulating weeds, clover, and other undesirable plants at the expense of the grasses.

Considerable progress has been made in the field of turf fertilization, but the job has not been completed. There remain such practical questions as the best nutrient ratios of the basic plant-food elements, the possible effects of potash and other materials on disease incidence, and the response of the grasses to a long list of minor and trace elements known to be necessary to plant growth. Unfortunately, the fertilizer practices acceptable for general agricultural crops cannot always be applied to turf without major changes, because of the use and abuse which turf receives. It is not the basic principles underlying sound fertilizer practice which constitute the problem, but the way in which these must be applied.

Finally, the greatest question of all is how best to get the answers to the many individual problems on which a sound turf-management program must be based. The production of good turf on the golf course is a practical job. The first consideration is to provide good playing conditions. While there is no doubt that much has been learned and can be learned from intelligent observation of the effects of day-to-day operations, it seems obvious that time and cost limitations will prevent any extensive experimentation by the individual club. The United States Golf Association has recognized this difficulty and has provided for the critical study of turf problems by its Green Section Committee. The major functions of this body are to conduct original investigations, to encourage and correlate studies at other research institutions for the development of sound turf-production principles, and to report the results of experimentation and interpret them in terms of their practical applications. Many local and regional golf associations are cooperating with the parent organization in this work. The Golf Course Superintendents Association and the Professional Golfer's Association which are national in scope, as well as local and regional turf groups, also have been vitally interested in the efforts to secure adequate solutions of technical and practical turf problems.

All of these agencies have been active in their support of research at state agricultural experiment stations and other institutions. In some instances, they have made liberal financial contributions to aid in the establishment and maintenance of turf experiments. This organized approach to the problems of turf management is a happy sign that within the foreseeable future the individual golf-course superintendent can build a program for the production and care of grass based upon a sound body of facts and with reasonable insurance against failure.

2

Soil and Turf Relationships

The physical and chemical properties of the soil affect most of the practical operations of growing and maintaining turf. For example, the quantity of water that a soil can store depends upon such characteristics as the size of the soil particles and the amount of organic matter in it. Similarly, the value of fertilizers is controlled by the chemical soil conditions, such as acidity, which determines how much of the plant food in the fertilizer can be used by the grass. Many such soil qualities can be modified to provide better conditions for turf production. This chapter is designed to provide a working knowledge of the nature of these, and of their relationship to turf establishment and maintenance, so that the best possible adjustment of them can be made to insure good grass-growing conditions.

Basic Soil Conditions for Good Turf

The basic soil conditions for good turf are (1) a suitable surface for the preparation of a seedbed, (2) good physical properties (aeration and drainage) for the development of a deep root system, (3) sufficient moisture-holding capacity to meet the needs of the particular grasses used, (4) adequate fertility to get grass off to a good start and for growth afterward, (5) favorable conditions for the activity of desirable soil organisms, and (6) freedom from harmful chemical qualities.

1. Grass needs a well-prepared seedbed. It should be firm and reasonably fine. The presence of rock outcrops and large boulders may seriously hinder tillage operations. The removal of stumps, roots, and other undesirable material is essential but may be impractical because of excessive costs. Heavy, intractable clays sometimes cannot be worked adequately, except with heavy equipment, and cannot be properly prepared unless extensively modified with sand or peat, which is expensive. The danger of excessive erosion during the period of soil preparation and seed germination must be considered in determining whether the site can be used with a fair chance of success.

2. Grass roots need air for healthy, normal growth. They get it from the open spaces (soil pores) between the soil particles. A soil is not suitable for growing grass when the individual particles are so small and are packed together so tightly that the air spaces between them are limited. Soils are unsatisfactory when they are poorly drained because of impervious subsoil, a high water table, or poor structure. All these factors cause water to fill the pore spaces, at the expense of air.

3. Soils vary widely in moisture-holding capacity owing to differences in the size and arrangement of the individual particles and in the quantity of organic matter present. Where irrigation is not practical, the soil must be able to supply sufficient water for the grass during dry periods. It also must contain sufficient moisture for many of the fundamental processes that affect soil fertility.

4. Soils must supply plant food for turf growth throughout the entire playing season. When natural soil fertility is low, needed plant food can be provided by fertilization. The important thing is to recognize the necessity for adequate fertility and devise a feeding program that will meet the grass requirements.

5. Soil conditions must be favorable for the development of beneficial soil organisms. Many of the processes by which nutrient materials are made soluble and available for plant use are controlled by them.

Soils also harbor the organisms responsible for turf diseases and insects that feed upon the grass. Their abundance and activity depend in part upon factors such as soil acidity, aeration, drainage, and fertility levels.

6. The soil must be free from conditions and substances that

injure turf. These include high acidity or alkalinity and the presence of excessive quantities of soluble salts or amounts of individual nutrient materials which may interfere with the ability of the grass to use others. Materials essential for plant growth may be detrimental when present in large quantities. For example, excessive amounts of available nitrogen are definitely injurious, particularly to seedling grass. Many of the trace elements are extremely toxic when present in more than minute amounts. The accumulation in soils of poisonous chemicals resulting from the use of herbicides, insecticides, and fungicides which have not been sufficiently tested must be considered.

All of these basic requirements for growing turf successfully may be met to a large degree by a good management program. Most of the physical and chemical soil factors affecting turf growth can be readily controlled, particularly on greens and other limited areas. A working knowledge of the way in which these properties of the soil operate is the foundation of successful turf production.

Physical Properties of Soils as Related to Turf Management

The soil mass is made up of three kinds of matter: (1) solid, the soil particles; (2) liquid, the soil water; and (3) gas, the soil air. The proportions of each and their effects upon one another are vital to the well-being of living plants and are particularly important to grass, because turf is relatively permanent. It is difficult to correct faulty physical soil conditions after sod becomes established. Recognition of this fact is responsible for the development of special practices and types of equipment designed to overcome soil compaction, to change soil texture, and to increase its organic matter content.

IDEAL PROPORTIONS OF SOIL SOLIDS, WATER, AND AIR. The particles or mineral fragments that constitute the solid portion of the soil vary in size from stones and gravel to minute bits of silt and clay. Under ideal conditions the clay particles adhere to each other to form groups, or compound granules. Such a soil is said to have good tilth. The open spaces (pores or voids) between the individual particles and granules contain the soil water and the air. A good soil should consist by volume of approximately 50 per cent solids and 50 per cent pore space. The amount of air and water should be about equal, or one-quarter each of the total volume. When total pore space exceeds 50 per cent, water drains out so fast that the soil is droughty and requires frequent irrigation. When pore space is much below 50 per cent, the soil waterlogs easily, because water moves through it too slowly.

FIG. 2. Effect of soil physical condition on rooting of grass on greens. Good physical condition and root penetration (left). Medium to poor physical condition and root penetration (center). Very poor physical condition and shallow roots (right). (*Green Section.*)

IMPORTANCE OF AIR. Grass roots need air because of the oxygen which it contains. The beneficial soil microbes require air and oxygen also. When water forces the air out of the pore spaces, soils become sour, desirable bacterial activity stops, available plant nutrients are reduced, and grass roots stay near the surface where they can obtain air. Turf with shallow and restricted roots cannot make full use of soil moisture or available nutrients below the top few inches. The grass is more susceptible to injury, to attacks by diseases and insects, and to weed encroachment.

SOIL WATER. The physical properties of soils affect the soil water in three distinct zones. These are (1) the surface layer, which controls water absorption; (2) the intermediate or root zone, which supplies water to the grass roots; and (3) the zone below the root system, which is a reservoir that replenishes the supply above by upward movement of water. This zone is important also because

FIG. 3. Good root system in a well-aerated Green. (*Courtesy Sewerage Commission, City of Milwaukee.*)

it controls the rate of movement of surplus water out of the root zone.

The size of the pore spaces in the soil regulates the rate of water movement. When heavy soils with a high percentage of small particles and small pore spaces are used for greens and tees, water absorption and movement is slow. Compaction caused by trampling, mowers and other equipment further reduces the size of pore spaces. It does the same thing on fairways where the soil is heavy. Slow water movement in compacted soils keeps them saturated for long periods. Air cannot reach the root zone, and standing water in depressions causes scald and other serious injury.

The relative size and shape of the soil particles, the amount of pore space, and the total volumes which each occupies determine the quantity of water available to plants. Water is present in the soil as gravitational, capillary, and hygroscopic water or moisture. Gravitational water moves freely through soil owing to the pull of gravity. It percolates into the subsoil and drains away. Capillary water is the water held in the pore spaces by capillary attraction after the gravitational water has moved out. The water available for plant growth comes from this source. The hygroscopic water is the portion which remains as condensed moisture on the particles after the capillary water is removed. It is small in amount and so tightly held that it is not available to plants.

Soils in the best physical condition to produce good turf have pore spaces which are large enough to permit the rapid draining away of the surplus (gravitational) water, but small enough to retain capillary supplies equal to about one-fourth of the total soil mass. Turf grows so long as an appreciable quantity of capillary water is present. The details of water usage will be discussed in the chapter on Drainage and Irrigation. It should be noted here that the relation of total pore space to the amount of water available to the grass has a very practical bearing on watering practices. The coarser, more open types of soil are less subject to compaction and are less likely to become waterlogged. If ample supplies of water are available and frequent watering is possible, it is desirable to use these coarser soils with larger pore spaces to ensure good aeration and drainage at all times.

The third soil zone, the subsoil below the root zone, affects the moisture conditions in the soil above it. If it consists of heavy tight clay, it will not let water drain through it fast enough and causes waterlogging and poor aeration. When greens or other turf areas stay wet and soggy, the subsoil below the root zone should be examined by taking deep plugs, to determine whether water is moving through it at a rate that will permit surplus water to drain out of the soil above it. It may be acting as a dam that keeps the water backed up in the root zone. Poor physical condition of the subsoil zone also will reduce the rate of upward capillary movement of water into the root zone. In periods of hot windy weather when surface drying and evaporation from the leaves is high, water losses are not replaced rapidly enough to prevent wilting of the grass. When water movement out of the subsoil is slow, light sprinkling or syringing of greens several times daily during hot dry weather is a means of supplementing root-zone moisture and reducing wilting injury.

THE MINERAL SOIL FRACTION. The mineral portion of the soil is composed of rock fragments resulting from the weathering of parent rock. The fragments range in size from stones and gravel to very minute clay particles. They are divided into seven groups called soil separates, based upon the average size of particles.

TABLE 1

SOIL SEPARATES

Group	*Particle Diameter, In.*
Very coarse sand	1/12 –1/25
Coarse sand	1/25 –1/50
Medium sand	1/50 –1/100
Fine sand	1/100–1/250
Very fine sand	1/250–1/500
Silt	1/500–1/5000
Clay	Less than 1/5000

Soils are grouped into texture classes based on the physical character and crop-producing power of the various sized particles. The main soil classes, in order from coarse to fine, are, sand, loamy sand, sandy loam, loam, silt loam, clay loam, and clay. In general, sandy soils contain an average of 75 per cent or more of the various types of sands with less than 20 per cent clay. The loam soils have approximately 50 per cent sand and 50 per cent silt and clay, with clay less than 30 per cent of the silt-clay total. Soils are classed as clay loams when they contain 20 to 30 per cent of clay particles, and as clay when the clay content is 30 per cent or more.

Grasses will grow on a wide range of textures, but loam soils with a minimum of clay particles are best. The approximately equal proportions of coarse and fine particles in these soils provide good aeration and water movement through them. Their content of small particles is sufficient to meet the needs of the grasses for adequate storage of moisture and plant nutrients.

Except in the medium and coarser sands, the soil grains are grouped together into clusters (granules) of different size and shape. The compound granules are much larger than the individual particles composing them. This granulated condition is particularly important in the heavier types of soil because it results in the development of larger pore spaces between the granules. It increases aeration and speeds drainage without impairing the effectiveness of the individual particles to retain moisture and nutrients. The best soils for grass have a good granular structure. Under nonuse conditions granulation will increase under turf. It is assisted by alternate freezing and thawing in winter and alternate wetting and drying in summer. Granular structure is reduced or destroyed by strong acidity, poor drainage, excessive rolling, tramping, and by tractors, mowers, and other heavy equipment.

ORGANIC MATTER. The organic portion of the soil consists of plant and animal residues in various stages of decay, living plant roots, microscopic organisms, worms, insects, and rodents. As the organic matter undergoes decay humus is formed. It is a dark-colored, odorless material, quite uniform in its physical characteristics, but without definite chemical composition. Humus contains a high percentage of very fine particles (colloids) which strongly affect the physical properties of soils. It improves structure by causing granulation and thereby improves aeration and drainage. Humus has a high capacity to store moisture and plant nutrients. Active organic matter is needed by soil microorganisms as a source of energy food. The solvent action of the carbonic acid generated during decay liberates insoluble soil nutrients and makes them usable by plants. An ample supply of organic matter reduces injury to growing plants by toxic substances and excessive quantities of soluble salts. Partially decomposed organic matter also increases surface resiliency. This is an important quality on greens where resilience is needed to hold pitch shots without overwatering.

Organic matter is high under grass sod, owing to the extensive root system of grasses and the fact that they produce a new crop of roots each year. The quantity of true humus is much lower and varies with the rate at which dead roots, stems, and leaves decay. Mineral soils seldom contain more than 10 per cent of true humus by weight, and the amount may be 1 per cent or less where decay is checked by conditions such as high acidity and poor drainage. Likewise soils are low in humus when conditions favor very rapid decay of organic matter. In such instances the humus is decomposed as rapidly as it is formed. In regions where moisture and temperature are favorable, complete decay of organic matter is most rapid in coarse sandy soils and they will contain little or no humus.

It is impossible to specify the optimum quantities of humus which soils should contain for best growth of grass. Amounts vary with different soils. Maintenance practices designed to increase humus naturally or to provide additions of organic matter must be devised to fit each soil. The use made of the turf also determines the quantity required. Greens and tees which receive much more intensive wear than fairways require larger quantities to maintain adequate conditions than are necessary for the less used fairways. Soils having satisfactory physical properties and good fertility will produce high-quality fairway turf at humus levels which develop under normal maintenance treatment. Additional humus above the levels already present in native soil is needed for greens and frequently for tees. It is required also in composts prepared as topdressing material for greens.

ORGANIC MATERIALS. Rotted manure, spent mushroom soil, peats, and by-products like tannery sludge, sewage sludge, ground cocoa shells, and similar materials which may be available locally can be used as supplementary sources of organic matter. Their general character and rates of decay must be considered in estimating their value. Manures, for example, consist of 70 to 80 per cent moisture and 20 to 30 per cent dry matter. They decay rapidly and within a comparatively short time only about 2 to 3 per cent of the original weight of material remains in the soil as humus. Spent mushroom soil supplies even less humus than manure. It is a mixture of spent manure with the casing soil placed on top of the mushroom beds. One hundred pounds of average-quality mushroom soil contains approximately 20 to 30 lb. of water, 60 to 70 lb. of mineral soil, and 10 to 15 lb. of organic matter. The organic matter is the rotted-manure portion of the mixture removed from the beds after a crop of mushrooms is harvested. In the preparation of top-dressing material, mushroom soil is valuable for use as the soil portion of the mixture but does not supply sufficient humus to justify its use to increase soil organic matter permanently. Most of the other organic by-product materials, such as sewage and tannery sludges, are of the same general character as manure. They break down rapidly and leave relatively little humus for permanent improvement.

The peats are desirable forms of organic matter. The best ones are the residues of marsh plants (reeds, sedges, and mosses) which have been preserved under water. The type of decomposition to which they have been subjected left them in a form that is highly resistant to further decay. As a result their beneficial effects on the soil extend over comparatively long periods. In tests at the Pennsylvania Experiment Station, better than 70 per cent of the organic matter added by mixing peat into a well-drained nonacid soil to a depth of 5 in. was still present after a 10-year period.

Peats vary considerably in structure, stage of decomposition, capacity to absorb water, organic-matter content, and reaction. The moisture-absorptive capacity and organic-matter content are the most important items from the standpoint of effects upon physical soil properties. Peat should absorb four to five times its dry weight of water, and the organic-matter content should be 90 per cent or more by weight on a dry-matter basis. Because of their high water-holding capacity peats may appear quite dry when their actual moisture content is as high as 60 or 70 per cent. The quantity of moisture should be considered in purchasing commercial material. Peats vary in reaction from pH 4.0 to 7.5 or higher. Lime should be applied when the acid types are used.

Commercial peats, commonly called humus, can be grouped into four main classes: (1) raw peats, (2) cultivated peats, (3) moss peats, and (4) sedimentary peats. Raw peat is the material just as it comes from the bog or bed, which has been processed by drying, shredding or pulverizing, and screening. Deposits are widely distributed throughout the entire eastern part of the United States.

Most of the commercial product comes from Minnesota, Wisconsin, Florida, and Michigan, but deposits have been found in many states and are being used to supply local demand. Tests of peats from a number of different sources indicate that all have about the same value as soil conditioners, if used on the basis of their dry organic-matter content.

Cultivated peat is raw peat that has been tilled to break it up mechanically and to hasten the rate of decay. Cultivation stimulates the development of organisms responsible for decomposition. In peat of this type some of the more readily decomposable materials have been lost and the residue is more resistant to further breakdown. Because of the additional decay to which it has been subjected it has lost some of the coarsely fibrous condition characteristic of the raw type and is closer in composition to true soil humus. The commercial material is in excellent physical condition for thorough mixing into the soil. Its commercial value depends upon its moisture content, its capacity to absorb water, and the amount of actual organic matter which it contains.

Moss peat is composed principally of sphagnum mosses which have undergone partial decay. It is finely fibrous and very light and fluffy. Unless well pulverized, it is in poor condition for mixing into soils. Moss peat contains a larger proportion of readily decomposable materials than the raw peats. Because of its higher rate of decomposition and its extremely light spongy character it is not so suitable a soil conditioner for turf use as the raw and cultivated peats.

The sedimentary peats have little value for soil conditioning. They are composed of high percentages of very fine particles of organic matter mixed with silt and clay, which have been deposited in shallow lakes and ponds. They are often sticky and plastic when wet and highly compact and hard when dry. Small local deposits of sedimentary peat are widely distributed and, in some instances, have been used on golf courses with disastrous results.

Many other materials have been used, or suggested for use, as physical conditioners of soils for growing turf. Among the more important of these are charcoal, sawdust, rice and buckwheat hulls, peanut hulls, fused cinders, and some of the mica products regularly used for packing and insulating purposes. Charcoal has been the most widely used of these materials. Its moisture-absorptive capacity is greater than that of mineral soils but much lower than good-quality peats. In comparative tests with peats it has been of less value for reducing compaction and increasing the porosity of heavy soils. Its intermediate value and high cost have largely eliminated it from consideration for turf use. Raw sawdusts should not be used for growing turf without first composting with soil for a sufficient period of time to ensure thorough rotting.

Attempts to use various by-product hulls such as cocoa shells and hulls from rice, peanuts, and buckwheat as soil conditioners have not been very satisfactory, unless they have been composted first. These materials are light and fluffy and are difficult to mix into the soil uniformly. When composted or ground so that good incorporation can be secured, they provide a satisfactory source of organic matter. Their breakdown is rapid, and much heat is generated in the early stages. For this reason materials of this type should be composted before using or applied at least three to four weeks before seeding, and areas should be kept well watered during the intervening period to avoid injury to germination.

Various inorganic materials have been suggested for use as soil conditioners because of their porosity and high degree of stability. Those holding the most promise of being suitable are fused cinders that have been screened to remove coarse clinkers and processed mica products now commonly used for packing and insulating purposes. Since these materials are highly inert, they should persist in soils for long periods with relatively little change in their character. Currently, little is known of their value as compared with peats and other organic materials. They should be used on trial areas only, until more data are available as to their usefulness.

Chemical Properties of Soils as Related to Turf Management

Essential Plant-food Elements. A fertile soil is needed to grow good turf. It must contain all the essential plant food elements in sufficient amounts to meet the needs of the grass. The 10 main chemical elements needed are carbon, hydrogen, oxygen, nitrogen, phosphorus, potassium, calcium, magnesium, iron, and sulfur. Excepting iron, all are used in relatively large quantities. The carbon, hydrogen, and oxygen are obtained from air and water. The soil supplies the remainder. It also furnishes minute amounts of the trace or minor elements. The most important ones are manganese, copper, boron, and zinc.

Ordinarily one or more of the elements nitrogen, phosphorus, and potassium are likely to be deficient in soils. Nitrogen and phosphorus are usually present in relatively small amounts in proportion to the quantities required by the grass. Potassium, although plentiful, may be locked up in the soil. Magnesium and calcium deficiencies may occur on strongly acid soils. Barren sands and soils that are highly alkaline (opposite acid) frequently cannot supply sufficient quantities of available iron, sulfur, manganese, boron, and other trace elements.

Nitrogen is the key element in turf production. It is primarily responsible for color and vegetative growth. Constant liberal supplies are essential for good leaf density and satisfactory root development under sod. The soil nitrogen comes from organic matter. The gradual decay of organic materials provides a constant supply throughout the growing season. Nitrogen may be added to soils in organic and inorganic forms, and in synthetic Urea-form compounds which come within the accepted definitions of these materials for use as fertilizers (see Chap. 3). The organic and Urea-form nitrogen carriers must undergo a much longer process of decomposition in the soil than inorganic forms before their nitrogen becomes available. The latter usually are highly soluble and release nitrogen quickly. It is easily lost when in soluble form, due to leaching by surplus water draining through the soil.

Phosphorus is a necessary part of all living plant tissue. It is particularly important in stimulating the quick development of a good root system in newly seeded grass. Soils with a high proportion of silt and clay particles contain more of it than sandy soil. Phosphorus is not lost in the drainage water because it is quickly fixed in the soil. It redissolves slowly following precipitation, but sometimes solution is not rapid enough to supply adequate quantities.

Potassium is needed to help produce energy and plant structural materials. It aids in the production and movement of starches and cellulose. There is some evidence that potassium availability is related to the development and virulence of the organisms causing plant diseases. This fact has been demonstrated on cotton and may be equally true of turf. Like phosphorus, most of the potassium in soils occurs in the finer soil particles. Large total quantities are present in loam and heavier soils. Barren sands, mucks, and peats are the exception. These soils are consistently low in potassium and need regular fertilization with this element. Loam soils may show deficiencies due to high fixing power for potassium.

Calcium and magnesium are essential for vital growth processes. Deficiencies of both materials are very likely to occur on strongly acid soils. They are the cheapest and best materials for correcting soil acidity (see Chap. 3 on Fertilizers and Lime).

Iron, sulfur, and the trace elements are necessary for plant growth. Iron is required in the formation of chlorophyll, the green coloring matter of leaves. Sulfur, like phosphorus, is a necessary part of living plant tissue. These materials usually are adequate in the heavier soils that have a good organic-matter content. They may be deficient in poor sands and soils that are highly calcareous (high in lime content).

SOIL AS A SOURCE OF PLANT FOOD. Soils differ in their total content of plant nutrients and in the quantity available for use by grass and other plants. They seldom contain enough available nutrients to meet growth requirements of the turf grasses. Additional amounts must be supplied by fertilization. Intelligent selection and use of fertilizer require an understanding of the soil as a source of plant-food materials.

Deficiencies of plant nutrients may be due to shortages in the total quantity present in the soil. As previously noted, nitrogen and phosphorus often are present in amounts much lower than needed for satisfactory turf growth. Deficiencies also may be due to the fact that nutrients are in forms so insoluble that the grass cannot obtain enough to supply its growth requirements. Some soils have a high fixing power. When liberal quantities of fertilizer are added to such soils, very little of it may be available for use by the grass in a relatively short time after it has been applied. The nutrients have been changed to insoluble compounds or are held so tightly by the soil particles that their rate of solution is too slow to supply plant needs adequately. Good management practices will adjust fertilizer applications and soil conditions so that maximum quantities of available nutrients are produced.

Adjustment of soil reaction can materially affect nutrient availability. Table 2, page 25, shows the relative availability of various materials at different levels of soil acidity and alkalinity (see the following section for a discussion of soil reaction). Since grasses are heavy users of phosphorus, potassium, magnesium, and calcium, the best pH range for turf is between the limits pH 6.0 to 7.0 where maximum quantities of these materials are available. Soil reaction also affects available supplies of nitrogen. Soil organisms responsible for the decay of organic matter and the production of available nitrogen from this source do not grow well in highly acid or alkaline soils. The pH level that is best for maximum availability of the other elements also favors nitrogen production by these organisms.

Nutrient deficiencies may develop when excessive amounts of one or more elements are present in a soil and the quantity of others is limited. Under such conditions the balance which nature attempts to maintain in the available supplies of the various materials is upset. Those present in limited quantities are thrown out of solution entirely because of the excess of the others. For example, in soils that are highly alkaline (have an excess of basic materials such as calcium or magnesium) elements such as potassium, manganese, iron, and boron may be unavailable even though the soil contains sufficient quantities of them to supply the needs of grass under normal conditions. This situation occurs most frequently on mucks and peat soils with a high lime content and on some soils in dry areas that have a high content of soluble salts. There are several practical remedies. Frequent light applications of the deficient materials dissolved in water can be made, so that the grass has a chance to get them before they become unavailable. Also, it is sometimes possible by heavy watering to leach out the excess of materials that are causing the trouble.

Soil Reaction. The chemist divides matter into three classes based on "reaction." Substances are acid, neutral, or alkaline. Acid soils are those in which acids predominate. Similarly, alkaline soils have large quantities of alkaline materials. Acids and alkaline

TABLE 2

Some pH Values and Special-purpose Turf-grass Relationships (After Scarseth)

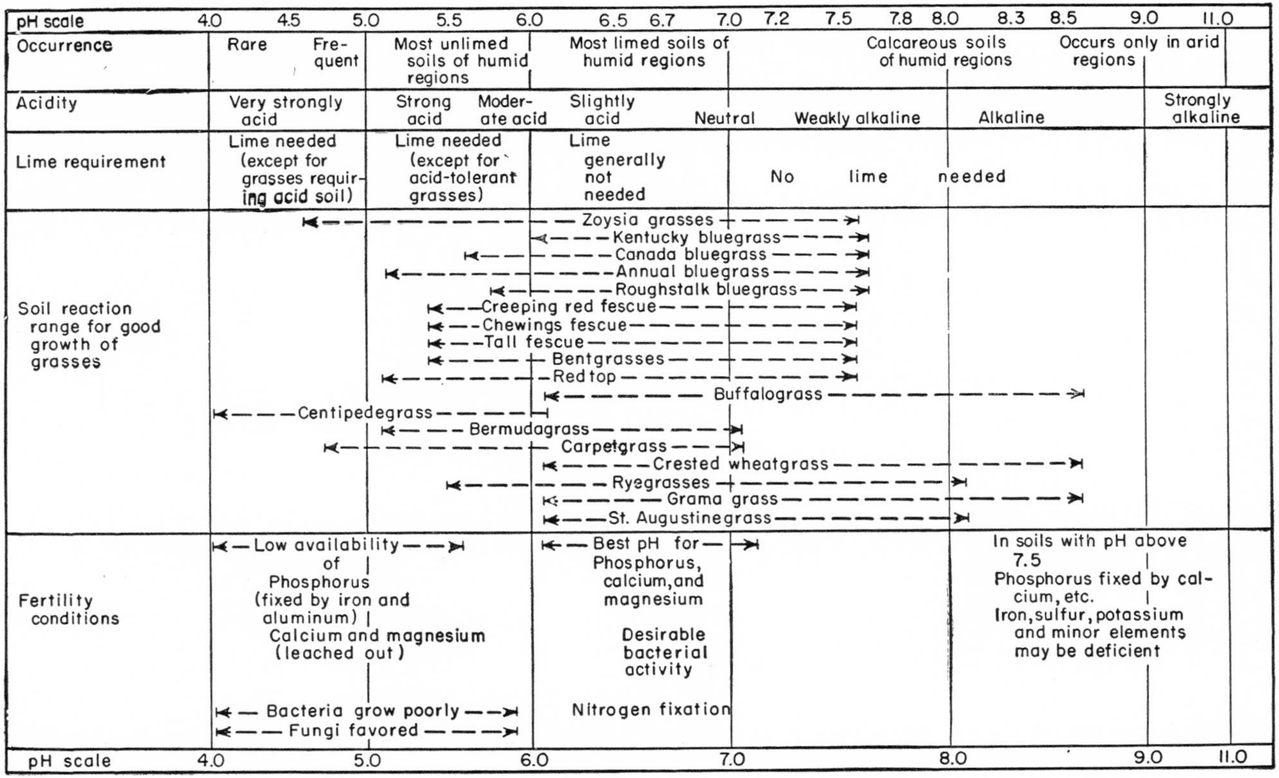

pH scale	4.0 4.5 5.0	5.5 6.0	6.5 6.7 7.0	7.2 7.5 7.8 8.0	8.3 8.5 9.0	11.0
Occurrence	Rare Frequent	Most unlimed soils of humid regions	Most limed soils of humid regions	Calcareous soils of humid regions	Occurs only in arid regions	
Acidity	Very strongly acid	Strong acid Moderate acid	Slightly acid Neutral	Weakly alkaline	Alkaline	Strongly alkaline
Lime requirement	Lime needed (except for grasses requiring acid soil)	Lime needed (except for acid-tolerant grasses)	Lime generally not needed	No lime needed		
Soil reaction range for good growth of grasses	Zoysia grasses Kentucky bluegrass Canada bluegrass Annual bluegrass Roughstalk bluegrass Creeping red fescue Chewings fescue Tall fescue Bentgrasses Red top Buffalograss Centipedegrass Bermudagrass Carpetgrass Crested wheatgrass Ryegrasses Grama grass St. Augustinegrass					
Fertility conditions	Low availability of Phosphorus (fixed by iron and aluminum) Calcium and magnesium (leached out) Bacteria grow poorly Fungi favored		Best pH for Phosphorus, calcium, and magnesium Desirable bacterial activity Nitrogen fixation		In soils with pH above 7.5 Phosphorus fixed by calcium, etc. Iron, sulfur, potassium and minor elements may be deficient	
pH scale	4.0 5.0	6.0	7.0	8.0	9.0	11.0

materials balance each other in neutral soils. The degree of active acidity or alkalinity is measured by determining the concentration (quantity) of acids and alkaline materials in the soil solution. It is expressed in terms of a unit called pH (potential of hydrogen). An arbitrary scale has been set up which runs from 0 to 14, with 7 as the dividing point, or neutrality. Acidity increases as figures decrease below 7. Alkalinity increases as the figures increase above 7. The degree of acidity represented by each number differs by a multiple of 10. Thus, pH 6.0 is 10 times, pH 5.0 is 100 times, and pH 4.0 is 1,000 times more acid than pH 7, the neutral point. Similarly pH 8.0 is 10 times more alkaline than neutral. Soils fall in a pH range of 4.0 to above 8.5, but they usually come within the narrower range of about pH 5.0 to 7.5.

ACTIVE AND POTENTIAL ACIDITY. Soil acidity is active and potential. Active acidity refers to the soluble acids in the soil solution. They are called active because they are directly harmful to plants. The pH determination is a direct measure of the soluble acids. Acid soils also contain insoluble acids which are the reservoir or potential source of active acidity. Potential acidity resides in the silt, clay, and humus fraction of the soil. Loam and heavier soils have a higher potential acidity than sandy ones. A sandy soil and a clay soil may have the same pH reading (active acidity), but the clay soil will require more lime because of its higher potential acidity.

Acid soils develop in regions where annual precipitation is 25 in. or more. Acidity also develops where watering is so frequent and heavy that large amounts of surplus water are constantly moving down through the soil and draining away. Calcium, magnesium, and other basic or alkaline materials are dissolved and carried away by this drainage water. Where leaching of alkaline materials does not take place because of limited water movement, soils contain materials that produce alkaline reactions.

Soil acidity is accentuated by crops grown continuously on soils without adequate provision for replacing the basic materials which they remove. Permanent grasses are heavy users of basic materials. Acidity may develop under intensively managed turf unless prevented by good fertilization and liming practices.

Some fertilizers increase the active and potential acidity, and some reduce it. Nitrogen-supplying materials have the greatest effect on soil reaction. Acid-forming nitrogen carriers include such materials as ammonium sulfate, ammonium nitrate, ammonium phosphate, and urea. Ammonium sulfate and ammonium nitrate effects are the most pronounced because the sulfuric and nitric acids which they contain are very powerful. Urea is converted into nitric acid through a process of chemical and biological changes in the soil. It increases soil acidity. Cyanamid, sodium nitrate, and calcium nitrate reduce acidity. The calcium in Cyanamid changes to hydrated lime in the soil. When the nitrogen in sodium and calcium nitrates is used by the plant, the residues of sodium and calcium reduce acidity.

Among the organic nitrogen carriers, dried blood tends to increase acidity because it carries only small amounts of calcium and other alkaline materials. Bone meal and tankages (animal and fish) contain large amounts of calcium and produce an alkaline reaction. Many other organic materials such as conditioned sewage sludge and the seed meals (cottonseed, linseed, and soybean) have no appreciable effect on soil reaction. The synthetic Ureaform compounds will produce only a very slight increase in acidity. The general tendency of superphosphate and the principal potassium-carrying materials (muriate and sulfate of potash) is to reduce soil acidity, although there may be a temporary increase when potassium is applied.

Effect of Soil Reaction on Grasses. Some grasses tolerate a wide range of reaction and will grow on acid, neutral, and alkaline soils. Others will do well only within a narrow pH range on either side of the neutral point. A few tolerate soil that is more acid than ph 6.0. Table 2, page 25, gives the optimum reaction range for the more important turf grasses.

Effects of Soil Reaction on Availability of Nutrients. Grasses differ in their ability to absorb and utilize calcium and similar nutrients. Grasses that have the lowest requirements for calcium are the most tolerant to acid conditions. High acidity interferes with the ability of grasses to utilize ammonia. Many fertilizers carry nitrogen in the ammonia form. When soils are not more than very slightly acid, the ammonia can be assimilated satisfactorily. Under strongly acid conditions it accumulates in the plant and becomes toxic. The nitrate form such as sodium nitrate is the best to use on such soils.

In highly acid soil, soluble aluminum compounds may be formed which are absorbed by the grass. The aluminum is precipitated (thrown out of solution) within the plant and clogs the conducting tissues. Liming acid soil changes the aluminum to an insoluble form, which cannot enter the plant.

The availability of applied phosphate is reduced in acid soils. At reactions below pH 6.0 to 6.2 highly insoluble compounds of iron and aluminum are formed. At reactions above pH 6.2 the phosphate unites with calcium to form compounds which are readily available to the plant. Acidity increases the solubility of trace elements. Where the soil contains excessive quantities, enough may go into solution to become toxic. In contrast, high alkalinity reduces their solubility to a point where grass cannot get the limited amounts needed for normal growth.

EFFECTS OF REACTION ON TURF QUALITY. Excessive soil acidity is one of the major causes of poor root development. Under normal conditions grass roots are grayish white in color and densely fibrous with many fine branches. They are deep and occupy the entire root-zone region. In strongly acid soil roots are shallow, restricted, brownish in color, and the fine-feeding rootlets are reduced or entirely absent.

Acidity is one of the reasons, although not the sole cause, of the thatching of turf. Grasses renew a large part of their root systems each year. When soils are not too acid, the old roots slough off and decay. Dead roots, stems, and leaves accumulate in acid soil, forming a thatch that acts like a tightly woven felt blanket. It impedes the penetration of air and water and is largely responsible for the formation of localized dry spots. It also creates excellent conditions for the development of disease-producing fungi.

EFFECTS OF REACTION ON SOIL ORGANISMS. Reaction affects the numbers of worms, bacteria, and fungi present in the soil. Earthworms are less numerous and less troublesome in acid soils. While fungi develop over a wide reaction range, they are most prevalent under acid conditions. Many of them are desirable and necessary because they are responsible for the initial decay of organic matter, but certain groups are disease producing. Dollarspot and brown patch, for example, are aggravated by excessive acidity and are checked when acidity is controlled by proper liming. Most groups of bacteria that are active in the destruction of plant residues and in the production of available nutrients prefer a soil reaction near the neutral point.

Rapid Chemical Tests for Soil Reaction and Available Nutrients

SOIL-REACTION TESTS. Field tests for soil reaction are accurate to within a few tenths of a pH and are satisfactory for practical use in determining the degree of soil acidity or alkalinity. Any one of several inexpensive commercially available test kits are suitable. They are similar in principle. Appropriate dyes which develop distinctive color shades depending upon the reaction are used as indicators. Standardized color charts are provided so that reaction can be determined by matching colors. These are accompanied by tables showing the quantities of lime required to correct different degrees of acidity.

In making the test, the indicator solution is added directly to the soil. Various methods are used for draining a small quantity of the solution from the soil, or a powder is sifted on the soil indicator. The color develops on the white powder background and can be compared with the standard color chart. The indicator solutions should be reasonably fresh and should be allowed to remain in contact with the soil for a sufficient time to develop maximum color. The quantity of moisture in a soil to be tested is not important for most of the colorimetric types of soil-reaction tests.

The so-called Comber test depends upon a different principle. It is based upon the fact that acid soils contain dissolved iron. The amount of iron is roughly proportional to the degree of acidity. When soil containing dissolved iron is treated with a chemical called potassium sulfocyanate, a red-colored compound is formed. The intensity of color is proportional to the degree of acidity. A test based on this reaction is sold under the trade name Rich-or-Poor Test. It is a simple, rapid method and works well in all soils except those lacking in soluble iron. The method works best when the soil is reasonably dry.

It is best to make soil-reaction tests on samples from various depths throughout the root zone. Sometimes strong acidity is confined to the surface layer of only one or two inches, or it may occur throughout the deeper soil. In the latter case more lime and a longer period will be required to correct the acid condition than where acidity is confined to a shallow surface layer. Cultivation or spiking to allow the lime to penetrate more deeply is desirable.

SOIL TESTS FOR AVAILABLE NUTRIENTS. Rapid chemical tests of various types are widely used as an aid in determining fertilizer needs. They attempt to differentiate between easily soluble and difficultly soluble forms of plant-food materials and tell nothing about the total amounts which may be present in a soil. Only the available forms are determined, presumably the amount plants can use in a short period of time. The tests are made by treating the soil for a definite period of time with an extracting solution. Methods differ principally in the type and strength of the extracting solution employed. The quantity of nutrient present in the solution is then measured by the use of standard color charts or by the degree of cloudiness (turbidity) of the liquid.

The practical usefulness of soil tests depends upon (1) correct and careful sampling in the field, (2) the accuracy of the testing method and its adaptability to the particular soil being examined, and (3) skill in interpreting results.

SAMPLING. The most accurate test is of very little value if the sample is not representative of all the soil in the area. Usually the soil on greens and tees is uniform. One composite sample consisting of 8 to 10 plugs taken at as many locations is enough. When turf shows evidence of different growth characteristics in certain areas, separate samples should be taken from these areas. In sampling fairways, separate samples of 8 to 10 plugs each should be taken for each area where soil may be different in color or texture, or because of previous fertilizer treatment, drainage, erosion on knolls, or similar causes. Standardization of sampling depth is very important. Plugs should be taken to an exact and uniform depth of 2 in. The 2-in. sampling depth should be measured below the surface thatch of turf. The latter should be discarded in preparing the soil for testing. When information about the soil below is desired, separate samples representing that zone should be collected. A very satisfactory type of sampling tube can be made from a discarded steel golf-club shaft (see Fig. 4).

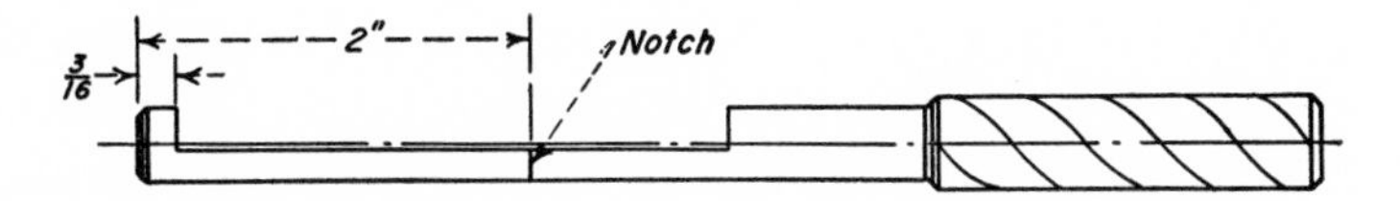

FIG. 4. Soil sampling tool made from discarded steel golf club shaft. The simple, practical soil sampler illustrated above is made on an emery wheel from a golf shaft with a heavy side wall. Those of light stock break easily. The cutting edge is only 3/16 in. to facilitate removal of plugs and is sharpened. The slot is ground just below center so plugs slip out easily and the mark for measuring plugs is EXACTLY 2 IN. (*Courtesy Sewerage Commission, City of Milwaukee.*)

INTERPRETATION OF RESULTS. There has been an unfortunate tendency to use soil tests without discrimination. Correct interpretation of quick tests for anything but pH depends first upon the use of a reliable method, adapted to the particular soil. Results are of practical value only when they are interpreted by a person who knows the soil, who has had fertilizer experience with turf, and who thoroughly understands the problems of its maintenance.

TESTS FOR NITROGEN. Soil tests for nitrogen are of little value for grassland areas. Grasses absorb available nitrogen as fast as it is formed. Samples from areas on which the grass is thrifty generally show little or no soluble nitrogen. Stored nitrogen in the soil exists in the organic or humus fraction which has a low solubility in water and dilute acids. The rate of decomposition is affected by soil temperature, moisture, and reaction factors which are not susceptible to chemical test. Need for nitrogen can be judged by the behavior of the grass, because nitrogen is the growth element. Poor color, slow growth, thin turf, etc., are the best signs.

TEST FOR PHOSPHORUS AND POTASSIUM. Tests for phosphorus and potassium must be interpreted by someone who understands how the grass growing on the soil responds to applications of these materials.

Most of the quick test methods express phosphorus and potassium availability in three to five categories from low to high. When past experience shows that the test results are a true indication of the need for these nutrients, applications of phosphorus and potash should be made when available quantities are below the "fair" level on fairways and the "high" level on greens.

In interpreting the results of phosphorus tests it is necessary to know whether the soil under investigation has received applications of arsenic compounds such as arsenate of lead or sodium arsenite. Chemists have demonstrated that arsenic gives the same reaction as phosphorus in the testing methods commonly used. Where medium to heavy applications of arsenic compounds have been made as weed killers or insecticides, tests may show more available phosphorus than the soil actually contains.

TESTS FOR MAGNESIUM AND CALCIUM. Soil tests for available magnesium and calcium are dependable for determining deficiencies or excesses of these elements. They are particularly valuable as a measure of the need for lime, when used in connection with pH determinations of soil reaction. In some acid soils available magnesium is extremely low. Because of their high rate of water solubility under acid conditions, magnesium and calcium deficiencies are likely to occur wherever there is excessive drainage. By using a lime of high magnesium content (20 to 30 per cent reported as magnesium oxide) to correct acidity, the possibility of magnesium deficiency is eliminated. When abnormally high amounts of available magnesium and calcium are present, they may cause deficiencies of other elements. When such a condition occurs, someone should be consulted who is familiar with the local soil and suitable methods for reducing concentrations of these materials.

TESTS FOR IRON, MANGANESE, AND OTHER SOIL CONSTITUENTS. Satisfactory rapid tests have been developed for the determination of soluble iron and manganese in soils. As previously noted these nutrients may be deficient on barren sandy soils or where there is excessive alkalinity. When grass becomes yellow or chlorotic on soils of this type and is not responding to normal fertilizer treatment, tests for iron and manganese may supply the key for correction of the trouble. Deficiencies of trace elements such as boron, copper, and zinc also may be responsible for turf deterioration or failure on these types of soils. No satisfactory quick-test procedures have been developed for these materials. Deficiencies must be determined by field-trial methods.

Aluminum is not classed as a grass nutrient. Sometimes it is desirable to determine whether soluble compounds of it are present, because of their toxic effects. Tests for aluminum are available and can aid in the diagnosis of undesirable soil conditions due to its presence. They are particularly valuable when correlated with pH determinations. Moderately acid soils may or may not contain active aluminum, and tests for it may be of direct assistance in determining the quantity of lime that is needed.

PLANT-TISSUE TESTS. Rapid plant-tissue tests determine, approximately, the quantity of raw plant-food materials in the conducting tissues of the plant. They do not measure nutrients that have been converted into the complex products of plant growth. When the tissue test for a particular element, such as nitrogen, is positive, the soil supply of that element is considered to be adequate. Tissue tests are designed to determine whether nutrients actually are getting into the plant. They will indicate deficiencies before the symptoms characteristic of starvation for the nutrient are evident.

Satisfactory tissue tests for nitrates, phosphates, and potash have been developed. Various testing methods are in use, and several test kits are available commercially. The basic principles of the different testing methods are similar. Grass clippings are crushed between filter paper which absorbs the juice. The paper is then treated with suitable solutions which indicate the presence of the various nutrients by characteristic color or turbidity (cloudiness) of the solution.

3

Fertilizers and Lime in Turf Production

Fertilizers

Fertilization to supplement the natural plant-food supplies of the soil is one of the most important factors in turf management. Turf needs liberal feeding—without interruption—throughout the growing season, because it grows continuously from spring to fall. It differs from economic crops in this respect. Their requirements for plant nutrients are less as they approach maturity. A successful feeding program for grass must be based upon an understanding of fertilizer materials and a knowledge of the turf requirements on greens, tees, fairways, and roughs.

Commercial Sources of Plant-food Elements. The essential elements required by turf, together with their sources and functions, were outlined in Chap. 2. From a commercial standpoint, fertilizer materials are the individual substances that contain one or more of the three most important elements: nitrogen, phosphorus, and potassium. Fertilizers contain one or more of these elements in forms that plants are able to utilize. The fertilizer trade uses the term nitrogen for that element, but speaks of phosphorus as phosphoric acid and potassium as potash. Fertilizers do not carry the elements in pure form, but in chemical compounds combined with other elements or as by-products of vegetable or animal (organic) origin. Chemical fertilizers may come from natural sources, for example, Chilean nitrate of soda. They may be manufactured, like superphosphate, and the Urea-form compounds, or produced as by-products from manufacturing processes, like ammonium sulfate. The vegetable and animal materials include animal manures, by-products from the utilization of plants and animals, or by-products from waste products, Guano, tankage and vegetable meals, and sewage sludge are examples, respectively, of manures, by-products, and waste materials.

In the trade, fertilizer materials are grouped into carriers of nitrogen, phosphate, or potash, depending upon the principal element in them. Some materials may fall into more than one class. This is true of natural organic fertilizer materials and several of the inorganic ones. Thus, fish scrap and animal tankage contain both nitrogen and phosphoric acid and are classed as both nitrogenous and phosphatic organic fertilizer materials. The same is true of Ammo-Phos, an inorganic material, containing both nitrogen and phosphoric acid. Table 12, page 291, lists the principal fertilizer materials with the percentages of nitrogen, phosphoric acid, or potash in each.

Fertilizer materials are classified also on the basis of their effects on soil reaction. Some materials increase acidity, some reduce it, others have no material effect. Materials which contain nitrogen in the form of ammonia, or in forms which are converted into ammonia in the soil, increase soil acidity unless sufficient lime or other alkaline compounds are present to offset its effect. Other sources of nitrogen, such as sodium nitrate, having an alkaline reaction reduce soil acidity. Most of the phosphatic fertilizer materials have little or no permanent effect on soil reaction. Their tendency is to make the soil less acid. The principal carriers of potash are neutral. They temporarily increase the active or soluble acidity of an acid soil, but the permanent effect is slight and of no practical significance. Table 12, previously referred to, summarizes the effect of the principal fertilizer materials on soil reaction.

NITROGENOUS FERTILIZER MATERIALS AND THEIR VALUE FOR TURF. Nitrogenous fertilizer materials are of three classes, based on the rate at which the nitrogen they contain becomes available. The first group includes inorganic chemical compounds such as ammonium sulfate and ammonium nitrate, and synthetics like urea and cyanimid. All of the materials in this class are highly water soluble. The nitrogen they contain is converted rapidly into ammonia and nitrates which are absorbed quickly by the grass roots. When applied at rates of more than 1 to 1½ lbs. of actual nitrogen per 1,000 sq. ft. they may cause excessive stimulation that results in a soft, succulent type of growth which has low resistance to disease and other adverse conditions. Because they are highly water soluble they are lost easily from the soil by leaching during periods of heavy rainfall or if irrigation is excessive. All will cause severe burning of the turf, even when applied in moderate quantities, unless watered in promptly or mixed with liberal quantities of soil or top-dressing material.

The natural organics constitute the second class of nitrogenous fertilizers. Materials such as processed sewage sludges, tankages, and the seed meals belong to this group. Availability of the nitrogen in the various products differs to some extent, but on the average, its rate of release is appreciably slower than from the first group. The natural organics contain only very small quantities of soluble compounds, so there is much less danger of burning the grass than with soluble fertilizers. For the same reason, their effects last over a longer time. They are particularly valuable for use where turf is fertilized only at monthly or longer intervals. Most of the natural organics contain less total nitrogen than the soluble forms, but they also carry moderate quantities of phosphates and sometimes appreciable amounts of trace elements. This may be important on open, sandy soils where essential trace elements often are deficient. The first cost of the nitrogen per pound in this class of materials is appreciably higher than in soluble compounds. Easier handling, less danger of burning, lower leaching losses, less possibility of over stimulation, and a longer period of availability largely compensate for initial price differences.

The Urea-form compounds belong to the third class of nitrogen fertilizers. They are plastic type materials produced by combining urea and formaldehyde under carefully regulated conditions. When the process is properly controlled, a product is formed which gives up its nitrogen at a slower and more uniform rate than other nitrogenous materials when subjected to the biological decomposing processes in the soil. Under standard methods of production for fertilizer use, Urea-form compounds will contain approximately 38 per cent nitrogen. About one-fourth of this quantity is in a form that becomes available at nearly the same rate as the nitrogen in materials like ammonium sulfate and urea. The remaining three-fourths is classed as insoluble nitrogen. Its rate of availability is indicated by the term *availability index*. This is the per cent of the total insoluble nitrogen that is assumed to become available gradually during the current season of application. It is generally accepted that a Urea-form formulation should have an availability index of at least 40 to be desirable for fertilizer use.

There are several methods used in the manufacture of Urea-form fertilizers. In some of these the process cannot be held under as rigid control as in others, with the result that the product will vary widely in the percentages of quickly and slowly available nitrogen it contains. Critical studies have shown that such products may contain as little as 20 per cent of slowly available nitrogen. In such cases, they are of little more value than the inorganics. The cost per pound of actual nitrogen in the better Urea-form compounds is approximately the same as in the natural organics. The same factors of greater simplicity and ease of handling, reduced problems of burning, low leaching losses, etc., that characterize the natural organics, also apply in comparing the cost of these materials with the quickly available class of products.

PHOSPHATE FERTILIZER MATERIALS. The sources of phosphoric acid can be grouped into three classes. These are (1) organic carriers, (2) superphosphates, and (3) ammonium phosphates. Bone meal is the principal organic source, but natural guano, the animal tankages, fish scrap, sewage sludges, and vegetable meals also carry moderate amounts. The phosphoric acid is not available in these materials until they undergo decay in the soil. Release of phosphoric acid is hastened by fine grinding. They are excellent sources of phosphoric acid for turf. Steamed bone meal has a higher phosphoric acid content than raw bone meal, and the phosphoric acid is more quickly available.

Superphosphates are the most important commercial source of phosphoric acid. They are produced by treating raw phosphate rock with sulfuric acid to convert the phosphoric acid into soluble or readily available forms. Superphosphates contain 16 to 50 per cent phosphoric acid. In the soil the phosphoric acid changes to insoluble forms which redissolve gradually. The type of compound formed and the rate of re-solution depends upon soil reaction. When the soil is moderately to strongly acid, highly insoluble compounds are formed.

The ammonium phosphates contain 20 to 48 per cent phosphoric acid and 11 to 20 per cent nitrogen in addition. The phosphoric acid is completely water soluble. The nitrogen exists as ammonia and is water soluble. Ammonium phosphates are quick-acting fertilizers and and must be used with caution. Otherwise they will burn turf badly.

Soil reaction and other soil conditions strongly influence the availability of phosphoric acid. Although reaction is of chief importance, other factors such as organic-matter content and soil texture affect its solubility. Because phosphoric acid can be changed quickly into difficultly soluble forms, soil deficiencies may occur even though the total quantity present is high. For this reason, regular applications may be required to maintain a sufficient supply for normal growth.

POTASH FERTILIZER MATERIALS. The principal commercial potash fertilizers are water soluble. Muriate of potash is the outstanding source. The muriate produced in this country contains 60 to 62 per cent potash. Some potassium sulfate containing 47 to 52 per cent potash is available commercially but at present costs more per unit of potash. Other potash carriers are potassium nitrate, cotton hulls, unleached hardwood ashes, and tobacco stems. The muriate is the form most commonly used for turf. Soils of high clay and silt content are higher in potash than sandy soils, but it may not be available because of fixation. The regular use of potash is necessary on very sandy soil, because of rapid losses by leaching, and may be needed on heavier soils when the soil supply is fixed in difficultly soluble forms.

SOURCES OF SECONDARY AND TRACE ELEMENTS. Fertilizer materials contain other essential plant food elements in addition to nitrogen, phosphoric acid, and potash. Calcium is present in varying quantities in superphosphate and in other phosphatic materials, except ammonium phosphate. The nitrogenous materials Cyanamid, calurea, and Cal-Nitro contain appreciable quantities of calcium. Sulfur is present in superphosphate, ammonium sulfate, and in potassium sulfate. Magnesium requirements are met most readily by the use of dolomitic limestone of high magnesium content. Epsom salts (magnesium sulfate) is used to correct an acute deficiency quickly. Sources of the trace elements include sulfates of manganese, copper, zinc, and iron. Borax is the common source of boron. All of these compounds are water soluble. Grasses and other plants require them only in minute quantities. They must be used cautiously because even small excesses may be highly injurious. Animal manures, many of the natural organic fertilizers, and superphosphate contain trace elements in appreciable quantities.

MIXED FERTILIZERS. Most of the fertilizers sold in the United States, except organics, are mixtures of fertilizer materials containing the primary ingredients nitrogen, phosphoric acid, and potash. When all of the elements are present in mixed goods, the mixture is called complete fertilizer. The quality of a commercial mixed fertilizer is determined by its analysis, grade, and formula. The analysis states the percentages by weight of nitrogen, phosphoric acid, and potash in that order. For example, a 10-6-4 fertilizer contains 10 per cent nitrogen, 6 per cent phosphoric acid, and 4 per cent potash. The term analysis also applies to the percentage of plant-food elements in an individual fertilizer material. A 20 per cent superphosphate contains 20 per cent phosphoric acid. It is an 0-20-0 fertilizer.

The fertilizer grade is defined as "the minimum guaranty of its plant food expressed in terms of nitrogen (not ammonia), available phosphoric acid, and water-soluble potash." Thus, a fertilizer containing 7 per cent nitrogen, 7 per cent available phosphoric acid, and 7 per cent water-soluble potash would have a minimum grade of 21 total units of plant food. Many states have laws specifying the minimum quantities (grade) of total plant-food materials which a mixed fertilizer must contain before it can be sold. In some states the fertilizer industry meets annually with representative growers and experiment-station workers. Together they determine what grades (above the legal minimum) and analyses will best meet requirements of the major crops produced. Turf has received little consideration from them up to the present time.

The Association of Official Agricultural Chemists (AOAC) has adopted the following definition for a fertilizer formula: "A fertilizer formula shall express the quantity and grade of the crude stock materials used in making a fertilizer mixture. For example: 800 lb. of 16 per cent superphosphate, 800 lb. of tankage (7.40 per cent nitrogen and 9.15 per cent total phosphoric acid), and 400 lb. of sulfate of potash-magnesia (26 per cent potash)." In the illustration the quantities of the crude fertilizer materials used to supply the desired amounts of the various elements total exactly 1 ton. If the fertilizer materials needed to secure the desired quantities of nutrients had totaled less than 1 ton, the formula would have included the amount of filler needed to make the total 1 ton.

A fertilizer ratio states the proportion of plant nutrients in relation to each other. Thus, a 7-7-7 fertilizer has a 1-1-1 ratio, or 1 part nitrogen, 1 part phosphoric acid, and 1 part potash. An 8-8-8 or a 10-10-10 has the same ratio. Similarly, a 4-8-4 or a 5-10-5 fertilizer has a 1-2-1 ratio.

FERTILIZER FORMULAS AND ANALYSES FOR TURF. The specific fertilizer formula and analysis that should be used will depend on the character of the turf, the intensity of management, soil fertility levels, and many other considerations which will be discussed in detail in later chapters on establishment and maintenance. There are inherent differences in the fertilizer needs of turf on greens and fairways. On greens, management is more intensive, a faster rate of growth is required, and clippings are removed. More liberal, and often more frequent, fertilizer applications are necessary. Also, larger quantities of nitrogen and potash in proportion to the phosphate often are needed for greens turf than for the less intensively managed fairway areas. Return of clippings reduces the need for high potash applications on fairways.

It may become necessary sometimes to modify or supplement standard fertilizer mixtures with other materials, or to make up mixtures to meet specific needs, based on soil requirements or the feeding requirements of individual grasses. For example, Kentucky bluegrass needs more available phosphate than red fescues and bentgrasses. Similarly, bermudagrasses require higher nitrogen levels than zoysias.

A wide range of nutrient ratios are available in complete fertilizers for general use on golf course turf. These can be grouped into three classes: (1) Those in which the nitrogen content is twice, or more, as high as the amounts of phosphate and potash (ratios like 2-1-1, 3-1-1, 4-1-1); (2) Those in which the nitrogen, phosphate, and potash is approximately equal (1-1-1); and (3) Those which contain higher amounts of phosphate or potash than of nitrogen (1-2-1, 1-2-2, etc.). In most cases, specialty fertilizers for turf that have the higher ratios of nitrogen to phosphate and potash contain materials that will supply 50 per cent or more of the total nitrogen in slowly available form. (Exceptions to this are the high analysis liquid or completely soluble dry concentrates.) If such fertilizers are not available, they can be prepared easily by modifying common inorganic mixtures with slowly available nitrogen sources. Table 3 illustrates how an all-inorganic 10-10-10 fertilizer may be modified to maintain the 1-1-1 ratio, but have at least 50 per cent of the nitrogen in slow form. Higher proportions of slowly available nitrogen can be obtained by varying the quantities of ingredients, as shown in Table 4. If a 2-1-1 ratio is desired, in which three-fourths of the nitrogen is slowly available, it can be prepared as illustrated in Table 5, in which part of the nitrogen is derived from activated sludge and part from Urea-form, and in Table 6, where all of it comes from Urea-form compounds.

The analysis of commercial mixtures always is based on the actual percentage of each nutrient per ton of fertilizer. Adjustments to a desired ratio and nutrient content are made by deter-

TABLE 3

Material	*Total pounds*	*Pounds of nutrients*		
		N	P_2O_5	K_2O
10-10-10 inorganic fertilizer	850	85	85	85
Activated sludge (5.5% N, 4.0% P_2O_5)	600	33	24	
Urea-form (38.0% N)	130	50		
Superphosphate (20.0% P_2O_5)	300		60	
Muriate of potash (65.0% K_2O)	120			78
Total	2,000	168	169	163
Approximate ratio		1	1	1
Approximate analysis		8.4	8.4	8.1

TABLE 4

Material	*Total pounds*	*Pounds of nutrients*		
		N	P_2O_5	K_2O
10-10-10 inorganic fertilizer	420	42	42	42
Activated sludge (5.5% N, 4.0% P_2O_5)	660	36	26	
Urea-form (38.0% N)	230	87		
Superphosphate (20.0% P_2O_5)	500		100	
Muriate of potash (65.0% K_2O)	190			124
Total	2,000	165	168	166
Approximate ratio		1	1	1
Approximate analysis		8.2	8.4	8.3

TABLE 5

Material	*Total pounds*	*Pounds of nutrients*		
		N	P_2O_5	K_2O
10-10-10 inorganic fertilizer	800	80	80	80
Activated sludge (5.5% N, 4.0% P_2O_5)	250	14	10	
Urea-form (38.0% N)	600	228		
0-20-20 inorganic fertilizer	350		70	70
Total	2,000	322	160	150
Approximate ratio		2	1	1
Approximate analysis		16	8	7.5

TABLE 6

Material	*Total pounds*	*Pounds of nutrients*		
		N	P_2O_5	K_2O
5-10-10 inorganic fertilizer	1,440	72	144	144
Urea-form (38.0% N)	560	213		
Total	2,000	285	144	144
Approximate ratio		2	1	1
Approximate analysis		14.2	7.2	7.2

mining what per cent of the ton (2,000 lbs.) each of the total nutrients supplied by the various ingredients represents.

Lime

The causes for soil acidity and its effect upon the physical and chemical properties of the soil have been outlined in Chap. 2 (section on Soil Reaction). Soil reaction directly affects the health and vigor of the turf grasses. It also affects grass growth indirectly because of its influence upon the availability of nutrients and other soil properties. It is essential to keep soil at or near the best reaction for optimum turf growth. Periodic applications of lime, based on soil-reaction tests, is the best way to control soil reaction and avoid excessive acidity.

Functions of Lime. Lime improves the physical condition of heavy soils by promoting granulation. It causes the minute silt and clay particles to form aggregates which help increase the air and moisture supply. On sandy soils it acts as a binding agent and makes them more loamy in character. Lime increases the availability of many plant nutrients. The supply of calcium, magnesium, and available phosphorus is restricted in acid soils and is improved by liming. The amount of nitrogen, sulfur, phosphorus, potash, and other elements is affected by the rate of organic-matter decay. Applications of lime to acid soils increase their availability. Many soil organisms responsible for organic-matter decay will not thrive when the soil is more than very slightly acid.

Lime reduces toxic conditions caused by excessive quantities of soluble iron and aluminum—and sometimes copper and zinc—that may be present in strongly acid soils. It also creates more favorable conditions for the assimilation of ammonia by the plant. When soils are strongly acid, plants have difficulty using nitrogen from ammonium sulfate and other fertilizers in which the nitrogen exists as ammonia.

The fungus diseases which attack grass are aggravated by insufficient lime. Although the relationship is not thoroughly understood, there have been many instances where serious damage from dollar spot, brown patch, and snow mold have been reduced materially by lime applications. It is not intended to suggest that lime be used as a substitute for fungicides, but it seems certain that lime assists in disease prevention and control.

Lime affects grass aggressiveness and in that way helps turf resist weed encroachment. For example, Kentucky bluegrass does not persist on acid soils or compete successfully with more acid-tolerant bentgrass and fescue. The general vigor of grass is reduced by high acidity; this is also true of the acid-tolerant ones. They are more seriously weakened by drought and other adverse conditions when the soil is acid to a marked degree. Weeds such as sorrel, which have a very high acidity tolerance, are particularly troublesome under such conditions.

Lime directly affects turf quality. Moderate to strong acidity reduces root penetration and injures the root tissues. The sod becomes thin, loses its color, and develops a starved appearance. Under such conditions it is highly susceptible to injury, is less drought tolerant, loses its playing qualities, and is slow to heal. Undesirable matting develops because dead roots, leaves, and stems do not undergo decay. In some instances the mat becomes so tight that water is completely excluded and local dry spots develop.

The extent to which liming affects the quality of the turf produced by individual grasses is determined by their range of tolerance of acidity. Table 2, page 25, shows the optimum soil-reaction range for the important turf grasses. Grasses of both the Northern and the Southern climatic regions vary widely in their lime requirements. In the North, the bluegrasses are very sensitive to acidity. They make their best growth where lime is applied regularly to maintain a pH reaction above 6.0. The fescues and bents grow over a wide reaction range and have a much lower lime requirement than the bluegrasses. In the South, Bermudagrass produces the best turf where lime is used on moderately to strongly acid soils, but its lime requirement is not so high as that of carpetgrass. The zoysia grasses grow over a wide reaction range but respond to lime when soils are distinctly acid. Centipedegrass may be seriously injured by lime applications on soils where iron deficiencies develop when acidity is reduced. All the native grasses adapted for turf use in the West Central region have a low acidity tolerance.

KINDS OF LIME. Lime is obtained principally from deposits of limestone rock. Some lime is produced also as a by-product of chemical industry. There are two types of limestone. One is called calcite (limestone) because it is composed largely of calcium carbonate. The other is dolomite and is a variable mixture of calcium carbonate and magnesium carbonate. Other liming materials used for correcting acidity include marl, oyster shells, and slag. The first two are principally calcium carbonates similar to limestone. Blast-furnace slag is used occasionally. It is a silicate of calcium. When raw limestone is burned, calcium oxide is formed (burned lime). Hydrated lime is produced by adding water to the calcium oxide, or burned-lime, form. Commercial lime may be purchased in the form of carbonates, hydrates, or oxides of lime.

The value of raw ground limestone depends upon its chemical composition and degree of fineness. The composition of the commercial product may be expressed as the percentage of calcium and magnesium oxides which it contains or as the percentage of carbonates, or both. When the percentages of calcium and magnesium carbonates are shown separately, these should be totaled to determine the value of the material. The combined value should not be below 90 per cent. The composition is sometimes expressed as "calcium oxide equivalent" or as "neutralizing power." These terms are used for ground limestone that consists of mixtures of calcium and magnesium carbonates, because magnesium carbonate has a greater neutralizing power than calcium carbonate. Based on calcium carbonate, or pure limestone, as 100, 74 lb. of pure hydrated lime and 56 lb. of pure burned lime have the same neutralizing power.

The rate at which ground limestone dissolves varies with particle size. Finely ground material acts faster than coarsely ground limestone. For turf use at least one-half should pass a 100-mesh screen, and all should pass a 10-mesh screen.

Burned lime, the calcium oxide form, is seldom used. The danger of severe burning of the grass due to its caustic properties eliminates it from consideration as a liming material for use on turf. The value of other forms such as marl, slag, and by-product materials will depend directly upon their neutralizing power. Some contain large amounts of inert clay, silt, or sand and are lower in neutralizing value as a result. They can be used to good

FIG. 5. Hand spreader for lime, fertilizer, top-dressing, and seed. (*Courtesy Sewerage Commission, City of Milwaukee.*)

advantage when available from nearby sources at low cost. The additional cost of handling larger quantities of material must be considered in determining their value.

RATES, FREQUENCY, AND TIME OF LIME APPLICATIONS. The rate and frequency of lime applications depend upon several factors. Soil reaction expressed as pH determines the quantity of lime needed to bring soil reaction to a desirable level. Where soils are only moderately acid, it is practicable to apply the full amount of lime needed in a single dose. Ordinarily, this requires 1 ton, or less, of pulverized limestone per acre (see Table 7). Acidity tests should be made annually, and applications should be repeated whenever an undesirable reaction develops.

It is seldom desirable fully to correct strong acidity by a single application of lime. The large amount required may depress the solubility of phosphorus, iron, and many of the trace elements and actually retard rather than improve growth. The best plan is to apply hydrate or finely ground limestone annually at a rate of ½ to 1 ton per acre until the desired pH is reached.

The rate of lime applications is affected by the character of the soil and the kind of grass. Less lime is required to correct acidity on sandy soils than on loam and clay. The degree of tolerance of different species of grasses also will affect the quantities used. The type of area influences the rate of application to some extent. Usually it is desirable to make relatively heavier applications on fairways than on greens, because of the increased time and labor involved in making frequent light applications on large areas. Frequent light applications are desirable on greens because they lessen the danger of scorching the grass, particularly when hydrate is used. The lime may be desirable also for reducing injury by disease. Table 7 suggests satisfactory rates of application of ground limestone for different kinds of soil on fairways and average rates for greens.

The most convenient times to make lime applications are in late fall, winter, and early spring. Raw ground limestone can be applied at any time, but the summertime rate for hydrated lime should be under 1,000 lb. per acre, or 20 to 25 lb. per 1,000 sq. ft. Lime should not be applied immediately before or following the use of fertilizers containing ammonia. When a soluble phosphate fertilizer or arsenate of lead is needed and the soil is strongly acid, it is best to apply lime first, preferably several months earlier.

Other Soil Amendments. Gypsum (calcium sulfate) is used occasionally for correcting unfavorable soil conditions. It is not an efficient material for reducing acidity because sulfuric acid is formed first. It must be leached out of the soil before acidity is reduced. Sulfur is the most desirable material for reducing the alkaline reaction of soils. When this element is added, it must be converted to sulfuric acid by soil organisms before it is effective

TABLE 7

Soil pH	Degree of acidity, approx.	Fairways, lb. per acre		Greens lb. per 1,000 sq. ft.
		Sandy loams	Loams and clays	
6.6–7.0	Neutral	0	0	0
6.1–6.5	Very slight	1,000	1,500	0–10
5.6–6.0	Slight	1,500	2,000	10–20
5.1–5.5	Moderate	2,000	3,000	20–40
4.6–5.0	Strong	3,000	4,000	40–60
4.0–4.5	Very strong	4,000	6,000	60–80

Note: Quantities indicated for fairways are designed for Kentucky bluegrass, Burmudagrass, and other grasses that have a narrow tolerance to soil acidity. Quantities should be reduced by one-half for grasses having a high tolerance to acidity, such as fescues and bentgrasses.

in reducing alkalinity. This process usually takes 3 to 6 months. One pound of sulfur will neutralize 3 lb. of calcium carbonate, so that approximately one-third as much sulfur must be used to reduce alkalinity as carbonate is used to reduce acidity.

4

Drainage and Irrigation

The capacity of soils to absorb, store, and transport water affects drainage and irrigation. The characteristics typical of a well-drained soil provide ideal conditions for irrigation. Conversely, poorly drained soils of poor texture, bad structure, and low organic matter content are bad irrigation risks, especially when the subsoil is compact and impervious to water movement.

Good drainage and irrigation are important both in regions of abundant and of limited rainfall. In the former, drainage is the first necessity because of the high precipitation rate and the prevalence of heavy surface soils and impervious subsoils. Supplemental irrigation is desirable during periods of drought. In regions of limited rainfall, irrigation is a maintenance necessity. Good drainage is just as important. Free movement of water through the subsoil is required to prevent the accumulation of soluble salts in the root zone.

Drainage

Drainage improvement is needed when any conditions occur which prevent the movement of surplus water out of the soil or concentrate water in limited areas. The methods commonly employed are improved surface drainage, installation of tile drains, or modifying the physical condition of the soil to facilitate water movement.

EFFECTS OF POOR DRAINAGE. Saturated soil affects playing conditions adversely. Players cannot walk or make a satisfactory shot on wet soggy fairways. Tractors cannot operate on them. Slippage of the traction wheels prevents adequate mowing and scars the turf. A waterlogged green lacks resilience, the surface bakes badly because of sparse grass coverage, and putting quality is poor because of surface irregularities caused by deep ball marks and footprints. A saturated soil on tees does not provide the firm stance required for tee shots.

Poor drainage reduces the use of a course. Swampy fairways and rough compact greens are not attractive and result in loss of membership by private clubs and reduced revenue on public and fee courses.

Wet soils are cold soils. Growth starts slowly in the spring and stops early in the fall. Where grass is thin because of poor drainage, freezing may cause honeycombing and heaving of the soil, with further loss of grass by winterkilling. Poor drainage checks the activity of beneficial soil organisms and causes shallow root systems. Grass with a shallow root system is apt to wilt on hot windy days. Unless watered lightly several times a day the turf withers, turns brown, and dies. Then scald and algae become pronounced. Poor drainage destroys soil structure, which reduces the ability of the soil to store air and moisture. It also hastens the development of soil acidity.

In dry regions where water must be used in large quantities, good subsoil drainage is a necessity. Water must move down through the soil and pass away through the subsoil or through tile drain lines. Otherwise, upward movement by capillarity of the salt-laden water carries the dissolved salts to the surface where they are deposited as the soil water evaporates. Heavy deposits develop eventually that are toxic to grass.

DETERMINING DRAINAGE REQUIREMENTS. It is easy to determine the need for better drainage. The presence of persistently wet soggy soil and of ponds is one indication. The occurrence of sedges, *Poa trivialis*, or other moisture-tolerant vegetation is further evidence. Soils that puddle when wet, bake severely when dry, or honeycomb when frozen are usually poorly drained. A blue or mottled color of the subsoil is a sure indication of poor drainage. The iron in these soils is unoxidized owing to a lack of air, and they do not develop the characteristic rusty brown color typical of good aeration. Shallow root systems may be the result of serious compaction and consequent poor drainage in the surface layer. The seriousness and extent of the drainage problem and the type of corrective measures required can be determined by carefully observing and evaluating these factors.

SURFACE DRAINAGE. Poor surface drainage is evidenced by standing water in depressions and may be due to one, or both, of two distinct conditions. It may be caused by compaction in heavy soils. The water-moving channels in the soil have been so reduced in size that water moves through the compacted layer very slowly, if at all. This condition is common on greens and tees which are compacted by trampling and by mowers, and other maintenance equipment. It may occur on heavy fairway soils that are subjected to concentrated use and to frequent operations of heavy maintenance equipment. Poor surface drainage may be the result of bad contouring which concentrates large volumes of surface water in restricted areas. In such instances soils, even though they are otherwise satisfactory, may not be able to absorb and move the water fast enough to prevent saturation. Surface ponding also may be aggravated by impermeable subsoil which prevents movement of water out of the surface layer, causing saturation and surface accumulation in low areas. In either case the effects are the same. Root systems of the desirable grasses become shallow and restricted. The plants turn yellow and scald out rapidly. A black scum of algae appears or undesirable types of vegetation come in that can tolerate saturated soil conditions.

SUBSURFACE DRAINAGE. Drainage is essential whenever root zones stay wet continuously. The type of installations to use depends upon the character of the soil and the source of the water. Tile drains are commonly used to remove surplus water. They function best in soils with internal passageways that are large enough to move water quickly. Tile lines must have sufficient fall to permit gravity flow to the outlet. Systems should be laid out in such a way that the tile will not become clogged with roots of trees and large shrubs. Tile drainage is least satisfactory when soils are highly alkaline or contain high proportions of very fine sand, silt, and clay. Materials of this type will be washed into the lines through the joints and fill up the tiles. This condition occurs most frequently in irrigated sections of dry regions. Under such circumstances, other drainage methods such as open ditches or subsoil knifing must be used. Knifing can be employed to break a relatively shallow clay pan below a fine silty or clay soil. The clay layer is opened by a deep chiseling tool attached to a long colter. The equipment operates like a plow except that it cuts a deep groove instead of a furrow.

TILE SYSTEMS. No fixed pattern can be established for the arrangement of a tile drainage layout. Sometimes poor drainage is caused by an impervious subsoil which occurs at a comparatively uniform depth throughout the area, or the impervious soil layer may be irregular and form wet basins sometimes obscured by a covering of porous soil. Water dams up to form ponds or swales. In other instances water may form springs or concentrate on seepage areas by moving above impervious strata on slopes or by following highly porous gravel layers. Seepage breaks out at the foot of the slopes or on the slopes themselves. Drainage systems must be designed to meet these varying conditions.

KINDS OF TILE SYSTEMS. There are two general classes of tile systems: (1) regular, and (2) intercepting. Regular systems are used when drainage requirements are uniform over all or part of the area. The arrangement of tile lines of regular systems are known as gridiron, herringbone, and random. Diagrams of these types are shown in Fig. 6. The gridiron or herringbone types are used when uniform drainage is required over the entire areas. The size and shape of the areas will determine which of the two designs is the most efficient and economical. Random systems are used when irregular portions of an area require drainage.

Intercepting systems are used to eliminate seepage at the foot of slopes or along the slopes themselves. If seepage is at approximately one level, a single line of tile running across the slope a short distance above the upper edge of the wet area can be used to intercept the water; otherwise several lines or more are needed. Test borings should be made to determine how deep the tile line must be placed to cut off the water effectively.

Tile systems may be designed in connection with catch basins to remove surface water more rapidly than it will be absorbed through the soil. Catch basins also are useful where it is necessary

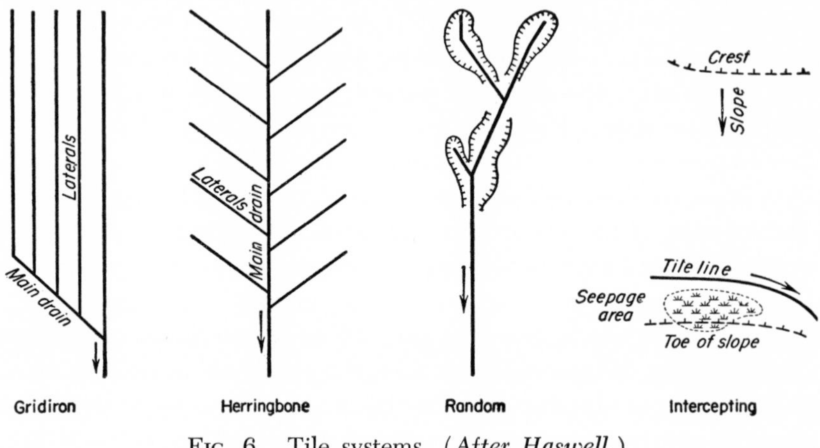

FIG. 6. Tile systems. (*After Haswell.*)

to decrease the grade of a tile line. The bottom of the basin should be at least one foot below the lower tile in order to collect sediment.

INSTALLING TILE DRAINS. Convenient tables are given in the Appendix (Tables 31 and 32) showing tile capacities and sizes required for mains and laterals of various lengths. The spacing between lines, the depth, and the grade depend upon the character of the soil to be drained and other local factors. Tile always should be laid deep enough to avoid possible damage from frost and equipment operation. An average depth of 24 to 30 in. usually is sufficient. Tile lines should be as straight as possible with sweeping curves where direction changes are necessary. The ditch bottom should be cut to the required grade and the tile laid directly upon it. Joints should be fitted as tightly as possible and should be protected by some type of covering to prevent infiltration of soil or root penetration into the lines. This is particularly important where tile is used to drain sand traps and similar areas of loose soil. Porous fiberglass strips that are available in rolls of varying length and width are excellent for this purpose. The tile opening at the upper end of each line should be closed off and the outlets protected by substantial screens. Outlets of tile lines should be above the surface of the water. Tile systems assist materially in soil aeration when the outlets are not sealed off by water, so that air is excluded from the lines. The original soil can be used for backfilling the ditch after the tile is laid, or it can be backfilled with coarse material such as cinders, gravel, or stones. The latter method is more desirable where it is necessary to remove surface water rapidly.

A complete map should be made of all drained areas showing the location of tile lines. This will be of very practical value when repairs or additions to the system are needed.

Other Drainage Methods. Open ditches sometimes can be used to advantage in providing drainage for areas where soils or the terrain are not suitable for tile drains. The capacity and grade of ditches will be determined by the size of the area to be drained and the volume of water they must carry. Water 2 to 3 ft. deep will have a velocity of 3 ft. per second in a ditch with a fall of ½ to 1 ft. per mile. Higher velocities with this volume of water will cause cutting of the banks. The fall can increase as the volume of water decreases. Water of less than 1 ft. in depth can have a fall of 50 to 60 ft. per mile without causing serious bank cutting. Ditch banks should be so constructed that they can be cut with power mowers and other maintenance equipment can be used on them.

Numerous small seepage areas may be due to water from deeper sources breaking through to the surface. In such instances it may be possible to tap the source of the water by sinking wells and pumping it out. This is a technical matter requiring the services of a good drainage and irrigation engineer.

Mole drains have been used successfully to improve drainage. They are made by drawing a heavy colter to which a cartridge-type mole, a ball, or a bell is attached, through the soil below the normal root zone. The usefulness of mole drains is limited to areas where satisfactory outlets for the channels can be obtained and to types of soils in which the channels will remain open for a reasonable time. They must be installed when the soil is in proper moisture condition. It is difficult to draw the mole through soils that are hard and dry. When soils are too wet, the channel walls will develop a glaze that interferes with water percolation. Mole drainage is a temporary corrective and must be repeated periodically because the channels tend to clog and lose their effectiveness.

SURFACE DRAINAGE OF GREENS AND TEES. The principal causes of bad drainage on greens and tees are poor surface contours, soil compaction, impervious subsoil, and seepage. Good architectural plans should provide designs for the surface contours of greens and tees that avoid pondlike depressions in which water can stand. Contours that concentrate water in relatively narrow runoff channels of low gradient are undesirable. They should be broad and shallow with a grade of at least 1 per cent to permit water to flow out of the turf at a reasonable rate. Surface contours should be designed so that most of the water is taken off where traffic is least concentrated. Draining water to the front of a green should be avoided, whenever possible. Most of the traffic onto the green is from the front; so concentration of water at this point intensifies compaction problems.

In many cases the best remedy for poor surface drainage on established greens and tees is reconstruction. (Other improvements, such as correction of physical condition and provision for underdrainage, can be made at the same time.) Installation of tile drains is seldom satisfactory for the removal of excess surface water. This is particularly true where poor drainage is due to a combination of bad surface contouring and tight soils. Unless grades are relatively sharp, water will not flow rapidly enough through the turf to the low point above the tile to prevent soil saturation. Percolation through tight soils to the tile is so slow that drainage conditions are not adequately improved except in the narrow strip immediately over the tile lines.

UNDERDRAINAGE OF GREENS AND TEES. Provision for adequate subsurface drainage of greens and tees should be made when they are constructed. Some type of underdrainage is necessary, except where foundations are composed of material through which water can move rapidly. Where tile drains are used, tiles should not be smaller than the 4-in. size. Lines should be at least 2 to 2½ ft. below the final surface. The sides of the trenches in the subgrade should be gently sloped toward the tile and the trenches backfilled with cinders or some other type of highly porous material to within 8 to 10 in. of the surface. Compacted pockets in the surface of the subgrade will trap the water and should be avoided. Spacing between lines can be from 10 to 25 ft., depending upon the type of foundation soil in which they are set. When greens are built up so that the outlets can be opened at the foot of slopes, each tile line can be installed independently of the others and sloped from the center in both directions. A connecting system should be provided when the water must be carried to a low point such as a creek or ditch. All connections should be made outside the area of the green whenever practicable.

A second method of providing for good underdrainage of greens and tees has been recommended by the United States Golf Association Green Section. It consists, essentially, in constructing the subgrade at a minimum elevation of 14 in. below the finished grade. The subgrade next is contoured to conform with the contour design of the finished grade. Trenches for receiving tile lines are cut into the subgrade to the necessary depth to provide a fall in the lines of from 0.5 per cent to 3.0 per cent. Suitable types of drain tile (clay, concrete, plastic, or asphalt paper) are laid on a firm bed of ½ to 1 in. of gravel, or directly on the bottom of the trench if the soil is of such character as to make washing into the lines unlikely. Joint fitting and protection against soil and root penetration should be as previously outlined. Tile lines should be spaced at a maximum distance of 20 ft. The trenches are backfilled with some type of highly porous material, such as pea gravel, clean pit-run gravel, or crushed stone, and a 4 in. layer of the same material spread uniformly over the entire subgrade. This should be covered with a layer of finer textured material to a depth of 1½ to 2 in. The particle size of this material should average from 5 to 7 times smaller in diameter than that of the base course. A minimum of 12 in. of prepared topsoil should be used for the surface course. This allows for 4 in. of settling to meet the finished grade requirements (see Chap. 6, page 130, for details of topsoil preparation).

Correcting Poor Drainage on Established Greens or Tees. The successful correction of poor underdrainage depends (1), upon a correct diagnosis of the cause, and (2), upon the choice of a method that will produce the desired improvement. Poor drainage due to compaction in the top four or five inches of the surface layer of soil can be corrected by the use of various types of aerating equipment. Where the trouble is confined to limited areas, the tubular tine fork is suitable for opening drainage channels through the compact layer. Mechanical aerating equipment can be used to advantage on larger areas. The holes it makes always should be filled by working top-dressing into them, except after late fall aeration. When aerated at this time they should be left open over winter to take advantage of freezing and thawing action to improve physical soil condition (see Chap. 7).

Greens or tees located along the side or at the bottom of hills may be wet because of seepage from the hill. The seepage can be trapped by placing a tile line between the green and hillside, in a direction to cut across the line of water movement. The tile must go down to or below the water-bearing strata and the trench backfilled to the surface with porous material. A porous backfill is important and necessary. Otherwise the water will flow across the top of the tile and into the green or tee. Seepage water moves under pressure from above.

It is difficult permanently to improve the underdrainage of greens and tees that have been constructed with heavy impervious soils. The successful functioning of tile drain, mole drains, or other drainage methods will depend upon the rate at which water moves through the soil to the lines. In some types of heavy clay soil, a good crumb structure develops upon drying. Channels to the tile are formed which increase the rate of water movement through the soil. Tile drains function satisfactorily on such soils. Installation methods outlined for new construction are suitable. Soils that are plastic and sticky or have been severely puddled during construction operations develop satisfactory structure for good water movement very slowly. In extreme cases, they may never open up sufficiently for drains to function properly. Before an expensive program of drainage correction is undertaken, it will be wise to make a thorough examination of the soil. A core of plugs should be pulled for this purpose to a minimum depth of 2 to 2½ ft. The assistance of a drainage engineer, or some other individual familiar with drainage problems, should be sought to determine whether the soil is such that tile drains will operate successfully. If the verdict is negative, the only alternative is complete reconstruction.

FAIRWAY DRAINAGE. Fairway-drainage problems are similar to those of greens and tees. Inadequate surface drainage, surface compaction, impervious subsoils, and seepage are the major causes of waterlogging that prevent good turf development.

As previously noted, the ponding of surface water in depressions may be due to the development of surface compaction. It also may be due to impervious soils below the root zone. In either case soils in such areas become saturated and turf either scalds, smothers, or freezes out. In irrigated sections the pocketing of surface water is particularly serious. In addition to the usual types of injury to the turf, toxic concentrations of soluble salts frequently develop in such areas. Where surface compaction is the chief source of trouble, it can be corrected effectively by the use of the turf Aerifier if the soil below is sufficiently porous to permit good water movement. When set to its full operating depth, the spoons on this machine usually penetrate through the compacted zone. Periodic use of equipment of this type is necessary.

Where water ponds in surface depressions because of impervious subsoils, subsurface drainage plus surface grading, where practicable, is the best remedy. In Northern regions, where water collects in depressions when the soil is frozen it causes freezing out of the turf. Tile drains are of no value under these conditions since they do not function when the ground is frozen. Surface grading or the use of tolerant grasses such as the bents is the only satisfactory solution.

Tile systems or open ditches can be used to correct poor drainage caused by impervious subsoils or high ground-water levels. Tile drains are preferable wherever suitable outlets can be provided and soils are of such structure that water will move out of them into the tiles. Soils also must be of such texture that fine particles will not flow into the tiles and clog them. Intercepting

FIG. 7. Ponded water in depression on a green. (*Courtesy Sewerage Commission, City of Milwaukee.*)

tile lines for seepage areas, as described for greens, also are suitable for fairways. Where fairways are constructed on heavy soils that require uniform drainage over the entire area, a simple system of two or three lines of tile running lengthwise of the fairway usually is satisfactory. Each line may have its own outlet, or the lines may be connected to a main at the lower end. Types of tile systems and methods of installation have been outlined.

Open ditches can be used to drain fairways where tile drains are not satisfactory because of high ground-water levels or unsuitable soils. These may be shallow swales that are completely turfed and are designed to carry off surplus water in periods of excess precipitation. Open ditches may be constructed also to carry a constant flow of water as previously discussed. They sometimes can be designed as hazards when used for fairway drainage.

FIG. 8. Bent survival on seepage area in fairway. (*Courtesy Sewerage Commission, City of Milwaukee.*)

DRAINAGE OF TRAPS. When traps must be placed on impervious soils, they should be designed with the trap floor sloping toward an open side through which water can drain out of the sand. Otherwise tile drainage is necessary. The floor of the trap should be sloped toward the tile line and the tile laid in a shallow trench running in the direction of the long axis of the trap. The principal problem in trap drainage is to prevent sand from getting into the line through the joints. Various methods have been used. Joints have been covered with pieces of sod or carefully packed with a good grade of loam topsoil. Strips of tar paper or asphalt-treated burlap also can be used satisfactorily to cover the joint. A tar-treated fiber conduit, with holes on the underside and convenient slip collars that completely cover the tile, has been developed. It provides good protection against clogging.

Irrigation

The intelligent use of water on golf-course turf depends upon an understanding of the water requirements of grass and its functions in plant growth. Knowledge is needed of the effect of soil conditions upon absorption, storage, and release of water for growth processes. Good judgment in correlating these basic facts with weather conditions and requirements for play is essential.

Water Relationships

FUNCTIONS OF WATER. Water is needed by plants in every stage of their life cycle. The processes of germination, tissue formation, and food manufacture require liberal supplies of moisture. From 500 to 600 lb., or more, of water is needed for every pound of dry matter produced by grass.

Water acts as a solvent and carrier of plant-food materials. The compounds of nitrogen and the other essential elements dissolved in the soil water are absorbed by the grass roots and carried through the plant in an unbroken stream that extends from the tip of the root to the top of the uppermost leaf. In addition to being a part of food compounds, water is essential for the processes of elaboration (digestion) of raw food materials in the leaves and for transporting the finished product to the various parts of the plant. Large amounts are required for these processes because the quantities of nutrient materials in the soil solution normally are very dilute. Heavy concentrations of dissolved substances in the water absorbed by plants would seriously injure the tissues. Water also regulates the rate of food manufacture and use in the plant. It equalizes temperature by the cooling effect of evaporating water from the leaves. Plants wilt when the soil is unable to supply water as fast as it is evaporated from the leaves.

Adequate supplies of soil moisture are necessary for good development and activity of the organisms that decompose the grass clippings, dead roots, and other organic residues. Undecayed materials of this type produce unhealthy turf that is hard to maintain in good playing condition. Good decomposition adds humus which greatly improves the water-holding capacity and other physical soil properties.

QUANTITIES USED BY TURF. Many factors affect the day-to-day consumption of water by turf. The growth rate of an individual grass will affect the quantity of water used. Slow-growing grasses like the fescues require less moisture than fast-growing types such as creeping bent and Bermudagrass. Larger amounts will be needed when soil and weather conditions are favorable for rapid turf development. Sod density, depth of root systems, and height of cut also influence the rate of water consumption.

Transpiration (evaporation from leaf surfaces) is an important factor affecting the quantity of water used by turf. It controls the amount absorbed from the soil by the grass roots and affects the rate at which water moves through the plant. Weather conditions, such as rain, humidity, temperature, sunshine, and wind, influence transpiration. It is affected, also, by the quantity of moisture present in the soil. When soil moisture is plentiful, nutrients usually are more dilute. Then the plant is forced to absorb and transpire larger quantities of water to secure sufficient food to meet its normal requirements. When the soil solution contains a higher concentration of nutrients, plants secure sufficient food from lower volumes.

The daily consumption of water by turf varies widely, owing to differences in the factors noted above. Estimated quantities range from less than 10 to more than 60 gal. per 1,000 sq. ft. These wide differences emphasize the necessity for careful adjustment of irrigation practices to the needs of the turf.

SOIL CONDITIONS AFFECTING WATER AVAILABILITY AND LOSSES. Soil properties and their relation to water movement and storage were discussed in Chap. 2. As previously noted, the water available to plants is that part of the total quantity in the soil that is held loosely as films on the soil particles by capillary attraction. Soils are in the best condition for turf growth when available water in the pore spaces constitutes about one-fourth of the total volume of the soil mass. A sandy soil requires between ¾ and 1 in. of water to satisfy its capillary capacity to a 6-in. depth. Loam soils need between 1 and 1¾ in. and clay soils, between 1¾ and 2½ in. Grasses wilt when the amount of available water in the root zone falls below minimum requirements for growth. On the other hand, injury occurs because of poor aeration when the pore spaces persistently contain too much water—quantities appreciably larger than the one-fourth volume noted above.

Losses due to runoff, percolation, and evaporation materially increase the total amounts of rainfall and irrigation water needed to ensure optimum storage in the soil. Runoff losses are increased by steep slopes and hard, compacted surfaces. They can be controlled by proper grading and improvement in soil conditions to increase absorption. Runoff is necessary in regions of heavy precipitation when surplus water must be disposed of rapidly to avoid soil saturation.

Percolation losses occur whenever the total quantity of water entering a soil is greater than its absorptive (storage) capacity. Percolation is undesirable only when excessive. Highly porous soils are subject to serious leaching of plant nutrients and dry out too quickly. A moderate rate of percolation is essential to ensure good aeration. In regions where rainfall averages 2 to 3 in. per month, leaching losses from the root zone of a loam soil will amount to about one-fourth of the total water received. Loss of irrigation water will depend upon the rate and the amount applied.

There is no satisfactory method to differentiate between water losses due to direct evaporation from the soil and losses caused by transpiration from the grass leaves. Usually these losses are considered together in determining the total amount of water required for plant growth. They are highly variable, depending upon turf density, the occurrence of cracks and fissures in the soil, and the influence of climatic conditions.

Determination of Water Requirements. Adequate supplies of available water in soils must be maintained by natural precipitation, supplemented when necessary by irrigation. The capacity of an irrigation system and the rate of water applications will depend upon the proportion of total needs which the system must supply. In regions of limited rainfall or where precipitation is seasonal, systems must be designed to meet full water requirements. Where rainfall is more abundant and uniformly distributed, irrigation capacity should provide the additional water required during drought periods.

It is impossible to establish a fixed standard for all irrigation systems. Requirements on individual courses vary greatly. All of the factors previously outlined affect the efficiency and proper use of any irrigation system. All factors should be evaluated and correlated with local climatic conditions before planning the layout and determining water-management practices. Data on rainfall and temperatures over a period of years should be obtained. The average period of time between rains and the average precipitation during the growing season should be known. Other local conditions such as high wind velocities must be considered. They affect evaporation and water consumption. Experience and good judgment are required to evaluate the effects of all of these factors. A sufficient knowledge of the mechanical design of irrigation systems is essential to ensure efficient and economical installation and operation.

Irrigation Systems

The three general methods of applying irrigation water to turf include (1) sprinkler-type irrigation, (2) surface flooding, and (3) subsurface irrigation. Sprinkler-type systems have a wide adaptation and are generally used. Surface flooding and subsurface irrigation have a very restricted application for golf-course use. They can be used only under special conditions of topography and soil and where they do not interfere seriously with play.

1. Sprinkler Systems. The four essential features of sprinkler-type irrigation systems are an adequate water supply, a suitable means of providing pressure, water-transmission lines of adequate capacity, and efficient equipment for distribution.

Sources of Water. Some golf courses can obtain water from the public mains of the municipal system. Before choosing this source assurance should be obtained that the supply will be adequate at all times. Some courses have been deprived of water during periods of severe drought. The choice of this source also depends upon the initial cost of the water plus the cost of installation and operation of pumping equipment, which is sometimes necessary for boosting the pressure to provide adequate sprinkler efficiency. These costs must be compared with the cost of providing the same quantity of water from nearby surface or ground-water supplies. Surface sources include natural lakes, ponds, and streams. When stream flow will not supply a sufficient volume of water to meet irrigation requirements, it may be possible to construct artificial dams or impounding reservoirs. Many state agricultural experiment stations and extension services issue bulletins containing detailed directions for building dams and ponds. These can be of material assistance in constructing impounding basins. Where surface supplies are not available, various types of wells are used to obtain underground water. The question of capacity is a principal consideration in using wells as a source of supply. A total volume of 1,350,000 gal. of water is required to apply 1 in. of water to 50 acres of golf-course turf. Where sprinklers are operated 10 hr. per day, a well must supply approximately 320 gal. of water per minute to produce the required volume in a 7-day period. It is always wise to have local sources of water examined by a competent chemist to determine whether they carry soluble substances in concentrations sufficient to be harmful to turf. In some states the state geologist can supply this information. The information is particularly desirable in sections where water commonly carries high concentrations of sulfur, salt, or similar materials.

Pressure Equipment. The three types of pumps commonly used for sprinkler irrigation are centrifugal, displacement (plunger-type), and turbine pumps. The one best adapted for any particular system depends upon the suction lift needed from the supply to the pump, the capacity, and the head of water required. Where the lift is limited to 15 ft. or less, it is customary to use centrifugal pumps because of their high capacity and pressure. Displacement pumps also have a limited lift (maximum approximately 22 ft.) and are used primarily to deliver water from surface supplies. The turbine-type pumps are best for deep wells requiring a high lift. Pump capacities and horsepower requirements for various elevations are given in Tables 25 to 28, pages 336 to 338.

PIPE LINES. The sizes of pipe required to transmit water from the source to the distributing point depends upon the volume and head needed. Capacities and friction losses in head are shown for pipe sizes and fittings in Tables 21, 23, pages 332, 333. Pipe lines should be constructed of pressure piping throughout their entire length. It is not necessary to lay them below the frost line if they are equipped with drain valves at the low points so that they can be emptied whenever necessary to prevent freezing. The arrangement of the lines depends upon the design of the areas to be watered. System layouts vary from single long mains with short laterals to branched lines radiating in various directions. In some instances it is possible to construct them in the form of a loop, which is considered highly desirable by some engineers.

SPRINKLER HEADS. Sprinklers are of the fixed, the whirling, or the slow-revolving type. Selection will depend upon the piping system and the size and shape of the area to be watered.

Fixed sprinkler heads have no moving parts and cover the area with a continuous spray. They are designed for full-circle, square, half-circle, or quarter-circle coverage. They vary in size for spacings of 8 to approximately 20 ft. and operate on pressures of 15 to 40 lb. Variations of fixed sprinkler heads include pop-up types. The heads automatically rise about 2 in. above the turf when the valve is opened, falling back to a flush position when not in operation. They have a maximum coverage of about 30 ft. in diameter and operate on pressures of 10 to 50 lb., depending upon their size. Pop-up sprinkler heads also may be of the rotary type. These have a higher capacity and coverage than the fixed types and require higher pressures for satisfactory operation.

Whirling sprinklers are usually of small to medium capacity

and are designed to operate on relatively low pressures. Most types have two nozzles set at an angle with the sprinkler arm. They rotate rapidly owing to the jet reaction. There are many different arm and nozzle types designed to break up the spray and give uniform coverage. The larger sizes cover a circle of about 50 ft. in diameter at pressures of 15 to 20 lb.

Slow-revolving sprinkler heads are designed primarily for large areas. They have capacities up to 100 gal. or more per minute, and the largest types cover circles in excess of 200 ft. in diameter. Depending upon their size, operating pressures of 35 to 100 lb. are needed. They are designed for a slow rate of rotation and usually have some type of vibrator to prevent stopping when adjusted to slow speeds. Sprinklers are designed to operate from hose connections or as snap-on types that attach directly to risers from the mains. Where hose is used, the sprinklers usually are mounted on rollers or skids to permit moving without damaging the turf.

Important characteristics to be considered in selecting a sprinkler head include the uniformity of water distribution (water pattern), the pressure required for efficient operation, and the effective coverage area. Some types of heads are designed to give effective coverage at rather low pressures. When pressures are lower than the minimum for which the sprinkler is designed, the spray is coarser and more water is thrown to the outside edge of the pattern. High pressures cause a finer spray that distributes more water near the sprinkler. The spacing between individual heads should be limited to that area receiving uniform coverage. This will avoid too close spacing, which results in excessive moisture in the overlap areas, or too wide spacing, which produces inadequate coverage in the overlap centers. Sprinklers that have cone-shaped patterns with the greatest amount of water at the head and tapering off gradually to the outer rim are the most suitable. The best spacing of these types is about one-half of the total diameter covered.

The capacity of a sprinkler head depends upon the size and type of the nozzles and upon the water pressure. The discharge will be increased 41 per cent when the pressure is doubled. When pressure is tripled, the discharge will be increased by approximately 74 per cent.

A modification of the slow-revolving type is known as the traveling sprinkler. This consists of a whirling sprinkler mounted on a wheel at the outer end of a radial arm that is attached to a rotating drum at the inner end. The arm is a length of 1-in. pipe through which the water is carried to the sprinkler. A wire cable is anchored at one end or side of the area to be watered, and the other end is attached to the drum mounted on a skid. The action of the sprinkler winds the cable on the drum, and the traveling sprinkler moves forward slowly. A variation of this type of traveler is designed to attach the inner end of the radial arm to a stationary supply pipe with a swivel connection. The sprinkler travels in a circle without moving forward on a cable. A third type of traveler has the cable drum mounted with the sprinkler on a two-wheeled carriage that moves forward as the cable winds on the drum. The drum is driven by an auxiliary whirling sprinkler independently of the slow rotating main nozzle.

TYPES OF SYSTEMS. There are two kinds of sprinkler systems: the underground type and those with rotating sprinklers. Underground systems with fixed or pop-up heads are suitable for greens and tees where lines can be laid in such a way that the heads do not interfere with play. In some cases slow revolving pop-up heads can be used satisfactorily. Half-circle heads can be placed at the edges on long narrow tees and sometimes can be used for greens. Heads must be set close enough to give uniform coverage, and pipe sizes must be sufficient to provide the necessary pressure to operate the sprinklers. Underground systems are best adapted to limited areas.

Systems that distribute the water with rotating sprinklers usually are more satisfactory and economical on areas of more than two to three thousand square feet. Supply lines can be equipped with risers having self-closing snap valves to which portable sprinklers can be attached with a coupling device. Swivel hose couplings also can be connected to snap valves so that sprinklers can be used on hose lines. This permits adjustment of sprinkler locations to compensate for wind. The pipe-line sizes must be adequate for the number of sprinklers, to furnish the required amount of water and to provide necessary pressure for efficient operation of each sprinkler.

Either type of system can be designed for complete manual or for fully or semiautomatic operation. A manually operated system requires hand adjustment of valves controlling each sprinkler head. Semiautomatic operation controls batteries of sprinklers by a series of main valve adjustments. A fully automatic system is controlled from a central station by timing devices that are preset to control the rate and quantity of water used on any area.

Planning the System. Satisfactory performance of a sprinkling system depends upon an adequate pressure at each outlet to ensure efficient operation of the sprinklers. The pressure required at the main or at the pump will be determined by the number of sprinklers to be operated from a single line, their capacity, the pressure needed, and the friction losses in supply lines. These determinations require a complete plan of all areas to be watered, with a pipe-line design that will show the lines to each area and the number and size of sprinklers needed to supply the required amounts of water. The design also should include sizes of all pipe and fittings. Convenient tables for the determinations are given in Tables 21 to 24, pages 332 to 334. The calculated pressure needed at the heads plus the friction losses for the pipe line and all fittings will indicate the pressure requirements at the pump or at the city main.

Systems should be designed with the minimum length of piping and number of valves and other fittings that will provide efficient operation. Angle valves ordinarily are most satisfactory for installations. Their resistance is low, and they often eliminate the need for elbows. Valves usually are placed in boxes below the surface and are operated with a key.

The required capacities of sprinkler heads will depend upon the quantity of water they must deliver to a given area within a certain period. The quantity of water applied by a sprinkler can be determined readily by making the following simple computation.

$$\text{Inches applied} = \frac{96 \times \text{gallons per minute} \times \text{hours}}{\text{area covered (square feet)}}$$

Similarly, the time required to apply a certain number of inches can be determined by the following formula:

$$\text{Time, hours} = \frac{\text{depth, inches} \times \text{area covered, square feet}}{96 \times \text{gallons per minute}}$$

Spacing of outlets must be adjusted to provide uniform coverage for the rated capacity at the available pressure as indicated in the manuafcturer's performance chart. Where more than one sprinkler is fed from the same line, there will be a drop in pressure to the outlets that are located farthest away from the control valve. There is no exact method for adjusting heads so that all will deliver the same amount of water. Delivery rates can be regulated within practical limits by adjustment of volume and area controls on the sprinklers and by adjustment of rotation speeds.

2. SURFACE FLOODING. Surface flooding is used in a few instances for turf irrigation, especially on fairways. Its value is limited to areas that are flat enough to permit the water to cover the surface uniformly and to soils that are sufficiently porous to absorb it at a rate that will prevent ponding for any appreciable period of time. Flooding must be done at night or at other periods when it will not seriously interfere with play on the flooded sections. Some of the advantages of this method include elimination of expensive sprinkler and pipe installations and operation at a lower water head than is required where sprinklers are used. Flooding is not satisfactory for greens and tees because of the limited areas involved and the irregular surface grades and contours and their elevated position. It is sometimes useful to replenish soil moisture in periods when freezing of shallow pipe lines becomes a problem.

In making flood-type installations, grade levels should be run on all areas to be irrigated. Primary outlets are located at the high points so that the water will flow uniformly over the area. It is sometimes possible to use the same outlet to supply water to several sections that are at different levels. Portable quick-coupling pipe or canvas hose is used to transport the water to these locations. The total capacity of the system and the rate of flow from individual outlets must satisfy turf requirements for water. Careful determination should be made of the water-holding capacity of the soil and the rate at which it can absorb water. Reasonably accurate estimates of the quantity of water required within a given period to keep good supplies of available water in the soil also should be made. The total capacity of the system and the size of lines to the various outlets will be determined by the size of the area and the total volume of water that it must receive within the estimated time. Estimates of total water requirements are difficult because of higher percolation losses near the outlets than at the outer boundaries of the irrigated areas.

3. SUBSURFACE IRRIGATION. The practicability of subsurface irrigation is limited to those areas where soil conditions are adapted to its use. In this case water is required to move upward through soils instead of downward as with other systems. There must be an impervious layer of soil below the surface zone to act as a dam and prevent rapid percolation losses. A high ground-water level functions in the same way.

Subsurface systems adapted for turf use consist of parallel lines of open-joint tile into which the water is fed. It is discharged into the soil through the open joints between the individual tiles. Lateral lines usually are constructed of 4-in. tile and are not more than 6 to 8 ft. apart. Ordinarily, they are connected in series of three to a perpendicular riser pipe or supply pocket that extends above the surface of the turf. The opposite ends of each line are connected with similar risers called stop pockets. Each is equipped with a plug which permits drainage from the line into a ditch. Water is fed into the system through the supply pocket at one end and seeps out of the line into the soil through the open joints. As the system fills, water rises in the stop pockets at the opposite end of the lines, thus keeping a constant pressure in the laterals. For satisfactory use on golf courses quick-coupling risers are required at the ends of the lines, so that they can be removed when the system is not in operation. When the soil has absorbed a sufficient quantity, the supply is cut off and the plugs in the stop pockets are pulled, permitting the water remaining in the lines to drain out into the open ditch. The time of operation required to provide the quantity of water necessary to maintain adequate soil moisture may be determined by periodic sampling of root-zone areas to check the rate of moisture rise.

Subsurface irrigation is best adapted for use in light types of soils because they move water rapidly. It is not satisfactory for heavy types that are highly resistant to water penetration. Overwatering is not a serious problem where the system is installed under conditions that will permit it to function properly. It can act as a drainage system as well. When too much water has been used and the soil becomes saturated, the drain plugs can be opened and the surplus water permitted to drain out.

Water Management

The irrigation system is a management tool. When properly used, it will help to maintain better grass. Water applications must be regulated, just as fertilization, clipping, and other maintenance practices are adjusted, to best meet the needs of the turf. It would be just as reasonable to apply all the fertilizer that a spreader will hold to a limited area, without estimating nutrient requirements, as it is to base the amount of water applied upon the capacity of the irrigation system. The quantity, time, and frequency of water applications depend upon grass requirements, the capacity of the soil to store and move it, and the factors of climate and weather affecting its consumption and loss. Because all of these vary, it is impossible to establish arbitrary standards for water use.

Watering must be adjusted to the existing conditions on each green, tee, and fairway of the golf course. The watering schedule on each of these areas should be based upon how much water the turf needs to keep it in good condition, how fast the water in the root zone of the soil is lost, and how much must be used to replace it. Applications must be adapted to the rate at which the soil will absorb water. The use of a sprinkler that throws 100 gal. per minute on a soil that can take up water only half as fast is poor economy and bad practice from the standpoint of its effect on the turf. Water schedules depend also upon how effectively the grass growing on an area can use water at any particular period. Where growth is checked by high summer temperatures or other adverse climatic factors, watering may serve only to stimulate weeds.

Unless watering practices are adjusted to fit these various conditions, water may be a greater liability than an asset in turf maintenance.

Watering New Seedings and Vegetative Plantings

Water should be applied to new seedings and vegetative plantings in a fine spray that will not wash the soil away from the base of the young plants. It must be applied slowly so that the surface will not puddle and crust. Crusting of seedbeds is caused by too much water applied too fast. The soil becomes saturated and flows together, baking into a hard crust like the surface of a mud puddle when it dries out. Only sufficient quantities are needed to keep the top inch of soil damp, until the young plants start to grow. In dry periods it may be necessary to sprinkle several times daily to keep the surface from drying out. As roots become deeper, intervals between waterings should be lengthened and the quantity of water used in each application increased.

Watering Greens

The basic watering problems that are common to every green on all golf courses are the questions of how much water is needed, how often it must be used, and how fast it can be applied. These problems are concerned primarily with the needs of the grass for sufficient quantities of water to maintain satisfactory growth. Water is used also to protect the turf against adverse conditions, such as excessive temperatures in summer and severe drying out (desiccation) in winter.

QUANTITY OF WATER. There is no substitute for good judgment in determining how much water should be applied to a green at any one time. The amount of moisture in the root zone is the best indication of the quantity needed. The small sampling tube illustrated in Fig. 4 (page 31) is a convenient tool for checking the moisture content of the soil. Plugs should be taken from high and low areas on the green to a depth of at least 6 in. Usually, a little practice in correlating the appearance and feel of the soil with the condition of the turf will provide a basis for a close approximation of water needs. Sampling also will show the uniformity of water distribution. If water is running off the high areas too fast or is not penetrating localized dry spots properly, low sections of the green will become saturated before the other areas have absorbed sufficient amounts. Moisture conditions on both areas will be unsatisfactory for good grass growth. The best remedy is thorough aeration of the dry spots to secure faster water penetration on these areas. This will eliminate the necessity for overwatering of low areas to secure sufficient moisture in the drier sections. It should be emphasized that applications of sufficient water to moisten the soil to a 6-in. depth do not require soil saturation. If the soil is in good condition physically or is thoroughly aerated, water will move down through it without filling the pore spaces with free water for an appreciable period of time.

The quantity of water that must be applied at any one time to provide sufficient moisture for plant needs will depend upon the total amount which the soil can store without becoming saturated. It will depend also upon the losses that have taken place between water applications. Light sandy soils can retain about 1 in. of available water in a 6-in. depth of soil. This is approximately 623 gal. per 1,000 sq. ft. Average loam soils will retain approximately 1¼ to 1¾ in. to a 6-in. depth, and clay loams 2 in. or higher. Where soils contain the average amounts of organic matter used in seedbed and top-dressing preparation (one-third to one-fourth of their volume), their moisture-retaining capacity to a 6-in. depth will be increased by about ⅓ to ½ in. of available water. When grass is growing vigorously and the weather is hot and dry, the losses in moisture will average from ½ to 1 in. of water every 2 to 4 days. The above figures are averages and must be adjusted for each individual soil. They emphasize the importance of determining how much water the soil on a green is capable of retaining. Applications of quantities that are greater than this capacity will result only in soil saturation and excessive losses.

FREQUENCY AND RATE OF WATERING. The quantity of water a soil can retain and the rate of loss due to grass consumption and weather conditions will determine how often water must be used. Light soils will retain less available water. Applications on these soils must be more frequent than on heavier types and on those having a higher organic-matter content. Ordinarily, the better loams with a good organic-matter content will supply sufficient water for good grass growth for periods that are two to three times longer between waterings than the lighter soils.

The physical condition of the soil on a green will determine the rate at which water can be applied. A heavy type of loam soil with a good sand and organic-matter content will absorb water at a rate that is four to five times as fast as the same soil without admixtures of these materials. The extent of surface compaction also will affect water intake by soil. As previously noted, compaction can be broken and absorption rates increased by good aeration. When surface flooding occurs for any appreciable length of time, the water is being applied too fast. The result is saturation of the surface layer and the increased compaction of this zone if trampled while it is wet. Sprinklers should be adjusted to deliver water at a rate that will avoid this danger.

EFFECT ON TURF DISEASE. The organisms that cause serious turf diseases develop most rapidly when soil moisture is high. The relationship of watering practices to disease prevention and control is discussed in Chap. 9, Turf Diseases.

WATERING TO HOLD SHOT. Water often is used to keep the surfaces of greens soft so that they will hold a pitch shot. This is not the answer to the problem of providing suitable playing conditions. Overwatering results in serious soil compaction and weakens the turf and destroys resiliency. A vigorous turf and the right kind of soil will provide the qualities necessary for holding a shot that is played properly. They are the results of good construction and intelligent maintenance. Where greens cannot be maintained properly to meet playing requirements without overwatering, more frequent use of top-dressing to build a good surface soil or complete renovation is the solution.

TIME OF WATERING. Local conditions and the demands of play are the controlling factors in determining the time of day when

FIG. 9. Syringing a green to check wilting in hot weather. (*Courtesy Sewerage Commission, City of Milwaukee.*)

water should be applied. On many courses where play is heavy, watering is done at night. The time of watering is largely a matter of local management. When temperatures are high, the safest watering periods probably are at night and in the early morning. If water is applied properly, daytime watering will not cause injury. It is dangerous if the amount of water used is excessive or if it is applied too fast.

WATERING TO PREVENT WILTING. Turf on greens can be protected against wilting in periods of hot windy weather by frequent applications of limited quantities of water to reduce transpiration rates and soil temperatures. Wilting occurs when plants transpire (evaporate) water from the leaf surfaces faster than the roots can absorb it from the soil. Under extreme conditions it may be necessary to spray (syringe) greens two or three times daily to prevent injury. Applications can be made by hand or with automatic equipment if it has good capacity for quick coverage. Signs of wilting are bluish color, severe footprinting of the turf, and loss of the normal luster of the leaves.

Watering to Prevent Winter Drying. In areas where rainfall is limited, late-season watering of greens often is necessary. When turf goes into the winter under low soil-moisture conditions, excessive drying out (desiccation) of the grass may take place during the winter months. A late fall application of water to restore soil moisture will protect the turf from winter injury due to dry soil.

Seasonal Factors. Other seasonal factors influence the use of water on greens. The most important are the relation of water to root development, its use in regions having alternate wet and dry seasons, and adjustment to precipitation in humid regions. These factors are particularly important in watering fairways. They are discussed in the section on that subject.

Watering Tees

The same basic principles that affect watering practices on greens apply to tees. The quantities of water used, sprinkling frequency, and rates of application must be adjusted to the needs of the turf, to soil and weather conditions, and to the specialized playing requirements on teeing areas. The turf is subject to the same seasonal factors that affect the use of water on fairways and greens. In addition, watering practices must be adjusted to the specialized type of play from tees. A reasonably dry surface is required that will provide a firm stance and make the turf tough and resistant to wear. Stretching time intervals between sprinklings will aid materially in meeting these requirements. Tees should be watered at periods that will allow the longest possible time between applications and heaviest play. Where tees are large, it is sometimes practicable to design underground watering systems or make portable sprinkler sets in such a way that the tee can be watered in sections. This will permit adequate drying of the surface before play is shifted to the freshly watered area.

Fairway Watering

The methods of determining the water requirements of fairway turf are fundamentally the same as for greens and tees. They are based upon the kind of soil, the weather conditions, and the type of turf. Estimates of the amount needed are complicated because it is difficult to control all factors to meet conditions on large turf areas. The danger of overwatering and its injurious effect upon soil compaction and turf vigor is greater than on greens and tees because of less control over distribution. Water losses from surface runoff and evaporation usually are high on fairways. Grasses vary widely in requirements, and practices must be adapted to the particular variety present. Applications must be regulated to prevent excessive weed stimulation. Fertilizer losses by leaching must be considered because of the practical difficulties involved in frequent replacement of nutrients on large areas. While these things affect the use of water on all turf areas, they are of the greatest importance on fairways. One or more of them often are the controlling factors in determining when to water and how much to apply.

Seasonal Adjustments of Watering Practices. Early season watering should provide favorable conditions for the development of a deep root system. Periods between waterings should be stretched as far as possible to allow the surface layer of soil to dry out to a depth of 2 or 3 in. When it becomes necessary to water, a sufficient quantity should be applied fully to satisfy the soil-storage capacity to a 6-in. depth or more (see Watering Greens, Quantity of Water). Grasses make most of their new root system during this period. Permitting the surface to dry out between waterings encourages deeper penetration of the new roots. When spring dry periods occur and are relieved only by scattered light rains that provide limited precipitation, it may be desirable to provide additional water even though the grass may show no immediate need for it. Soils should be examined following a rain to check on water penetration. If moisture has moved down to less than a 2- or 3-in. depth and the soil is dry below, water should be applied. Otherwise, root systems will be shallow throughout the season, and heavier watering and feeding will be required to maintain satisfactory turf.

Seasonal effects are important in determining when to water in regions having alternate wet and dry periods. In these areas irrigation must be relied upon almost entirely during the dry months. High temperatures or other adverse climatic conditions which occur during these periods require careful adjustment of watering practices to avoid turf injury. The approximate capacity of the soil for available water must be known and quantities and rates of application adjusted to it. When water is applied at a slow rate that prevents the surface layer of soil from becoming heavily saturated, sprinkling can be done at high temperatures without serious injury. Water should be used sparingly during the transition from the wet to the dry season, with maximum periods between waterings. This will help to produce a hard turf with a deep root system and a slow growth rate that is more capable of withstanding adverse conditions. It will permit withholding water during unfavorable weather for a longer period than is possible when grass is in a succulent condition.

Seasonal factors also are important in humid regions. In these sections it is necessary to adjust watering to precipitation. Careful study and full use of weather reports is of material help in determining when to start sprinklers, but will not avoid the effects of sudden showers and high humidity immediately following water applications. Adjustment of quantities and rates of application to soil capacity will eliminate some of the danger of injury in such cases. Good early-season management of limited water, good fertilizer, and aeration are important in preventing the development of soft turf with a shallow root system that is easily injured by soil saturation.

In areas where rainfall is limited, late-season watering of fairways is just as necessary as it is on greens and tees to prevent winter injury by desiccation of the grass due to dry soil. Fairways should receive a good application of water to restore soil moisture before going into the winter.

Seasonal adjustment of watering will assist in controlling weeds that have peak periods of seed germination. If the surface layer of soil is permitted to dry out thoroughly between waterings during the period of crabgrass seed germination (6 to 8 weeks during late spring and early summer), many seedlings will be killed before their roots can reach the moisture in the lower soil. The germination of annual bluegrass seed in the early fall can be reduced in the same way (see Chap. 8, Weed Control).

TYPE OF GRASS AFFECTS WATER USE. Watering practices should be adjusted to the requirements of the predominating grass on the fairway. Some kinds of grasses will thrive at lower levels of available soil moisture than others. The fescues have the lowest total water requirements among the permanent turf grasses of the Cool Humid region. They are followed, in order, by Kentucky bluegrass, colonial and velvet bents, rough bluegrass, and the creeping bents. In the Southern region the zoysia grasses, Bermuda, and centipede need less moisture than carpetgrass and St. Augustine. Buffalo and the other native grasses of the West Central region are highly tolerant to limited moisture.

The most satisfactory way of adapting watering to the needs of the various grasses is by adjusting the time between applications. The fescues and Kentucky bluegrass, for example, can grow on drier soils than the bentgrasses and do not require as frequent watering. The condition of the grass will provide a basis for estimating whether water is needed. By using the soil-sampling tube previously described, the approximate moisture content of the soil at any particular time can be determined. The quantity applied should be based upon the estimated losses of available water from the soil between sprinklings. When it is determined that water is needed, the full amount required to replace these losses should be used. It is unsatisfactory to attempt to reduce the quantities applied to the more tolerant grasses below this point. All grasses need well-developed deep root systems. The limited water penetration resulting from applying less than is needed to moisten the soil to full root-zone depth results in shallow and restricted rooting.

Cool-weather grasses such as fescue and the bluegrasses grow slowly during periods of high temperatures and cannot be forced into rapid growth by watering. The principal effect of frequent heavy watering of these grasses during hot weather is to stimulate rapid weed development at the expense of the grasses. Water applications should be spaced at the longest possible intervals and should be made only when it is necessary to prevent drought injury. When water is applied, the quantity should be sufficient to penetrate to a minimum depth of 6 in., and it should be applied slowly enough to prevent soil saturation. Watering of the bents and the southern grasses can be more frequent. These grasses will respond to water applications because of their ability to make good growth during the summer months.

SOIL QUALITY AND SURFACE DRAINAGE. Differences in the capacity of sandy, loam, and clay soils to absorb and store water were noted in the discussion of greens watering. When fairways are reasonably level and the soil is fairly uniform, estimates of the total quantity of water required and the time in which it can be applied are relatively simple. For example, if the soil is a typical loam it can store 1¼ to 1¾ in. of available water, or about 1,000 gal. per 1,000 sq. ft. in a 6-in. depth. In dry weather and for average-quality turf the water losses from a soil of this type would be approximately ½ in. every 3 days. The day-to-day condition of the turf usually will indicate when sprinkling is necessary to replace losses. Ordinarily, bent turf begins to show the effects of low soil moisture when available soil water is reduced to one-third or one-fourth of capacity. Kentucky bluegrass will grow at somewhat lower levels, and fescues are not seriously affected until available soil moisture has been almost wholly exhausted.

When the character of the soil varies between individual fairways or on a single fairway, estimates of water needs must be made for each set of conditions. The differences may be found to be sufficiently large to justify individual sprinkler adjustments for application of smaller quantities or at slower rates where heavier types of soil predominate.

Sloping terrain also requires adjustments of water applications because of runoff and concentrations in low areas that may cause uneven distribution. Thorough aeration of the soil on slopes will increase the rate of absorption and reduce runoff from these areas. A slower rate of application that will permit the soil to absorb the water as it is applied also ensures more even distribution. Under such conditions frequent use of the soil-sampling tube is desirable to determine what is happening to the water that is applied.

Relationship between Watering and Fertilization. Fairway watering practices and fertilizer programs must be correlated. Overwatering causes leaching of soluble nutrients from the soil and may injure turf more seriously than low moisture supplies. Where completely soluble forms of nitrogen are applied, excess water may remove them within a relatively short time. The use of slowly available forms will reduce losses, but it is not a substitute for careful adjustment of the quantity, rate, and frequency of water applications to the absorptive and storage capacity of the soil. When soils are not overwatered, leaching losses are negligible.

Watered fairways require heavier fertilization than where no supplemental irrigation is used. The grass is active throughout the entire growing season and uses more plant food. Available nutrients are used at a faster rate. Leaching losses also will be greater, unless extreme care is used in system operation to avoid application of excess water. Because of greater consumption and the possibility of larger losses, it is essential that fertilizer programs be carefully adjusted throughout the season to the normally heavier turf requirements.

5

The Special-purpose Turf Grasses

Choice of the right grass to meet the specific requirements of soil, climate, and use which will be imposed upon it often spells the difference between success and failure in growing good turf. There are over 1,100 native and introduced grasses in the United States. Less than 40 of these are of proven value for general use on the golf course. Even within this limited group there are wide variations in their turf-forming qualities and in their reaction to environment, use, and management. Selection of the best types for greens, tees, fairways, and roughs, therefore, depends upon a knowledge of the characteristic growth habits and a reasonably accurate estimate of the conditions to which the turf will be subjected. As an aid in choosing the best grasses to meet any given set of requirements this chapter will cover (1) climatic adaptations of the turf grasses on a regional basis, (2) their value for various uses on the golf course, and (3) descriptions of the individual species and of improved strains where such exist.

Climate Affects the Choice of a Grass

The grasses that will survive naturally in any given region over a long period of time are those which have been able to adjust themselves to the extremes of temperature, moisture, and other factors that limit growth. Many of the conditions normally occurring in nature are widely modified in the process of growing turf on the golf course. The job will be relatively easier when grasses are chosen which have a good natural adaptation to the climatic conditions of the region where they are to be used. Temperature extremes are the most important consideration because their effects can be controlled only to a limited extent. Natural moisture supplies also are a controlling factor where irrigation is impracticable. In choosing a grass it will be wise to determine whether the location where it is to be used falls within the general region of its normal adaptation, particularly from the standpoint of temperature and moisture.

Grasses for the Northern Cool Humid Region

This region includes two widely separated areas in the United States. The first covers all of the northeastern states and most of the north-central states and extends south into the mountainous sections of eastern Tennessee and western North Carolina. The second area is located in the Pacific northwest and comprises approximately the western thirds of Washington and Oregon and a part of northwestern California.

PERMANENT GRASSES. The grasses best adapted for permanent turf on golf courses within the region fall into three groups: bluegrasses, fescues, and bentgrasses. The bluegrass group includes Kentucky bluegrass, roughstalk bluegrass, Canada bluegrass, and annual bluegrass. The fescue group consists of creeping red fescue, Chewings fescue, sheep fescue, and tall fescue. Species of the bentgrass group are the creeping bents, the colonial bents, and the velvet bents. Sometimes certain types of Bermudagrass and the zoysia grasses can be used to advantage for permanent turf along the southern limits of the region.

TEMPORARY GRASSES. The most important species in this group are redtop, perennial ryegrass, and Italian ryegrass. Mixtures of perennial and Italian ryegrass are sold under the name of domestic ryegrass. The primary value of the temporary grasses lies in their ability to develop rapidly and establish cover quickly. They are short lived under close clipping and for this reason are used only where temporary cover is needed or in seed mixtures with permanent types for protection against weeds and erosion while the slower growing permanent grasses are developing.

Miscellaneous Grasses. In addition to the permanent and temporary species noted, several other grasses have a limited value for golf-course use under certain conditions. The most important of these are timothy, orchardgrass, tall oatgrass, and bromegrass. All are tall-growing types which form a loose open turf under close clipping. They are sometimes economical, considering seed costs and availability, for use on outlying areas where protection against erosion and weeds is needed and frequent clipping is not required.

Grasses for the Southern Warm Humid and Southwest Irrigated Regions

These regions include, respectively, all of the southeastern states and that section of the Southwest as indicated on the map in Fig. 1 (page 3). Although the two areas are widely different in natural rainfall, their temperature conditions are very similar, except at the higher elevations in the Southwest. Rainfall is so limited in the Southwest that none of the desirable grasses for golf-course use will survive unless additional water is supplied by irrigation. Where water is available, the species adapted to the southeastern area normally are grown. At the higher elevations grasses of the Cool Humid and Central regions may be used.

Permanent Grasses. The best grasses for permanent turf in these regions are Bermudagrass, centipedegrass, carpetgrass, St. Augustinegrass, Manilagrass (zoysia), Japanese lawngrass (zoysia), and Bahiagrass. Not all of these species are equally well adapted over the entire area. Bermudagrass and the zoysia grasses probably have the widest range of usefulness. They will grow well in most sections if sufficient water is available and soil factors are properly adjusted. On the other hand, St. Augustinegrass will do well only in the warmest sections. At the higher elevations in the southwestern region the bentgrasses, Kentucky bluegrass and other permanent cool-climate grasses can be grown if water is available.

Under drier conditions buffalo and grama grasses are suitable. The specific adaptations of each grass will be fully covered in the discussion of the individual species.

TEMPORARY GRASSES. Requirements for temporary grasses for use on golf courses in the regions are primarily for types that will make active growth during the winter period when the permanent grasses are dormant. Redtop, Italian ryegrass, and annual bluegrass are best suited for this purpose. Their use is confined largely to greens and tees and sometimes fairways where they are overseeded on the permanent turf in the fall when low temperatures check active growth. On some courses creeping bent and creeping red fescue also have been used successfully for this purpose. Good management is required not only to secure satisfactory establishment of the temporary cover but also to accomplish the transition back to the permanent turf when it begins active growth in the spring.

MISCELLANEOUS GRASSES. Species having limited value in the regions on nonuse areas for erosion and weed control include dallisgrass and Rhodesgrass in the Warm Humid section, and the lovegrasses, sand dropseed, and Indian ricegrass in the dry areas of the southwest.

Grasses for the Central Region of Limited Rainfall

This region includes all of the West Central states and extends from the Canadian border south to the boundaries of northern Texas, Arizona, and New Mexico (see Fig. 1). Average annual temperatures in the area approximate those of the Cool Humid region, and turf grasses adapted to the latter can be grown successfully wherever sufficient moisture is available. Because of limited natural rainfall, additional water must be supplied through irrigation to produce good turf with the bluegrasses, fescues, bents, and other species of the Cool Humid region. Where irrigation is impracticable, native grasses with relatively low-moisture requirements are the most suitable for general turf use.

PERMANENT GRASSES. All of the species used in the Cool Humid region can be grown successfully in the Central region where irrigation is practicable. On nonirrigated areas the native species best adapted for permanent turf are buffalograss, the grama grasses, crested wheatgrass, and smooth bromegrass. These grasses are suitable for fairways, tees, and roughs on the golf course but are not adapted for use on greens.

TEMPORARY GRASSES. Temporary cover can best be obtained by the use of cereal grains such as oats, wheat, and rye or of Sudangrass. Although these may not reach maturity because of moisture limitations, usually they will develop sufficiently to provide adequate protection against erosion. They may be used also to provide temporary cover for the protection of new seedings of the permanent grasses. When employed for this purpose, seedings of the permanent grasses should be made in the stubble only after the temporary grass has matured or has been killed by frost. Because of competition for moisture it is not satisfactory to seed the temporary and permanent grasses at the same time.

MISCELLANEOUS GRASSES. Grasses which have a limited value for cover on nonuse areas of the golf course in this region include western wheatgrass, little bluestem, and weeping lovegrass. The last named is well adapted only in the southern portion of the region.

Grasses for Specific Uses on the Golf Course

Any grass used on the golf course must fit its environment. It must meet the demands of the game and must be able to survive under the type of maintenance required for good playing conditions. Grasses used on greens, tees, fairways, and roughs must be able to adjust themselves to the requirements of these areas. Kentucky bluegrass is a case in point. The moderately coarse-textured somewhat open type of turf which it forms and its characteristic inability to withstand frequent close clipping bar it from use on putting greens and on closely clipped fairways. On the other hand, it will provide a very serviceable playing turf on fairways which are not cut too closely.

GRASSES FOR GREENS. Putting-green surfaces must be smooth, dense, and sufficiently firm to avoid footprints or other irregularities which might deflect the ball. The demands of play require that they be resilient without being spongy and that they be kept even and true at all times. Maintenance of turf under these very specialized conditions calls for frequent close clipping and many other management practices which seriously interfere with the normal growth of the grass. Only a very few grasses have been found that are capable of meeting putting-green requirements.

The creeping bents, colonial bents, velvet bents, and Bermudagrass are best adapted for permanent turf on putting greens. The bentgrasses, either alone or as mixtures, are used in nearly every section of the United States although they thrive best under moist cool conditions. The use of Bermudagrass is confined to regions with high summer temperatures.

Redtop, domestic ryegrass, and annual bluegrass also may be classed as putting-green grasses because of their value for temporary use as winter turf in the South. Because very little seed of annual bluegrass is available commercially, its use for winter turf is limited largely to greens where it has become established and reseeds itself naturally every year. Its value as a permanent putting-green turf in the North is restricted to the relatively few areas where it can be held during the hot weather of summer.

GRASSES FOR TEES. A good tee grass must be tough, capable of withstanding punishment and close clipping, and able to heal divot scars quickly. In the Southern region Bermudagrass meets all of these requirements and is in general use for summer tees except in shade. Centipedegrass and the zoysias also make excelent turf for summer use. Redtop and domestic ryegrass are best for winter turf on tees in this region.

The most useful grasses for tees in the Northern region are the colonial and creeping types of the bentgrasses, Kentucky bluegrass, mixtures of Kentucky and Canada bluegrass, creeping red fescue, Chewings fescue, and selected strains of tall fescue (Alta and Kentucky 31). Where cool moist weather prevails and where there is shade, annual bluegrass is ideal for tee turf. It should be noted, however, that this is a treacherous grass for any location where temperatures and humidity are likely to be high for periods of even two or three days.

In the West Central region the same grasses used in the Cool Humid region are suitable for tees wherever irrigation is practicable. For nonirrigated conditions buffalograss and the fairway strain of crested wheatgrass are the most satisfactory.

GRASSES FOR FAIRWAYS. Modern golf demands a smooth weed-free fairway turf that will give the player a firm stance, will carry the ball high, and will provide a cushion for the shot. These demands have created a gradual change in maintenance practices, with emphasis on close and frequent clipping and on heavy fertilization and watering to keep the grass in an active growing condition throughout the season. Some grasses, notably Kentucky bluegrass and the fescues, have not been able to adjust themselves to this type of treatment. In choosing a grass for fairway use, therefore, it is important to predetermine the type of maintenance which will be followed.

Bermuda and centipedegrass have the widest adaptations for fairway use throughout the Southern region. Carpetgrass will produce good turf on low areas where moisture supplies are liberal. All three species are low-growing creepers and are well equipped to survive under close clipping and other specialized maintenance practices. Additional grasses that are promising for fairway use include the zoysia grasses and selected strains of Bahiagrass. These are not in general use at the present time because of a lack of seed in commercial quantities and because of the cost and difficulty involved in vegetative planting of large areas.

In the Northern region colonial bent and creeping bent are the best grasses for fairways under intensive management practices of close clipping, heavy fertilization, and watering. Where the grass is cut reasonably high (1 to 1½ in.) and water is used sparingly or not at all, Kentucky bluegrass and the fescues will make satisfactory turf. Mixtures of Kentucky bluegrass, Canada bluegrass, and fescues also can be used to advantage under these conditions. Canada bluegrass should not be used alone because of the thin open type of sod which it produces.

Buffalograss, crested wheatgrass, and the grama grasses are the best species for use on unwatered fairways in the West Central region. The zoysia grasses have promise in the warmer sections of the region where limited water is available for irrigation. Where water is available for irrigation, creeping and colonial bentgrasses, Kentucky bluegrass, and the fescues are suitable provided that management practices are adjusted to the growth habits of each.

FIG. 10. Fescue on trap shoulders. (*Courtesy Sewerage Commission, City of Milwaukee.*)

GRASSES FOR ROUGHS AND TRAP FACINGS. Roughs are commonly the most neglected sections of the golf course. A common practice in the past has been to permit them to grow up to any type of vegetation occurring naturally on the area with occasional mowings when growth becomes so rank as to interfere seriously with play. The modern trend in course management, however, has been to seed the close roughs with the same species used on the fairway. An exception is creeping bent which is not satisfactory for close roughs. The required playing conditions are secured by adjusting mowing heights and fertilization. Where severe penalties are desired, roughs may be seeded with grasses having a heavy bunch habit of growth. Species of this type include sheep fescue, tall fescue, orchardgrass, timothy, and tall oatgrass for the Northern region. In the humid section of the Southern region, dallisgrass, the lovegrasses, and Rhodesgrass are suitable for erosion control on nonuse areas. Sand dropseed and Indian ricegrass can be used in the Southwest. In the West Central region native grasses such as western wheatgrass, crested wheatgrass, and the grama grasses are satisfactory.

The best species for stabilizing the dry sandy slopes of trap facings and bunkers are sheep fescue and the lovegrasses. Where maintenance is not a factor and cover is needed on dunes and similar areas, broomsedge and beachgrass sometimes can be used to good advantage.

Characteristics of Individual Grass Species

ALKALIGRASS (*Puccinnellia distans*) has high salt tolerance and will grow at alkali levels which other turfgrasses will not tolerate. It is slow growing, spreading by short rhizomes. It forms a moderately dense turf very simliar in appearance to that formed by red fescue. It has been used successfully by golf courses in the Western part of the United States where alkali soils are a problem.

ANNUAL BLUEGRASS (*Poa annua*) rarely lives for more than one year. Seed produced earlier the same season normally germinates in late summer and early fall, and the plants make their maximum growth during the late fall and early spring when other grasses are dormant. It matures and dies quickly under conditions of high temperatures and humidity. Because of its ability to grow at relatively low temperatures and its lack of tolerance to hot humid weather, it is of very questionable value for use as permanent turf in the North. These same characteristics make it useful for overseeding on the dormant permanent grasses for winter turf in the South.

Annual bluegrass has no rootstocks or creeping stems and produces a solid sod only because of the dense stand of individual plants. Under close clipping it makes a smooth even turf that has excellent putting qualities. Because of its quick germination and rapid growth during the active growing season, divot scars and other injuries heal in a relatively short time. It requires a cool moist soil of good fertility and low acidity and grows well in shade. Low soil temperatures are particularly important, and it is sometimes possible to hold it throughout the growing season by frequent light waterings on days when temperatures are excessive.

The ability of annual bluegrass to produce large quantities of seed at any clipping height and the fact that it makes most of its growth at periods when other grasses are dormant and give it little competition are primarily responsible for its abundance. Its presence may indicate some deficiency in the management program, such as overwatering or excessive compaction. While there is no sure method for its control, it is often practicable to check it within reasonable limits by adjusting maintenance practices to make conditions as favorable as possible for the permanent grasses. They include feeding only when the permanent grasses are active and best able to use fertilizers and restricting watering in periods when annual bluegrass is making its most rapid growth. There is some evidence that it may be injured by arsenicals such as arsenate of lead and sodium arsenite (see discussions of insecticides and herbicides).

Only very limited quantities of annual bluegrass seed are available commercially. This is due to the restricted demand and practical difficulties of harvesting and processing the seed. There are no improved strains of the grass at the present time.

BAHIAGRASS (*Paspalum notatum*) is a newcomer on the golf course, and to date it has not been sufficiently tested to warrant practical use. Trials of it at the Coastal Plain Experiment Station at Tifton, Georgia, indicate that it has definite possibilities for use as a tee and fairway grass. It is a low-growing perennial that spreads by short heavy runners and is best adapted to the Southern Coastal Plains of the Warm Humid region. It will survive on droughty sandy soils of low fertility.

Seed of two varieties of Bahiagrass is being increased in the United States, namely, the Paraguay and Pensacola. Only limited quantities are available at the present time. If its use is contemplated, it should be planted on limited areas on a trial basis until its practical value for golf-course turf has been more fully determined.

Beachgrasses (*Ammophila* spp.) are of principal value for use on golf courses for the stabilization of shifting sands in dune areas. They are coarse erect grasses with extensive rootstocks and will make a heavy growth on droughty sands of low fertility. They are best adapted along the north and middle Atlantic coast south to North Carolina and are found also to some extent on the Pacific coast.

Seed is not available commercially, and the grasses are propagated by vegetative planting of stems of old plants. The plants are collected when they are dormant during the late fall or early spring and are broken up into small clusters of stems (clones). These are set individually in hills spaced at 2- to 3-ft. intervals. Because of the large amount of handwork involved in this method of planting, the beachgrasses have been used only on those areas where other species easier to establish will not survive.

Bermudagrass (*Cynodon dactylon*) has a wide range of adaptability for golf courses in the Southern region. When properly managed it will make a very satisfactory turf on greens and tees. It is suitable also for fairways and is easily adaptable for roughs. It may be propagated from seed and also by sprig planting the creeping stems and underground rootstocks. Commercial seed supplies are produced in Arizona and Southern California but are not well suited for use in the more northern sections of the region. Vegetative plantings of types that have a higher cold tolerance than the turf produced from commercial seed are more satisfactory in these areas.

Under close clipping Bermudagrass forms a compact dense turf which becomes coarse and stemmy unless severely brushed and top-dressed frequently. It thrives best under warm to hot weather conditions and needs constant supplies of water in moderate quantities. It will not tolerate shade, poor drainage, and high acidity and will produce good turf only when soil fertility is maintained at a high level. Fertilizer experiments at the Coastal Plain Experiment Station at Tifton, Georgia, and elsewhere indicate that constant liberal supplies of available nitrogen are particularly important for maintenance of high-quality turf. Breeding and selection work to produce improved varieties of Bermudagrass is in progress at a number of state agricultural experiment stations, including the Georgia Coastal Plain Experiment Station, and the Florida, Kansas, Oklahoma, and Texas stations. A number of improved varieties have been developed. Brief descriptions of those most widely used, follow. Originating stations should be contacted for more detailed information on them.

Bayshore was developed in Florida and is used on greens, tees, and fairways. It is a light-green, fine-textured grass adapted only to the warmer sections of the South.

Everglades 1 also was developed in Florida. It is adapted primarily to use on greens and tees. It produces a dark-green, uniformly fine-textured turf. It is best adapted to Florida and other sections having similar climatic conditions.

Ormond is a variety selected in Florida primarily for use on fairways and tees. It produces a blue-green, vigorous, medium-textured turf. It has no cold tolerance and is useful only in the warmer sections of the South.

Sunturf originated in South Africa and has been tested by a number of experiment stations in the South. It is a dark-green, fine-textured type that can be used on greens, tees, and fairways. It has greater cold tolerance than the Florida varieties and does well throughout the mid-South.

Texturf 1F was developed in Texas. It is a light-green, fine-textured grass that can be used on greens, tees, and fairways. It has performed best in areas having climatic conditions similar to those in central and west Texas.

Texturf 10 is a selection made at the Texas Agricultural Experiment Station. It forms a dark-green, medium-textured turf that is most useful for fairways and tees. It makes early spring recovery from dormancy and produces very few seed heads.

Tifine originated at the Georgia Coastal Plain Experiment Station from crossing Common and African Bermudagrasses. It has good disease tolerance and is useful throughout the mid-South for greens, tees, and fairways.

Tifgreen also was produced at the Georgia Coastal Plain Station by crossing Common and African Bermudagrasses. It produces a very uniform, fine-textured turf with good disease tolerance. It makes an excellent putting green turf and is being used on many golf courses throughout the mid-South.

Tiflawn was selected at the Georgia Coastal Plain Station. It produces a medium-textured, highly wear-resistant turf that is best adapted for heavy duty on intensively used areas, as athletic fields and playgrounds.

Tifway was developed at the Georgia Coastal Plain Experiment Station. The leaves are tough and very dark green in color. It has high density and weed resistance, and is a sparse seeder. It is more frost resistant than Tiflawn, Tifgreen, and Common Bermuda. Because of its lack of softness it is better for fairway use than on greens.

U-3. The United States Golf Association Green Section developed this variety at Beltsville, Maryland. It is medium textured and more dense than Common Bermuda. It has shown higher cold tolerance than other improved Bermudagrass varieties but is less disease resistant. It has been widely used throughout the northern part of the warm humid region on tees and fairways.

Uganda is an African Bermudagrass introduced into the United States from the Gezira Golf Club, Cairo, Egypt. It is low growing and very fine textured. It spreads slowly and, although quite cold tolerant, develops a purplish cast with cool weather in the fall. Its use is confined mostly to putting greens.

BROOMSEDGEGRASS (*Andropogon virginicus*). The value of this grass for golf courses is limited to use on bunkers and dunes to control sand movement. It is tall and coarse and does not develop creeping stems or rootstocks. Seed is not produced commercially, and plantings are made by setting individual plants or divided tufts of individual plants in hills at 1½- or 2-ft. intervals on the area to be protected.

Broomsedge will grow on dry soils of low fertility. It matures early and develops a characteristic brownish color by the middle of the summer. It will not stand close clipping and should be planted only in the roughs and on nonuse areas.

BUFFALOGRASS (*Buchloe dactyloides*) is excellent for use on fairways, tees, and roughs of golf courses in the West Central region where water for irrigation is limited or unavailable. It is a low-growing, sod-forming perennial which spreads by creeping surface runners. It can be grown from seed or by planting 4-in. sod pieces on 2- to 4-ft. centers in a well-prepared seedbed. Buffalograss seed burs must be processed by soaking and chilling to ensure adequate germination. Treated seed is available commercially and should be used for turf establishment.

The turf is fine-leaved and dense and will withstand frequent close clipping. During its active growing period the foliage is grayish green but changes rapidly to a light straw color when growth stops. It grows best on the heavier types of soil that are fertile and well drained. Attempts to maintain satisfactory turf in areas outside its normal region of adaptation have not been very successful. Apparently it cannot adjust itself adequately to high humidity, disease, and soil conditions prevailing in these sections. Many state agricultural experiment stations in the West Central region are working to improve buffalograss. The value of new strains for turf is being studied, but no types for such use have been released as yet.

CANADA BLUEGRASS (*Poa compressa*) is of value principally in seed mixtures for fairways and tees. It is a sod-forming grass that spreads by underground rootstocks but produces a thin stemmy type of turf because of sparse leaf development. It is propagated entirely from seed which usually is available commercially in sufficient quantities to meet normal requirements.

Although the turf qualities of Canada bluegrass are poor, it produces a very tough sod, and will tolerate loose dry soils of low fertility, and grows well in shade. These characteristics sometimes justify its use in mixtures with the better grasses on areas which are subject to concentrated use or where soils are spotty in moisture-retaining capacity and fertility. It will not tolerate poor drainage, high acidity, and constant clipping to heights of less than about 1¼ in. No improved strains are available commercially.

CARPETGRASS (*Axonopus affinis*) is a low-growing perennial that spreads by aboveground creeping stems which root at every joint. It can be propagated vegetatively by planting these creeping stems, but the simplest method of establishment is by seed, which is abundant and cheap. It produces a dense compact turf under close clipping which is excellent for fairways and tees but is too coarse for use on putting greens.

It grows best on sandy to sandy loam soils that contain liberal quantities of moisture throughout the growing season, but it will not thrive on soils that are waterlogged for any appreciable period of time. Carpetgrass will produce a suitable turf for use on the golf course only when soil fertility is good and a program of liberal fertilization is followed. Large quantities of nitrogen, particularly, are essential. It is well adapted to close clipping and is one of the grasses that are most tolerant to heavy trampling. Breeding work for the development of improved types of carpetgrass is under way at several state agricultural experiment stations, but no superior types for turf use are yet ready for distribution.

CENTIPEDEGRASS (*Eremochloa ophiuroides*) is intermediate in appearance between Bermudagrass and carpetgrass. It is a low-growing perennial that spreads rapidly by short compact creeping stems that form new plants at every joint. Since seed is not available commercially as yet, it must be propagated vegetatively by planting the creeping stems. Centipedegrass produces a dense vigorous turf that is well adapted for fairways and tees. Like carpetgrass the foliage is too coarse to be suitable for use on greens.

It is adapted to a wide range of soil conditions, growing equally well on heavy clays and light sandy soils. It is tolerant also to high acidity and low fertility. Although it will persist on poor soils, it is benefited by applications of fertilizer. To produce a turf that has the required qualities for golf-course use it should receive a liberal annual application of a complete fertilizer high in nitrogen. It is sensitive to a lack of iron, and overliming may induce chlorosis. It is more severely injured by heavy trampling and intensive use than are Bermudagrass and carpetgrass and will not recover from injury as rapidly. No improved strains for use as special-purpose turf have been developed.

CHEWINGS FESCUE AND CREEPING RED FESCUE (*Festuca rubra*) are distinct forms of this species. The Chewings type is tufted and does not creep, while the creeping red has a predominantly creeping habit of growth by well-developed underground rootstocks. Since the adaptations and general value of the two types are very similar, they will be discussed together.

Both grasses are propagated entirely from seed which is produced chiefly in Oregon. Some seed is also imported from Canada, New Zealand, and Australia. Seed from New Zealand and Australia is of the Chewings type, while that coming from Canada is the creeping red type. Oregon grows both types. Under normal conditions commercial seed is abundant at a reasonable price. An important characteristic of fescue seed is that it loses its vitality rapidly if stored with a high moisture content at temperatures which average over 70°F. Where seed has been materially injured in storage, it deteriorates rapidly and is not a safe planting risk.

The turf produced by both grasses is excellent for fairways and tees when properly managed. The tough bristlelike leaves are highly resistant to wear and provide perfect playing conditions where the sod is good. Because of their slow growth rate these fescues will not heal quickly when injured nor resist invasion by other grasses under intensive management of frequent clipping, heavy fertilization, and watering.

Both types will grow on poor droughty soils, provided that drainage is good, and they have a wide tolerance to acidity. It should be recognized, however, that they grow in spite of these conditions and not because of them. Maintenance of good fertility by annual applications of moderate quantities of a complete fertilizer and the periodic use of lime to keep the soil above a pH 5.5 to 6.0 will aid materially in producing satisfactory turf for golf-course use. Both types grow well in shade and are widely used for this purpose.

Constant clipping to heights of less than 1¼ in. will seriously injure turf produced by commercial seed of both grasses, although there is some evidence that the creeping red is more tolerant to low cutting than the Chewings type. Tests of selected strains which are under way at a number of research institutions indicate that there is a wide degree of variability in this characteristic.

Improved varieties of creeping red fescue are Illahee, Rainier, and Pennlawn. The Illahee is a selection made from a seed field in Oregon. It has greater density and less disease susceptibility than common creeping red. The Rainier variety was found in Washington and is very similar in performance to Illahee. Pennlawn was bred at the Pennsylvania Agricultural Experiment Station. It is a synthetic variety produced by random crossing of three selected parents. It produces a denser and more uniform turf than the common creeping red and Chewings types, and has greater disease tolerance than the Illahee and Rainier varieties under Eastern growing conditions.

COLONIAL BENTGRASS (*Agrostis tenuis*) has a wide range of usefulness for greens, fairways, and tees on golf courses throughout the Cool Humid region. It is propagated entirely from seed, which is produced commercially chiefly in Oregon. Several types are available which have slightly different color and growth-habit characteristics. The most important of these types are the Astoria, Highland, and Oregon Colonial. Some seed is also imported from New Zealand and distributed under the name of New Zealand Colonial. In the past this has been known in the trade as New Zealand Browntop. The specific adaptations of these various types have not been adequately determined. No improved strains of the species have been released.

Colonial bent is essentially a tufted type of grass, occasionally producing very short rootstocks and creeping stems. In recent years seed has become badly contaminated with varying percentages of strongly creeping types. This has reduced its usefulness in mixtures with slower growing grasses, due to the aggressiveness of the creepers. When heavily seeded it develops a fine-textured dense turf under close clipping that makes an excellent putting surface, particularly when used in mixtures with creeping bent.

Because of its rapid growth rate, it requires a fertile soil and a program of liberal fertilization, particularly where used on greens. It will tolerate high acidity but makes its best growth when soils are reasonably sweet. Water requirements are relatively high, and it should be irrigated regularly during droughty periods. Its ability to withstand close clipping adapts it for use on fairways where this type of maintenance is demanded.

CREEPING BENTGRASS (*Agrostis palustris*) is by far the best adapted and most widely used grass for putting greens throughout the Northern Cool Humid region. In recent years its use has spread to other sections of the United States, and creeping bentgrass putting greens are in service in Texas, New Mexico, Arizona, and Southern California. Some types of this grass also are well adapted for use on fairways and tees under intensive systems of management.

As the name implies, creeping bentgrass spreads by creeping stems which have the ability to produce roots and shoots at every joint. It forms a very close-knit sod that makes a smooth true-putting surface with excellent resiliency. Because of its dense foliage and profuse creeping stems it requires close cutting, frequent brushing, and periodic top-dressing to avoid undesirable matting and graininess.

Creeping bentgrass will grow under a wide variety of soil conditions, but it produces the best turf where acidity is moderate to low and fertility, aeration, and water-holding capacity are good. Because of its rapid growth rate its moisture and feeding requirements are high. When used for putting greens and tees, systematic watering and fertilization must be practiced to ensure good-quality turf. When soils have become compact through heavy use, the root system becomes shallow and the turf becomes thin, permitting undesirable grasses and weeds to come in.

Two general classes of creeping bentgrasses are available commercially. One consists of a group of varieties developed by selection of individual plants from old established greens or from plant nurseries. All of these must be propagated vegetatively by planting the creeping stems (stolons). The second group includes the varieties that are propagated by seed. Planting stock of most of the vegetative varieties is available from a number of commercial nurseries in the bentgrass growing area. Seed of the second group is produced entirely in the Pacific Northwest.

The most widely used vegetatively propagated varieties are the Arlington, Cohansey, Collins, Congressional, Old Orchard, Pennlu, Toronto, and Washington. In addition to these, many selections of individual strains have been made by golf course superintendents and are being used locally. Since each vegetatively propagated variety has the characteristics and limitations of an individual plant, the performance records under the conditions similar to those to which the turf will be subjected should be checked carefully to determine which type is best suited to a particular location. Mechanical mixtures of stolons of several varieties often produce better turf than a single variety. For best results, color and growth characteristics must be similar; otherwise the varieties will eventually separate out and the turf will develop a patchy, irregular appearance.

The seeded group of creeping bentgrasses consists of two varieties for which seed is commercially available. These are Penncross and Seaside. Critical observations and comparative tests indicate that the Penncross will produce materially better turf than the Seaside over most of the area where creeping bents are used. The former is more uniform, has better density, is more disease resistant, and is adapted to a wider range of growing conditions. The seeded bents are less expensive to establish, both because of first cost of seed vs. stolons, and the difference in the time and labor required for planting. An added advantage is the greater simplicity in making overseedings on established turf when renovation is needed.

CRESTED WHEATGRASS (*Agropyron cristatum*) is a hardy perennial that thrives in the cool dry sections of the West Central region. Its primary value on the golf course is for tee and fairway use when irrigation is impracticable. It is also well adapted for use in roughs if seeded lightly and clipped only two or three times during the growing season. It is propagated entirely from seed, which is available commercially at reasonable prices.

Although crested wheatgrass is a bunch grass without creeping stems or rootstocks, it will form a fairly dense sod when seeded heavily and clipped regularly. This is due primarily to the heavy growth of basal leaves which it produces. It has a very deep fibrous root system which enables it not only to survive long dry periods but also to withstand heavy use without serious injury. Most of its growth is made during the spring and fall. It turns brown and goes into a semidormant condition during dry hot summer periods. In addition to its hardiness and drought resistance, it will grow on practically any type of soil and is fairly alkali tolerant.

Two improved strains of crested wheatgrass are available commercially: Standard and Fairway. The Standard strain is slightly more hardy and has somewhat greater drought resistance than the Fairway. It is coarser, however, and will not produce as dense and fine-textured a cover at normal clipping heights as the Fairway strain.

DALLISGRASS (*Paspalum dilatatum*). The value of dallisgrass for use on golf courses is limited to roughs and nonuse areas. It has a bunchy growth habit and forms an uneven open sod. It is propagated entirely from seed which usually is low in germination and must be used at heavy rates to secure good stands. It is not aggressive or particularly wear resistant under close and frequent clippings and readily permits weed invasion under these conditions.

Dallisgrass requires liberal supplies of moisture but will not tolerate poor drainage and high acidity. It prefers soils with a high organic-matter content. Where fertility is low it requires regular fertilization to keep it in adequate condition for turf use. Dallisgrass is a pest in fairways where seed is permitted to mature.

GRAMA GRASSES (*Bouteloua* spp.). Among the species of grama grasses native to the drier sections of the West Central region the blue grama (*B. gracilis*) is the most suitable for turf use. It is a low-growing hardy perennial that is highly drought resistant. Like crested wheatgrass it stops growth and turns brown during drought periods, becoming active again when moisture and temperature conditions are favorable. It is a bunch grass but will produce a good sod when seeded heavily and clipped regularly and is suitable for use on all areas of golf courses in its area of adaptation, except on greens. Seed is available commercially but is light and fluffy and difficult to distribute evenly.

Blue grama grass is adapted to a wide range of soil conditions, including alkali soils. It is less resistant to wear than buffalograss and cannot be clipped so closely and so frequently as the latter species. It will respond to both fertilizers and water, and the best turf is grown with it where management practices include these items.

No improved strains have been produced. There is a marked difference in the results secured with seed at a given location, depending upon where it was produced. Seed grown in the Dakotas and other northern states of the West Central region is not well adapted in the warmer sections further south. Similarly, seed produced in the southern areas is not suitable for northern planting. In areas where both species are adapted, excellent results may be secured by seeding a mixture of blue grama and buffalograss. The proportions for such a mixture should be approximately 2 parts blue grama to 1 buffalograss and the seeding rate 1 lb. per 1,000 sq. ft.

INDIAN RICEGRASS (*Oryzopsis hymenoides*) is a densely tufted perennial bunchgrass which grows from 1 to 2 ft. tall. Its value on the golf course is limited to nonirrigated areas of the dry Southwest where protective cover is needed for roughs and nonuse areas. It is highly drought resistant and somewhat alkali tolerant and often can be established on extremely dry sandy soils where practically no other grasses will grow. Seed is available commercially and when properly processed can be planted readily with a mechanical seeder. If initial thin stands are permitted to mature without clipping, natural reseeding will materially increase their density in years of good seasonal rainfall.

RYEGRASSES (*Lolium* spp.) Ryegrass is the name commonly applied to two closely related grasses: Italian ryegrass (*L. multiflorum*) and perennial ryegrass (*L. perenne*). Both are bunch grasses and form turfs very similar in appearance. True Italian ryegrass is an annual, while the perennial form will persist for four or five years under favorable conditions. The ryegrasses have two widely different adaptations for turf use. In the Northern Cool Humid region their principal value is in mixtures to make a quick cover while the slower growing, more permanent species are becoming established. In the Southern region they are used primarily for winter turf on greens, tees, and fairways.

Very little pure Italian ryegrass seed is produced in the United States. The Pacific Northwest produces perennial ryegrass and also large quantities of seed that is a mixture of annual, perennial, and intermediate types. This seed is often sold under the name of domestic ryegrass. It is less expensive than pure seed of the individual species and is equally good for use as temporary winter turf in the South. Its value in mixtures for permanent turf in the North is questionable. Many of the perennial and intermediate forms which are present in it are vigorous growers and seriously compete with the permanent grasses in their seedling year. Also, these types may persist as solid coarse clumps for several seasons, producing a ragged uneven turf and seriously crowding the more desirable species.

The ryegrasses require well-drained soils of good moisture-holding capacity. Because of their rapid growth rate they need liberal fertilization where soil fertility is medium to low. Good fertility is particularly important where rapid growth of the turf is required for winter use. They will not grow well on soils that are compact or strongly acid and are severely injured by hot dry weather. No improved strains adapted for turf use have been developed for use in the United States.

JAPANESE LAWNGRASS, zoysia (*Zoysia japonica*) has become a valuable addition to the group of grasses used for turf within its area of adaptation. While it has been grown successfully as far north as Boston, its principal area of usefulness will probably be south of 40° latitude because of its slow growth and quick loss of color in cool weather. It has a creeping habit of growth and forms a dense, tough sod that is very resistant to wear. Because of its coarse harsh type of leaf it is not adapted for use on greens although it will withstand extremely close clipping. Its exceptionally good wearing qualities should make it particularly useful for tees, fairways, and roughs. It is highly drought resistant, shade tolerant, and will thrive on a wide range of soil types. It will survive at low fertility levels but makes its best growth when fed regularly with liberal quantities of a complete fertilizer high in nitrogen.

Japanese lawngrass is a low-growing long-lived perennial that spreads both by creeping stems and rootstocks. Growth seldom reaches a height of more than 9 or 10 in. even when unclipped, and the mature sod forms a close woven mat that is highly resistant to weed encroachment. Because of the exceptional density of the sod and its good climatic adaptation, it should be particularly valuable for use in the southern part of the Cool Humid region and the northern section of the Warm Humid region where summer infestations of crabgrass are a serious problem owing to the limited adaptation of both northern and southern grasses to this area. It makes its most vigorous and aggressive growth during the crabgrass season and so is well adapted to resist invasion by this pest.

Interest in Japanese lawngrass has been restricted for several reasons. Seed is not as yet available commercially, and it must be propagated vegetatively by sprig planting the creeping stems or by spot sodding. Establishment of a mature turf by these methods is not very satisfactory because of the slow growth rate of the grass. Approximately two years are required normally to obtain complete cover. This period can be reduced to some extent by liberal use of fertilizers high in nitrogen and by heavy planting rates.

Two improved varieties, Meyer and Emerald, have been developed and are in general use in the zoysia growing areas. The Meyer is an individual plant selection made at Arlington Farms (United States Department of Agriculture) in 1940. It is medium textured and produces a tough, wear-resistant turf that is very drought tolerant. It has more cold tolerance than most of the warm-season grasses. Its greatest usefulness is on tees and fairways. The Emerald variety is an interspecies hybrid produced at the United States Department of Agriculture Plant Industry Station, Beltsville, Maryland. It is dark green and finer textured than Meyer, and has greater cold resistance than most of the Bermudagrasses. Planting stock of both Meyer and Emerald is produced for commercial distribution by several nurseries in the South.

KENTUCKY BLUEGRASS (*Poa pratensis*) has been widely used, both alone and in mixtures, for tees, fairways, and roughs on golf courses throughout the entire Cool Humid region and wherever irrigation water is available in the West Central region. It is a long-lived, perennial, sod-forming grass that spreads by numerous heavy underground rootstocks. The turf is medium in texture and density and of a pleasing brilliant green color. It is propagated entirely from seed which is produced largely in the Central states and Pacific Northwest and normally is in abundant supply commercially at a reasonable price.

Kentucky bluegrass prefers heavy well-drained soils of good fertility. It will not withstand poor drainage and makes its best growth where soil acidity is at or only slightly below the neutral point. Water requirements are high during the active growing period, but it is also highly drought tolerant owing to an ability to go into a semidormant condition during hot dry periods. Its drought and cold tolerance are dependent upon the extent of underground stem development. Close clipping or low fertility that reduces the number of these stems will lower its ability to survive under adverse weather conditions. It will make satisfactory turf only where soils are high in available nitrogen, phosphorus, and potassium. Where fertility is medium to low, fertilizer programs must be designed to apply these elements in liberal quantities.

Constant clipping to heights of less than 1 to 1¼ in. will seriously injure Kentucky bluegrass turf. Reduced rootstock formation under these conditions, with consequent failure to produce new shoots that will maintain satisfactory sod density, is the chief source of trouble. The grass also is seriously affected by soil compaction resulting from trampling and the use of heavy maintenance equipment when soils are saturated due to heavy natural precipitation or overwatering. This inability to adjust itself to the requirements of intensive course maintenance definitely limits the value of Kentucky bluegrass for use on the golf course. It will not produce adequate turf where close clipping, heavy fertilization, and frequent watering are a normal part of the maintenance program.

The wide variability in type among individual plants of the species, and the high percentage of asexual forms it contains offer excellent possibilities for the development of superior varieties. Improvement programs are under way at a number of state agricultural experiment stations and other research institutions in the region of Kentucky bluegrass adaptation. Named varieties resulting from this work include Aboretum, Delta, Merion, Newport, Park, and Troy.

Arboretum. Selected at the Missouri Botanical Gardens from collections of plants from old pastures and lawns in Missouri. Performance tests over a wide area of the Kentucky bluegrass growing region indicate that it is not materially superior to common Kentucky bluegrass, due probably to its high susceptibility to the leaf spot disease.

Delta. Selected at the Forage Crop Division, Experimental Farm Service, Ottawa, Canada. It is a fast, vigorous grower and new seedings develop rapidly. It has good density and marked resistance to mildew, but it's high susceptibility to the leaf spot disease limits its usefulness in areas where the fungus is prevalent.

Merion. A single plant selection from the Merion Golf Club course, Ardmore, Pennsylvania. It is a low-growing, dense, medium-textured variety that is more tolerant to close mowing than most of the other Kentucky bluegrasses. It has good heat and cold tolerances, and is highly resistant to the leaf spot disease. It may be superficially injured sometimes for limited periods by rust and mildew. It performs better than other Kentucky bluegrasses on golf course tees and unwatered fairways located in areas where the leaf spot disease is a perennially serious problem. It also is an excellent turf for lawns and athletic fields in such areas. Merion needs heavier fertilization than other varieties because of its vigor, density, and extensive root and rhizome development.

Newport. Selected at the Plant Materials Center, Soil Conservation Service, Pulman, Washington from a collection of individual plants made in the Pacific Northwest. It is a vigorous, medium low-growing type, dark green in color. New seedlings develop rapidly. Following the first year of establishment it often shows a marked tendency to thin out and become stemmy, even under liberal fertilization and favorable mowing height. It is more rust resistant than Merion but less tolerant to leaf spot.

Park. Developed at the Minnesota Agricultural Experiment Station as a composite of fifteen parent plant selections. Seedling growth is fast and new seedings establish quickly. It is more resistant to rust and mildew than Merion, but is highly susceptible to leaf spot. Critical tests in the East-Central and Northeastern states indicate that it is not materially superior to common Kentucky bluegrass in these areas.

Troy. Selected at the Montana Agricultural Experiment Station from plant introductions from Turkey. It is a tall, erect-growing, variety that develops a somewhat coarse, open turf. It is highly susceptible to leaf spot.

LITTLE BLUESTEM GRASS (*Andropogon scoparius*). The value of little bluestem for golf-course use is limited to roughs and nonuse areas where protective cover is needed. It is a vigorous perennial bunch grass growing from 1 to 3 ft. tall. When the plants mature in late summer, they develop a characteristic reddish-brown color. It is particularly well adapted for use under nonirrigated conditions in the Kansas-Oklahoma section of the West Central region. It has high drought resistance and will thrive under a wide range of soil conditions. It will not withstand continuous close clipping, and where used for roughs it should be cut only two or three times a year to heights of not less than 3 to 5 in.

MANILAGRASS, zoysia (*Zoysia matrella*) is closely related to Japanese lawngrass and has many of the same characteristics that so well adapt the latter species for turf use. It is shorter and finer textured than the Japanese type and is somewhat less cold resistant. It is highly shade tolerant and very wear resistant. Although it is similar in texture to Bermudagrass and will withstand close clipping equally as well, it is not as suitable for putting greens because of the harsh, stiff quality of its leaves.

Interest in Manilagrass has been limited by the same factors responsible for the slow adoption of Japanese lawngrass. Seed is not available commercially, and it must be planted vegetatively by sprigging or spot sodding. The relatively slow rate of turf establishment by this method and the high cost of planting material, coupled with the labor involved, have been important items in limiting its use. Selection and improvement work is underway to develop superior turf strains with good seed-producing qualities. When seed becomes available, turf establishment will be much less of a problem, and a rapid increase in the use of this grass can be expected.

ORCHARDGRASS (*Dactylis glomerata*). The value of orchardgrass on the golf course is restricted to nonuse areas or to roughs where severe playing penalties are desired. It is a tall growing perennial bunch grass which forms extremely heavy tufts. Under occasional clipping at heights of 3 to 5 inches it makes a dense basal leaf growth that is a good protective cover but creates very difficult playing conditions. It is tolerant to drought, shade, and low fertility but will not endure poor drainage and high acidity. It is propagated entirely from seed which is available commercially at relatively low cost.

REDTOP (*Agrostis alba*). The principal value of redtop for use on the golf course is, like the ryegrasses, for quick establishment of temporary turf. In the Northern region it is used for this purpose in mixtures to provide quick cover and protection against weeds while the more permanent grasses are developing. Although it germinates rapidly it does not compete seriously with the permanent grasses and gradually disappears as they develop into a mature sod. It is also used extensively for temporary turf on greens and approaches where annual bluegrass, crabgrass, and clover have crowded out the more desirable species, leaving bare areas where it is necessary to provide turf quickly to meet playing requirements. In the Southern region redtop is used primarily on golf courses for overseeding on the dormant permanent grass to produce winter turf. When seeded heavily on greens for this purpose and clipped early and often, it will retain its fine seedling texture until the following spring when the combination of high temperature, close clipping, and aggressive growth of the permanent grass will effectually check its further development.

Redtop is a short-lived perennial under close clipping. When clipped regularly at heights of 1¼ to 1½ in., it rarely survives for more than 2 or 3 years. When clipped constantly at normal putting-green heights, it seldom lasts more than a single growing season. The species consists of many individual types, ranging from definitely creeping forms that have well-developed rootstocks to plants that are noncreeping and have a decidedly bunchy habit of growth. The large majority of plants from commercial seed are of the latter type.

Redtop is tolerant to a wide range of soil and climatic conditions. It is highly drought resistant and yet will grow well on wet soils that are poorly drained. Fertility requirements are low, and it will survive under extremely acid conditions. It is also highly tolerant of temperature extremes and can be seeded successfully late in the fall or during midsummer when sufficient moisture is available for germination.

RHODESGRASS (*Chloris gayana*) is a tall-growing perennial sod grass which spreads by long creeping stems that form new plants at each joint. Its value on the golf course is limited to roughs and nonuse areas. When used for roughs it should be mowed periodically as the requirements of play demand. It requires a fairly moist soil and is adapted only in the southern part of the Warm Humid and Southwest Irrigated regions. Seed is available commercially but is sometimes of poor quality and should be checked for good germination before being purchased.

ROUGHSTALK BLUEGRASS (*Poa trivialis*) is a long-lived perennial that spreads by short aboveground runners. It is propagated entirely from seed most of which is imported from Europe. It has approximately the same texture as Kentucky bluegrass, but the leaves and stems have a tendency to lie flat, giving the turf a smooth, glassy appearance. It is highly shade tolerant and will withstand wet, poorly drained soil where acidity is not excessive. It is seriously injured by hot, dry weather and cannot be grown satisfactorily in open locations south of the New England states. It is a soft-textured grass with a shallow root system, and its wearing qualities are poor. While it occurs on many fairways and some greens within its area of climatic adaptation, it is of questionable value for these purposes. It can be used to advantage in mixtures for shady locations on clubhouse lawns and other nonplaying areas.

SAND DROPSEED (*Sporobulus cryptandrus*) is a tufted perennial grass that is well adapted for use in the low rainfall areas of the Southern region where irrigation is impracticable. Because of its sparse foliage and tufted habit of growth its value is limited to roughs and nonuse areas of the golf course. Its fertility requirements are low, and it will grow under extremely droughty conditions. Seed is available commercially and should be scarified or acid treated for quick germination if less than a year old.

SHEEP FESCUE (*Festuca ovina*) is adapted principally to roughs, bunkers, and trap facings on the golf course. It is a perennial bunch grass with a strongly tufted habit of growth. It makes a dense basal growth of long, stiff, needlelike leaves that are very tough and resistant to injury. Even when heavily seeded the individual tufts tend to separate and form a bunchy uneven turf. This may impose severe playing conditions, particularly since it cannot withstand frequent close clipping. It should be cut only occasionally at heights of not less than 2 to 2½ in. It is propagated entirely by seed which usually is available commercially in sufficient quantities to meet requirements.

Sheep fescue will persist on thin, droughty soils of low fertility. It will withstand high acidity and grows well in shade but will not tolerate wet soils that are poorly drained. It has a heavy fibrous root system which makes it particularly valuable for binding the loose sandy soil of trap facings, steep banks, and similar areas.

Smooth bromegrass (*Bromus inermis*) is adapted for use on roughs and nonuse areas of golf courses in those sections of the West Central region where annual rainfall is above 18 in. but where irrigation is impracticable. It is a sod-forming perennial with heavy rootstocks and an extensive root system which often penetrates to a depth of 4 to 5 ft. It produces an abundance of basal leaves that are coarse in texture but which become sufficiently fine under moderate clipping to produce an acceptable turf. It will not withstand frequent close clipping, but under conditions of favorable fertility and moisture and with good management it can be cut to heights of 2½ to 3 in. without serious injury. The turf is highly wear resistant and will endure heavy trampling and constant use with little permanent damage.

Smooth bromegrass requires a highly fertile well-drained soil and responds strongly to applications of fertilizers high in nitrogen. Although it is somewhat drought resistant, it will not grow under as low moisture and winter temperature extremes as such native grasses of the West Central region as crested wheatgrass and buffalograss.

Seed of two distinct types of bromegrass is commercially available. The northern type is adapted to states in the northern portion of the region where summer temperatures are moderate. The southern type does best where temperatures are higher and long dry periods are common. Improved strains of bromegrass include Lincoln, Achenbach, and Fischer. These types were developed primarily for hay and pasture use, and no determination of their value for turf has been made.

St. Augustinegrass (*Stenotaphrum secundatum*) is prevalent on fairways and tees of some golf courses located in the southern portion of the Southern region where good supplies of moisture are available. In some instances attempts have been made to eradicate it, because of its coarse spongy character. It is a creeping perennial which spreads by long runners that produce short leafy branches. It forms a dense, coarse turf that will withstand heavy trampling and wear without serious injury. It grows well in shade and is tolerant of close clipping. Seed is not available commercially, and it is propagated entirely by sprigging the creeping stems or by spot sodding.

St. Augustinegrass requires moist soils of good fertility. It is particularly well adapted on the muck soils of the Everglade section in Florida. It will also withstand salt spray, which adapts it for use in coastal areas. On sandy soils of medium to low fertility it needs liberal applications of fertilizer with a high nitrogen content.

SUDANGRASS (*Sorghum vulgare sudanese*) is included in the list of grasses for turf use on golf courses only because of its value as a temporary cover for the protection of new seedings of permanent grasses in the nonirrigated sections of the West Central region. In these areas new plantings are often seriously damaged by scouring from dust and sand blown across them by the almost constant winds characteristic of the region. Sudangrass is an annual and is well adapted to provide a protective stubble into which the permanent grasses are seeded. It is planted in the spring and either kept mowed during the summer or cut before seed has sufficiently matured to germinate and produce a volunteer reseeding. Either method will produce a good stubble which will last well into the following season. The permanent grasses are drilled into this stubble which serves as a protective cover but which does not compete with them for available moisture. Sudangrass is adapted to a wide range of soil conditions and is quite drought tolerant. It can be seeded at any time after the frost-free date in the spring to midsummer.

TALL FESCUE (*Festuca elatior arundinacea*) is a tall-growing long-lived perennial bunch grass. It develops a dense growth of basal leaves and a strong fibrous root system. When seeded heavily and clipped regularly it forms a fairly uniform sod that is coarse in texture but highly resistant to hard wear. Although it grows best on well-drained soils of good fertility, it has a wide range of adaptability from wet to droughty conditions and is moderately acid and shade tolerant. When mowed continuously to a height of less than 2½ in. it will gradually thin out and permit weed encroachment.

Tall fescue has not been used extensively for golf-course turf. However, interest is increasing in the possibilities of two improved types for use in mixtures for fairways and tees, because of their wide tolerance to soil conditions and ability to survive under heavy use and intensive management. These are the Alta strain, which is a selection made in Oregon in 1923, and Kentucky 31, which was found growing in Kentucky. There is good evidence that the latter is better adapted for Eastern conditions. It has been used successfully for athletic fields and other heavy-duty turf, and in mixtures with Kentucky bluegrass for fairways to produce quick cover. It has not proven to be objectionable for the latter because it disappears gradually under close mowing and the bluegrass takes over.

TALL OATGRASS (*Arrhenatherum elatius*). The value of tall oatgrass on the golf course is limited to nonuse areas where only occasional cutting is required. It is a tall-growing bunch grass that does not make a very good sod. Its chief claim for consideration is its ability to grow on dry soils of low fertility. Its use should be confined to those areas which it is not necessary or practicable to maintain intensively but where cover is required to check weeds and erosion. Seed is available commercially but is difficult to feed through mechanical seeders because of its light fluffy nature. An improved strain named Tualatin is being produced in Oregon and is shorter and finer in texture than common tall oatgrass.

TIMOTHY (*Phleum pratense*) is a coarse long-lived perennial bunch grass that forms an uneven clumpy sod. Its use for turf should be confined to roughs and nonuse areas where only occasional cutting is required. It is best adapted to the cooler portions of the Northern Humid region and is not a poor-soil grass. It prefers the heavier types of clay loam soils and will not withstand poor drainage or acid conditions. It requires regular fertilization and should not be cut to heights of less than 2 to 2½ in. It has a relatively slow growth rate and does not recover from clipping so rapidly as smooth bromegrass, orchardgrass, and other species that are available for roughs and nonuse areas. The fact that seed is abundant and cheap sometimes influences its use for turf purposes in locations where other species would give very much better results.

VELVET BENTGRASS (*Agrostis canina*) is a long-lived perennial that spreads by creeping stems which produce new plants at the joints. Under close clipping it forms a very fine-textured dense turf that is excellent for putting-green use. Although its growth rate is slow, it forms a very close-knit sod that is highly resistant to invasion by weeds. It occurs quite generally in old greens originally seeded with South German Mixed Bent as circular patches which can be recognized easily by their fine-textured velvety appearance. Formerly South German mixed bent seed was the only source of velvet bent, but more recently production has been developed in the United States and limited quantities of seed of several strains are available commercially.

Although velvet bentgrass will grow on a wide variety of soils, including wet and acid conditions and low fertility, it will produce the best turf where fertility is maintained at a high level, where acidity is corrected by additions of lime, and where drainage and soil aeration are good. Like creeping bent, its root system becomes shallow and restricted and the turf weakens when soil compaction develops. It has a tendency to develop a deep, feltlike mat which footprints badly. Where periodic top-dressing is a part of the regular putting-green maintenance operations, it must be carefully adjusted to meet velvet bent requirements. Because of the fine-textured dense character of the turf it does not require and will not withstand the frequent heavy dressings commonly applied to creeping bent. Top-dressings should be applied only once or twice per season, using finely screened material in limited quantities.

Individual plants of the species show wide variations in color, texture, and other characteristics related to turf quality. Many types have been selected at various times and given performance tests locally on the golf courses where they were found growing. Seed production of three of these, Piper, Kernwood, and Raritan, has been developed commercially, and limited quantities of seed of each are available.

WEEPING LOVEGRASS (*Eragrostis curvula*). The value of weeping lovegrass for golf-course use is restricted to nonuse areas, trap and bunker facings, and other places where the principal requirement is cover for weed and erosion control. It is a vigorous, tall-growing perennial bunch grass that is particularly adapted to the limited rainfall sections of the Southern Great Plains. It is propagated entirely from seed, which germinates quickly and produces an effective ground cover within a relatively short period. It is highly drought resistant and develops a heavy, fibrous root system that is very efficient in binding soils on bunker slopes and trap facings.

WESTERN WHEATGRASS (*Agropyron smithii*) is a perennial sod-forming grass that spreads by underground rootstocks. Its value for turf is primarily in mixtures for tees and fairways and for roughs and nonuse areas under nonirrigation in the West Central region. It forms a somewhat thin open type of turf, but when used in mixtures with crested wheatgrass it forms a wear-resisting sod of good quality. It is somewhat drought resistant but makes its best growth on the heavy soils characteristic of low areas when surface water collects and extra moisture is present. While it will persist on poor soils it will produce a suitable turf for use on golf courses only where good fertility levels are maintained. It is particularly suitable for roughs where it requires only a minimum of maintenance under normal soil and climatic conditions. Unless good fertility and moisture conditions exist, the turf is weakened by continuous close cutting.

6

Turf Propagation

Successful turf establishment depends first upon good soil preparation. Satisfactory drainage, good soil aeration and moisture-storage capacity, adjustment of soil reaction, and provision for adequate supplies of plant nutrients, which have been discussed previously, are involved. It depends, also, upon the selection of a grass, or mixture of grasses, adapted to the local climate and to the particular use and management to which the turf will be subjected. Grass establishment is concerned, further, with seed quality, mixture proportions, and the time, rate, and methods of seeding, vegetative planting, or sodding. Finally, it includes provision for adequate care of the young grass during the developmental period. Proper attention to these essentials will pay large dividends in reduced maintenance problems and lower costs.

SEEDBED PREPARATION. Seedbed preparation for turf includes fitting the soil to the depth of maximum root development. The necessary procedures will vary, depending upon soil type, size of area, purpose for which the turf is to be used, and available equipment. It is concerned primarily with the creation of good conditions for grass growth in the surface layer of soil. Seedbed preparation begins after grading operations have been completed and the necessary drainage and irrigation installations have been made. The essential steps include:

1. Loosening of the soil to the required depth.

2. Sterilization for weed and insect control.
3. Incorporation of soil-texture-improving materials, lime if required, and basic fertilizer reserves.
4. Soil pulverizing, smoothing, and firming.
5. Incorporation of starter fertilizer and final surface preparation for planting.

Each operation can be performed in many different ways and with a wide variety of implements. Some of the methods that have given satisfactory results on the various areas of the golf course are outlined in the following discussions.

SEED QUALITY. The most important seed qualities are purity and germination. Purity refers to the percentage of pure seed. Germination is the percentage of pure seed that will grow, as determined by standard germination testing methods. Most state seed laws require that the purity and germination of commercial seed be shown on the container. Table 17, page 322, gives the minimum percentage purity and germination for good-quality seed of the various turf grasses.

SEEDING. Most seeds of the turf grasses are relatively small. Very shallow covering and intimate contact with moist soil are essential for good germination and growth. Seedbeds should be permitted to settle or should be firmed by rolling before seedings are made. If surface crusts develop prior to seeding, they should be broken either by very shallow raking on small areas and with a spike-tooth harrow, weeder, or other appropriate tool on large areas.

DORMANT SEEDINGS. Construction operations sometimes are completed so late in the season that it is impracticable to secure satisfactory seed germination and turf development before cold weather begins. In such instances seedings should be delayed until average temperatures have dropped below the minimums for seed germination (35 to 40 deg.). The seed will lie dormant through the winter and germinate in the spring. The principal advantage in making dormant seedings is earlier turf establishment the following season. Spring seedings often must be delayed because of unfavorable soil and weather conditions for seeding operations. It should be emphasized that dormant seedings are practicable only in sections where winter temperatures are consistently low enough so that there is little probability that seed will sprout during mild periods.

Seedbed preparation and seeding methods for dormant seedings are similar to those used for normal seedings. Any area on the golf course can be seeded in this way if protection against erosion is provided by adequate mulching. Since protection is required over a relatively long period of time, maximum quantities of 1½ to 2 tons of mulching material per acre should be used. It may be necessary to tie down mulches on slopes and areas exposed to high winds by a system of stakes and strings. Mulches also can be stabilized by spraying with cut-back asphalt at 0.1 to 0.2 gal. per sq. yd.

MULCH SEEDING. Mulch seedings are made by spreading unthreshed grass straw containing mature seed upon the prepared seedbed. This method can be used for any species of grass for which sufficient quantities of seed-bearing straw are obtainable. It is particularly desirable for seeding roughs and nonuse areas because of its relatively low cost in comparison with more intensive seeding methods. Abundant material of the coarser grasses often can be obtained and applied at a price that is materially lower than the cost of separate seeding, covering, and mulching operations. Rates of approximately 1 ton per acre ordinarily are sufficient to secure good stands of most of the grasses. The material is handled and spread by the same methods used for ordinary mulching treatments. The straw should be handled as carefully as possible in transporting and spreading to reduce seed losses by shattering. It is seldom necessary to remove the straw after growth of the young grass has started. The weathering to which it has been subjected usually breaks it up sufficiently so that it does not interefere with turf establishment.

VEGETATIVE PLANTING. Vegetative methods of turf production are limited to those grasses which produce an abundance of creeping stems. Most of the improved strains of creeping bent, velvet bent, and Bermudagrass are propagated in this way. Other creeping types of turf grasses that produce only small amounts of seed usually are grown vegetatively. The more important of these are St. Augustine, centipede, and the zoysia grasses. Vegetative planting of buffalograss also has been widely used for establishing turf of this species.

Vegetative propagation of the turf grasses is based on the ability of the creeping stems to root and produce new plants at the joints.

FIG. 11. Bermudagrass plants approximately one month after row sprigging. (*Green Section.*)

Planting methods vary in different localities and for the different species of grasses. Turf of the creeping and velvet bents ordinarily is produced by broadcasting the creeping stems (stolons) over a prepared seedbed and covering with a light layer of prepared top-dressing material. Bermuda, St. Augustine, centipede, and the zoysia grasses can be broadcast or planted (sprigged) in narrow rows which quickly fill in to produce a solid sod. Buffalograss, and sometimes St. Augustine, centipede, and the zoysias, can be established vegetatively by spot planting small pieces of sod on 12- to 18-in. centers.

QUALITY OF VEGETATIVE MATERIAL. The first essential in vegetative propagation is good-quality planting material. Stolons and sprigs are injured easily by drying or heating and must be handled carefully to avoid serious reduction in their vigor and ability to grow. Commercial material should be unpacked promptly upon receipt. If not used immediately, it should be spread out in a thin layer and covered with wet burlap or protected against drying by some other convenient method. Nursery-grown material should be cut and shredded only as needed.

NURSERIES. Where needs can be anticipated in advance, stolons for vegetative planting can be produced in a nursery located on the course. This will assure an abundant supply of fresh material at a cost that usually is materially lower than when purchased from commercial sources. Establishment and maintenance of the stolon nursery is relatively simple. A good seedbed should be prepared by plowing or disking and harrowing. Moderately fertile soils are preferred, since too rapid growth will produce succulent stolons and excessive leaf growth. Stolons of the bent grasses should be planted in shallow furrows, with a minimum of 3½ to 4 ft. between rows. If good-quality planting material is available, approximately 1 sq. ft. of nursery sod will plant 75 to 100 linear feet of nursery row. The creeping stems should be distributed in a thin layer on the bottom of the furrow and covered lightly by drawing soil over them and firming with the feet. When plantings have been made properly, many ends of the stems will not be completely covered. It is essential that the zoysia grasses be left partially uncovered. Bermuda and other grasses that are propagated vegetatively under high temperature conditions should be planted at the bottom of furrows that are 3 to 4 in. deep and completely covered. The soil should be kept moist at all times until growth has started. Late summer or early fall is the best time to plant the nursery. Planting material is less succulent at this time and more resistant to adverse conditions. Also, the grass has a better opportunity to get well started before weeds become a problem.

SPOT SODDING. Turf can be produced vegetatively by spot sodding grasses that have a creeping habit of growth. This method has been used extensively for establishing buffalograss and less frequently for Bermuda, the zoysia grasses, centipedegrass, and St. Augustine. The method is most useful on areas where soil moisture is low and water for irrigation is not available or is limited. It consists, essentially, in setting 3- or 4-in. cubes of cut sod into a prepared seedbed at spaced intervals. Sods should be cut thick and handled in such a way that there will be minimum soil losses from the root mass of the cut pieces. For quick cover the sod pieces should be set on 12- to 18-in. centers. Planted areas should be rolled to firm the soil around the sod. Where water is available it can be used liberally on plantings of fast-growing grasses, like Bermuda. Slow-growing types such as buffalograss and the zoysia grasses should be watered sparingly to reduce competition by weeds. These grasses are highly drought tolerant and will root satisfactorily in soils low in available moisture. Spot sodding often can be used for quick turf establishment on limited areas such as tees. It is of doubtful value for fairways, because of the labor involved in cutting, transporting, and planting the sod pieces on large areas. Adequate turf usually can be established more economically on these areas by using grasses that can be propagated from seed.

SODDING. Sodding is the most expensive method of turf establishment. It involves the first cost of the sod, whether purchased commercially or grown in the nursery, and the relatively large amount of labor required in the sodding operations. Ordinarily, it is limited to greens and tees, or other areas where the need for turf in the shortest possible time justifies its use. A successful sodding job depends upon adequate preparation of the soil base, the quality of the sod used, and a high degree of skill and care in the sodding operations. The soil bed on which the sod is placed should receive the same type of preparation as seedbeds for seeding or vegetative planting. Surfaces can be rolled somewhat more firmly, and particular care should be taken that no depressions are left that might result in an uneven surface after the sod is laid.

SOD QUALITY. Sod that is grown for use on greens and tees requires the same type of care and management given established turf on these areas. It should be emphasized that the chief purpose of sodding is to produce a good playing turf quickly and not merely to provide a green cover on the area. The use of neglected nursery sod will materially increase the time required to develop good playing conditions and the amount of care and attention necessary in the process.

LIFTING AND TRIMMING. Where only small areas are involved, sod can be cut satisfactorily with hand tools. Essential equipment for this includes a cutting tool such as the half-moon type of turf edger, a 12- to 16-ft. board, 12 in. wide, and a suitable lifting tool. Several types of mechanical cutters are on the market and can be used where large areas are to be lifted. Individual sod pieces should be cut to a uniform size with square corners. Pieces that are 12 to 16 in. wide and 24 to 36 in. long are most convenient, particularly if handled by inexperienced workmen. Larger pieces will stretch badly unless carefully handled and are hard to lay uniformly. If the soil is loose and shatters off in rolling the pieces, they should be cut small enough to handle flat.

Sod should be cut as thin as possible. Good turf of the bents and Bermudagrasses can be cut to a thickness of ½ to ¾ in. Kentucky bluegrass, fescue, and other types which form a more open sod, require somewhat thicker cutting, but seldom in excess of 1 to 1¼ in. If cut sod must be held for several days before laying, it should be spread out flat, grass side up, in a cool place and kept damp. Stacked sod will yellow and weaken rapidly and will not be in good condition to start growth promptly when laid.

Hand cut sods usually require trimming to a uniform thickness before laying. When machine cut, trimming normally is not necessary. A suitable trimming frame can be constructed by nailing strips onto a broad plank or table top in a rectangular shape that is the exact size of the sod piece. The depth of the frame should conform to the desired thickness of the sod. The sod piece is laid in the frame, grass side down, and the excess soil shaved off with a scythe blade or other suitable tool that will ride on the sides of the frame.

LAYING. The surface on which the sod is to be laid should be firm and free from footprints or other depressions. A string or line of boards may be used as a guide for setting the first line of sod across the area. Sods of the next course are matched against the edge of this first line in such a way that the joints between the individual sod pieces in the two lines do not coincide. Successive courses are matched against the last line laid, in the same manner. All work should be done on boards laid on top of the sod to avoid footprints or other injuries to the surface.

The sod is tamped lightly as it is set to ensure good contact with the surface of the soil at all points. This is followed with a light top-dressing which should be worked into the seams between the pieces with a brush or mat. Rolling immediately after laying is not a good practice on large areas. Sod frequently creeps ahead of the roller and causes irregularities that are very difficult to correct. Water should be applied regularly to prevent drying of the edges. As soon as there has been sufficient root development to hold the sod firmly in place, water should be withheld until the surface has become reasonably dry. Additional top-dressing material can be applied at this time if needed and a roller used to level out minor irregularities.

Sodding can be done at any time during the growing season if the turf is handled carefully and watered properly. The quickest establishment is secured during the period of maximum root formation. The turf grasses make their most rapid root growth from mid to late spring, and this is the most desirable time for sodding operations. Where sodding is done on terraces or slopes, it should be staked down by driving a wooden peg through the sod and into the soil base. This will prevent slippage during heavy rains. The pegs can be removed as soon as the sod has rooted sufficiently to hold it in place.

Greens

Seedbed soil for greens must be in optimum condition for good grass growth. They must be resilient, highly resistant to compaction, and contain liberal quantities of nutrients. Normal soils seldom are capable of meeting these requirements, and their extensive modification is necessary. Essential modifications include adding texture- and structure-improving materials, the use of liberal quantities of plant nutrients, and the application of amendments such as lime and pesticides.

PHYSICAL CONDITIONING MATERIALS. Texture- and structure-improving materials most commonly used in greens are sand and

FIG. 12. A mechanical sod cutter being used to remove injured turf from a golf course tee, preparatory to resodding. (*Courtesy Landscaping Equipment Company.*)

suitable organic matter. There are wide variations in the quality of these materials. Some types of sand will not produce the porous conditions necessary in a greens soil. Many classes of organic materials decompose quickly and leave only limited residues that do not bring about effective permanent improvement.

SAND. The best type of sand for modifying the soil to improve its physical condition is one in which particle sizes range from *coarse* to *very coarse* (0.02 to 0.08 in. diameter). Fine textured material, as blow sand, is not satisfactory for use either in seedbeds or for top-dressings. When it is used in mixtures containing appreciable quantities of silt or clay it packs tightly and may reduce porosity and resiliency rather than improve them. Critical studies also have shown that ungraded sand, even after fines have been removed, has a greater compaction potential than a uniformly coarse textured product.

FIG. 13. Power equipment is used in modern green construction. (*Courtesy Sewerage Commission, City of Milwaukee.*)

ORGANIC MATTER. The qualities of the various types of organic materials for use as physical conditioners were outlined in Chap. 2. Results of both practical experience and critical studies indicate that the raw and cultivated peats are the best materials available at the present time. They should be fibrous in texture, and the coarse material in them should be reduced by grinding or screening to permit uniform mixing. Commercial products should be reasonably dry because there is no point in buying surplus water or paying transportation and handling charges on it. They should be purchased on the basis of moisture-absorptive capacity and organic-matter content based on dry weight. As noted in Chap. 2 a good-quality peat will have an organic matter content of 90 per cent or better and a minimum moisture-absorptive capacity of 400 to 450 per cent. When peats have been dried down to a low moisture content (less than 10 per cent) they reabsorb water very slowly. If material in this condition is used in the seedbed or in top-dressings, it will float out badly during periods of excessive precipitation. This difficulty can be eliminated by composting it with soil for 2 to 3 months before using.

FIG. 14. Piles of sand ready for spreading and incorporation into the seedbed of a green. (*Green Section.*)

The peats are preferable to the more readily decomposable types of organic materials such as manures, unconditioned sludges, and various by-product materials. The rapid rate of decay of the latter and the small quantity of residual humus added to the soil limit their value. These organic residues will not maintain the physical conditions required for greens. On the other hand, they may supply excessive quantities of plant food, even though their nutrient content on a percentage basis is low. Because of the large total volumes used and the rapid rate of decay, readily decomposable types of organic materials may release high amounts of nutrients within a relatively short period of time. This may cause the seedling grass to develop a soft type of growth that is highly subject to scald, damping off, and other types of injury.

The use of excessive amounts of peat is objectionable. Because of its high moisture-absorptive capacity peat will retain large quantities of water following rains or irrigation. Where too much has been used, soils will be soggy and lose their resiliency. They become unstable and footprint badly. As decomposition of the peat progresses, they will develop a tight gummy structure that is almost watertight.

OTHER PHYSICAL CONDITIONING MATERIALS. Several materials have been suggested and used to a limited extent as substitutes for sand and organic matter in modifying soils. The most prominent of these are blast furnace slag, various forms of processed micas (perlite, vermiculite, etc.), and calcined clays. All of them are more porous and have a greater moisture absorptive capacity than sand. Their cost and possible period of stability in the soil are factors that will limit their use until more adequate information is available on their long time effects.

SOILS. The kind of soil used in the seedbed mixture will affect the quantities of sand and peat required. A loam soil with a high content of coarse sand and good organic-matter residues will require a minimum of sand and peat. Very sandy soils will require relatively heavy quantities of organic materials and in extreme cases a limited amount of silt and clay. Where heavy soils with a high silt or clay content must be used, mixtures should consist of moderate quantities of organic material and high percentages of sand.

Very poor grades of topsoil can be improved by composting with various types of quickly decomposable organic materials in a soil bed. The organic materials should be plowed under and the bed thoroughly disked periodically. This will mix them with the soil, hasten decomposition, and destroy many weeds. The soil will be ready for use in one year following this treatment. Large quantities of organic matter must be used to produce any material improvement in soil quality. The maximum amount of any material that can be used will depend to some extent upon its condition and how thoroughly it can be incorporated into the soil.

Some of the heavier types, such as manure and raw sewage sludge, can be handled satisfactorily at rates of 3 to 4 cu. yd. per 1,000 sq. ft. of bed area. It will be necessary to use the lighter or fluffy types such as cottonseed hulls at lower rates.

Spent mushroom soil, if obtainable, can be used to advantage as the soil fraction of seedbed and top-dressing mixtures. A good grade of spent mushroom soil will contain 15 to 25 per cent of organic matter. Although the organic material decays rapidly, the residues give the soil the character of a good-quality loam. Normally, less peat is required for proper conditioning that is needed for topsoils of ordinary quality. The extra cost of the mushroom soil frequently is balanced by the reduced quantity of peat needed in the mixture.

RATIOS OF SOIL, SAND, AND ORGANIC MATTER. The best ratio of soil, sand, and organic matter for preparing seedbed or top-dressing mixtures must be based on good judgment. A survey of fifty-two golf courses was made by the United States Golf Association Green Section and, as reported in *Timely Turf Topics*, July, 1947, it gave the ratios shown in Table 8, on a volume basis. The wide variations in these demonstrate the necessity for making adjustments to compensate for fundamental differences in soil character. In doing this, there is no substitute for experience and good judgment, based on a practical knowledge of the ingredients to be used and how they will act when they become a part of the mixture.

The primary objective is to make a material that has high resistance to compaction, but is not so coarse and open that its ability to retain water and nutrients is reduced below practical levels. This is a vital consideration because the added labor and expense of frequent water and fertilizer use may more than compensate for the effort needed to correct the slight compaction that might occur in a less open soil.

Where sand and peat are used for soil modification their exact proportions will depend on the character of the soil with which they are mixed. The volume percentages of sand may vary from a minimum of 25 to 30 per cent of the total mixture to a maximum

TABLE 8

Parts soil	*Parts sand*	*Parts organic matter*	*Number of courses reporting*
1	1	1	19
2	1	1	13
3	1	1	4
2	1	2	3
2	1	0	3
2	2	1	2
1	7	3	1
1	4	1	1
1	3	2	1
1	1	2	1
1	2	3	1
3	4	3	1
4	1	2	1
5	1	0	1

of 70 to 75 per cent, with the extremes justified only in exceptional cases. The quantity of peat also will vary, but within a much narrower range. It is seldom necessary or desirable to use a greater volume than 10 to 15 per cent, unless a soil is exceptionally open and sandy. Excessive quantities may produce a chronically soggy condition, due to the very high moisture holding properties of peat.

A laboratory procedure for determining the correct quantities of conditioning materials to use in modifying soils for turfgrass has been suggested by the United States Golf Association Green Section. The detailed method has been described by Ferguson, Howard, and Bloodworth, United States Golf Association *Journal and Turf Management,* Vol. XIII, No. 5, September, 1960 (pp. 30–32). It consists, essentially, in correlating determinations of soil permeability and pore space with other physical characteristics, such as mechanical analysis, mineral derivation, aggregation, bulk density, and moisture holding capacity, as a basis for determining the extent of modification required for any particular soil. See Appendix, page 328, for a detailed description of this method.

Since the rates of destruction of good soil physical condition and of compaction development depend on the extent and intensity of use of the turf and on the type of management it receives, the laboratory data will be most useful when properly correlated with these factors. It should be used as a guide rather than an arbitrary measure of the extent of soil modification which actually will be necessary. Soil testing laboratories of several state colleges of agriculture offer service in making these physical measurements. A few private laboratories also are equipped to make the determinations.

SEEDBED DEPTH. The minimum settled depth of prepared soil on a green should be 8 in. (see Chap. 4, page 57). This will require from 25 to 30 cu. yds. of prepared material per 1,000 sq. ft. of area. To insure uniform depths of all three courses of materials (coarse base, sand-gravel, and top soil), the subbase of the green should be contoured and graded to the same design as the finished surface.

MIXING OPERATIONS. Soils for greens can be mixed either off the site or in place. In *off-the-site* mixing the required quantities of topsoil, sand, and organic matter are run through some type of mixing equipment such as a shredder, or rotary screen. This process is similar to that used in the preparation of top-dressing material. The mixed material is then spread on the area to the required depth. *In-place* mixing consists of spreading the materials on the surface of the green in layers and mixing them with a rotary tiller, disk, or other suitable tool. The latter method involves much less handling of large quantities of materials and is entirely adequate if done properly. Where this method is used, the screened topsoil should be placed first and the sand and organic material spread over it. This will avoid the possibility of layers of sand or organic matter developing because of a failure of the mixing equipment to penetrate to the full depth. Care must be exercised in the use of a disk for mixing, to prevent pocketing of sand on turns.

FERTILIZER, LIME, AND OTHER CORRECTIVES. Where soil tests show a need for lime, phosphate, and potash, these can be thoroughly mixed with the soil when the seedbed mixture is prepared, at rates indicated by the tests. If both phosphate and potash are low, a 0-20-20 fertilizer can be used to supply the needed quantities of these nutrients. If the fertilizer is thoroughly mixed into the soil to a depth of 5 to 6 in., rates of 50 to 60 lbs. per 1,000 sq.

FIG. 15. A solid sand layer in the root zone seriously interferes with root formation. (*Green Section.*)

ft. would not be excessive. The same quantities of superphosphate can be used when only phosphate is deficient, and 10 to 15 lbs. of muriate of potash when only potash is needed. When soil mixtures are made off-site, the materials can be added to the mixture at rates of 3 to 4 lbs. of 0-20-20 or superphosphate per cu. yd. of prepared soil, and 1 to 2 lbs. of muriate of potash. Other correctives, such as insecticides and herbicides, can be mixed into the soil at the same time (see appropriate chapters on these materials).

Starter fertilizer for the seedling grass should be applied prior to final surface grading and smoothing. It can be raked in to a depth of 1 or 2 in. in this operation. The fertilizer should have a ratio of 1-1-1 to 2-1-1. It is desirable that at least one-half of the nitrogen be in organic form as insurance against deficiencies of this element before reapplications to the young grass can be made. This will avoid the danger and difficulty frequently experienced in attempting to apply fertilizers to seeding turf, because of soft surface conditions and serious burning. Where completely inorganic forms are used, fertilizer applications should be adjusted to supply a maximum of 2 lb. of nitrogen per 1,000

FIG. 16. Soil layers on a Bermudagrass green resulting from improper construction. (*Green Section.*)

sq. ft. Higher rates may seriously injure germination if conditions are favorable for quick sprouting of the seed. Additional nitrogen must be applied within a period of 6 weeks to 2 months after seeding. Fertilizers in which at least one-half of the nitrogen is in slowly available form can be used at double the above rate with safety (4 lb. of nitrogen per 1,000 sq. ft.). Additional feeding of the grass normally is not required for periods of 4 to 6 months when fertilizers of the latter type are used.

ROLLING BEFORE SEEDING. Light rolling is sometimes necessary as a final operation in seedbed preparation. This is desirable when the soil is loose and fluffy and plantings are to be made before it has had an opportunity to settle and firm. Rolling should be done only when the soil is reasonably dry so that it will not compact. The standard 250-lb. water-ballast roller will be satisfactory under most conditions. The weight should be adjusted to meet local requirements. If rolling will not firm the seedbed underneath, it should be permitted to settle until a satisfactory condition has developed.

GRASSES. The improved varieties of creeping bentgrass are used almost exclusively for permanent turf on greens in the cooler sections of the United States and in Canada (see Chap. 5, section on Climatic Adaptation). They can be established either by seeding or vegetative planting. Where seed is used, the Penncross variety is preferred in most sections of the country. The Arlington, Cohansey, Congressional Old Orchard, Pennlu, and Toronto, are the most widely used vegetatively planted types.

The Astoria and Highland varieties of colonial bent are used to a limited extent in some areas. In most sections they will not produce as good turf as the better varieties of creeping bent.

The use of velvet bents for putting greens is confined largely to the Northeastern states. Apparently, they are better adapted climatically to this section than to other areas. The Kernwood and Piper varieties have been the most popular, although many greens have been seeded with common velvet from various sources with good results.

Improved varieties of Bermudagrass produce excellent putting green turf throughout the South. The most widely used are Bayshore, Everglades, Sunturf, Texturf 1F, and Tifgreen. Differences in temperature tolerance must be considered in choosing a variety for a particular location. None of the improved varieties produce true-to-type seed and must be planted vegetatively. Planting stock is produced by a number of commercial nurseries in the South.

RATE AND TIME OF SEEDING. The rate and time of seeding of both bentgrass and Bermudagrass can be varied within relatively wide limits. Optimum rates and times are indicated in Table 16, page 320. Rates can be varied from the quantities shown, depending upon local conditions. Good stands of the bentgrasses can be produced with as little as 1 or 2 lb. of good-quality seed per 1,000 sq. ft. It is seldom desirable to increase seeding rates above the top figures in the table because of the danger of severe competition among the plants for available supplies of nutrients and water. The best time for seeding the bentgrasses is in the fall or early spring. In the Cool Humid region where they are well adapted, successful seedings can be made at any time during the growing season if water is available for irrigation. Fall seedings are preferred in areas where early summer temperatures are high.

Bermudagrass makes very rapid growth when good moisture and fertility are available. It should be seeded at a somewhat heavier rate than the bentgrasses because of the difference in seed size (see Table 17, page 322, on seed-quality characteristics). It is not desirable to increase the seeding rate of Bermuda above the maximum of 5 lb. per 1,000 sq. ft. because of the competition factor. The optimum time for seeding Bermudagrass is in late spring. It can be seeded at any time during the summer or early fall in its normal region or adaptation if sufficient water is available for germination and to maintain normal growth.

Seeding Methods. Uniform distribution and even covering are the two most important items in making grass seedings. Seed can be broadcast by hand or spread with any good type of mechanical seeder. In addition to wheelbarrow seeders, several kinds of small mechanical seeders are available commercially that are suitable for use in seeding greens. All are of hopper-type construction mounted on two wheels and are hand operated. They have varying capacities and will seed a swath of approximately 3 ft. Either reel or screw-type agitators are used to feed the seed through holes or slits in the bottom of the hopper. Rates of seeding are varied by mechanical adjustment of the size of the openings. Dilution of the seed at the rate of 1 part of seed to 3 or 4 parts of finely screened topsoil or top-dressing material will assist in securing uniform distribution. Sand is not very satisfactory for this purpose because of the tendency of light types of seed to float out on top in mechanical seeders. Separation of the seed into two equal quantities which are seeded at right angles to each other also will assist in obtaining uniform distribution.

Seeds of the bentgrasses and Bermudagrass are very small and should not be covered to a greater depth than ¼ in. This can be done by very light hand raking. If the green was rolled prior to seeding to firm the surface, it should be scored lightly with a rake before the seed is applied. This will aid materially in securing uniform depth of coverage. Another method of securing uniform coverage is to broadcast a light layer of top-dressing soil over the surface after sowing the seed. When this method is used, it is not necessary to scarify rolled surfaces before seeding. The top-dressing can be spread by hand or with a suitable type of distributor. Approximately two-thirds of a cubic yard of top-dressing is needed for each 1,000 sq. ft. of area.

ROLLING AND MULCHING AFTER SEEDING. Areas should be rolled with a light roller immediately after seeding to press the seed into the soil. Mulching with a light covering of straw or hay that is free from objectionable weed seed is desirable. This will protect against excessive evaporation in the shallow surface layer of soil from which the seed must draw moisture for germination. It also will permit watering with less danger of washing out the seed and will prevent formation of a surface crust which may interfere with emergence of the seedlings. Approximately 75 to 100 lb. of mulching material will be required for each 1,000 sq. ft. of area. The mulch should be removed when the grass seedlings have made a growth of ½ to 1 in. This can be done satisfactorily with the common type of light bamboo or wire leaf brush.

VEGETATIVE PLANTING OF GREENS. The stolons or sprigs are prepared for planting by chopping or shredding so that they can be separated easily and distributed uniformly. Cut pieces should average not less than 6 in. in length. Bentgrass stolons usually are broadcast by hand over the prepared surface at rates of 8 to 10 bu. of stolons per 1,000 sq. ft. of area. Homegrown nursery stock can be planted at a rate of 1 sq. ft. of nursery sod on 8 to 10 sq. ft. of area. The stolons should be rolled to press them into the surface of the seedbed and covered with approximately ½ cu. yd. of prepared top-dressing material per 1,000 sq. ft. of area. Rolling should be repeated after the top-dressing has been applied. Thin areas, which have not received sufficient covering material, and slight depressions are dressed out by hand and again rolled.

Vegetative planting of Bermuda sprigs in rows is preferable to broadcasting them on the surface and covering by top-dressing. The row method permits planting to a depth where soil moisture is more constant and drying out is not so rapid. This method also

FIG. 17. Shredding creeping bentgrass stolons with a machine constructed from cylinder and concave of an old threshing machine. (*Pennsylvania Agricultural Experiment Station.*)

is more satisfactory for vegetating the zoysia grasses and other types adapted to the warmer climatic areas. In sprig planting greens and tees the rows should be 8 to 12 in. apart and are opened to a depth of 3 to 4 in. From 3 to 4 bu. of material will be required, at liberal planting rates, for each 1,000 sq. ft. of area. The sprigs can be completely covered and the entire area smoothed with a steel mat or by raking lightly. Rolling should follow the planting and leveling operations. Broadcast plantings by the same method used in planting creeping bent also can be used. Sufficient water must be used to keep the sprigs moist at all times until they have rooted. Broadcast plantings have the advantage of quicker establishment of turf than row plantings. They require two to three times as much planting material and need more attention.

Vegetative plantings require liberal supplies of moisture for good establishment. Planted areas should be kept moist at all times until the new growth is well developed. When the weather is warm and dry, it may be necessary to water three or four times per day to prevent excessive drying out. Water should be applied in a fine spray to avoid washing out the stolons and should be continued until it is certain that the new plants are well established.

Vegetative plantings must be kept well supplied with liberal quantities of available nitrogen. When soluble forms are used, as urea and ammonium sulfate, applications of ½ to 1 lb. of actual nitrogen per 1,000 sq. ft. should be made every 10 days to 2 weeks during the growing season. If slowly available nitrogen were used when the seedbed was prepared, reapplications at such frequent intervals are not necessary. The natural organics can be used at monthly intervals at rates to supply 2 to 3 lbs. of actual nitrogen per 1,000 sq. ft., and Urea-form compounds need be applied only at 6 weeks to 2-month intervals at rates of 4 to 5 lbs. Thorough watering after application of soluble forms is essential to wash the material off the leaves. Failure to do so invariably will result in serious foliage burn and often in permanent injury to the turf.

As soon as new stems have developed and have formed one or two joints the area should be rolled lightly and clipped to a height of ¼ to ⅜ in. The clippings should not be removed. Those which have jointed will produce new plants. They should be rolled down and covered with a light top-dressing of approximately ¼ to ½ cu. yd. per 1,000 sq. ft. Clipping, rolling, and top-dressing should be repeated at intervals, depending upon the growth rate, until the desired sod density has been reached.

WATERING. The surface layer of soil must be kept damp by frequent light watering with a fine spray during the germination period after seeding or vegetative planting and until the young plants are rooted firmly. It is often necessary to water three or four times daily in hot windy periods. After the grass is established, water should be used sparingly and with maximum intervals between applications. Frequent watering will result in shallow rooting and increase the danger of disease attacks. Serious damage from disease sometimes can be avoided by permitting the soil to dry out to a point where the grass shows some evidence of wilting before water is applied.

CLIPPING. Frequent light clipping is desirable. The most rapid turf development of the bents and Bermudagrass is secured when the grass is not permitted to grow to a height of more than 1 to 1¼ in. between clippings. Mowers should be set to cut at approximately ½ to ¾ in. until a sod begins to develop. Under normal growing conditions this will occur in 4 to 6 weeks after the first clipping. Subsequent clipping heights should be reduced gradually to ¼ to 3/16 in. over a 3- to 4-week period.

Winter Greens

TYPES OF GRASSES. Overseeding of Bermudagrass greens with quick-growing cool-weather grasses to provide winter turf is standard practice in the southern part of the United States. Italian and domestic ryegrass, red fescue, redtop, and occasionally bent are used for this purpose. Mixtures of the ryegrasses and redtop with Kentucky bluegrass or bentgrasses (colonial and creeping) also are suitable. They will produce excellent playing turf if proper seeding methods are followed. The ryegrasses and redtop have approximately the same germinating period and growth rates and can be seeded simultaneously by mixing the seed. Where turf mixtures of Kentucky bluegrass or bents with the ryegrasses or redtop are desired, the Kentucky bluegrass and bents should be seeded first. Overseedings with the ryegrasses or redtop should be delayed until the bluegrass and bents have germinated. The use of red fescue for winter greens has been very successful. It germinates quickly, forms a dense, fine-textured turf, and causes less difficulty than ryegrass during the spring transition period when the Bermudagrass starts to grow.

TIME OF SEEDING. The time of seeding winter greens will vary with the start of the dormancy period of Bermudagrass. In the more northern sections and at the higher elevations seedings are made in early October. Farther south they can be delayed to a much later date, usually late November and early December, depending upon when the Bermudagrass stops growth and loses its color.

In the warmer sections of the region the best winter turf is produced when seedings are made at two or more periods. A light seeding, equivalent to 20 to 40 lb. of ryegrass per 1,000 sq. ft., is applied first. A second, and sometimes a third, seeding is made after the initial planting is well started. This will reduce damage from smothering and damping-off. These are serious problems when heavy seedings are made while temperatures are still relatively high. As temperatures moderate later in the season there is less danger of injury. In the more northern sections turf must be established early in the fall while temperatures are still moderate. Under these conditions the entire seeding can be made at one time. Weather conditions for germination and seedling development usually are favorable, and heavy seeding rates can be used without serious danger of seedling damage.

SEEDING RATES. Suitable seeding rates for the various grasses when used alone are given in Table 16, page 320. Where turf mixtures of two or more grasses are desired, the recommended seeding rate of each grass should be reduced proportionately to the number of types used. For example, if a Kentucky bluegrass and domestic ryegrass mixture is used, the normal seeding rate of each when used alone should be reduced by one-half.

SEEDING METHOD. A firm base is needed for establishing winter grass on Bermuda turf. The Bermuda should be cut close and thinned out by aerating, verti-cutting, or similar treatment that will remove excess growth and thatch. Unless this is done the germinating seed of the winter grass cannot root effectively and will die out after starting growth. Following clipping and thinning, the greens are heavily top-dressed and fertilized. Where the double seeding method is used, a light top-dressing is applied to cover the seed following the second seed application. If Kentucky bluegrass has been used in the first seeding only a very thin dressing can be applied, as young Kentucky bluegrass plants are very susceptible to smothering. A sandy loam top soil that is low in organic matter is the most suitable type of top-dressing material. Heavy organic matter holds large quantities of water which will encourage seedling damping-off under warm temperature conditions and may cause damage from heaving due to frost action where the weather is colder.

FERTILIZATION. Fertilizer applications prior to seeding should consist primarily of treatments with phosphorus and potassium. From 15 to 20 lb. of 20 per cent grade superphosphate and 10 to 15 lb. of 60 per cent grade muriate of potash per 1,000 sq. ft. should be applied. Where minor elements are needed, they should be added at this time. Any necessary treatments to clean up injurious insects, such as mole crickets, also should be made prior to seeding. No nitrogen should be used, especially where straight ryegrass is seeded, until 3 weeks after seeding. Available nitrogen will produce a soft, succulent type of growth that will cause the seedling grass to be more susceptible to injury by diseases.

COVERING AND WATERING. Seedings can be made by hand or with any good type of mechanical distributor. The most uniform germination is secured if the seed is covered by applying a light top-dressing followed by rolling. Light watering with a fine spray nozzle will prevent washing out of seed. Water should be used at frequent intervals to keep sufficient moisture in the surface inch of soil for good seed germination. A light straw or hay mulch will prevent rapid drying out and permit more rapid watering with less danger of washing. The mulch can be removed by hand raking with bamboo or wire-leaf brushes without injury to the grass as soon as the seed has germinated and started growth. Mulching may not be desirable when seedings are made at average temperatures of above 65 to 70 deg.

FIRST CLIPPING. First clippings should be made when the grass is ¾ to 1 in. in height. The height of this first cut should not be less than ½ in. Heights can be reduced gradually to ¼ or 5/16 in. in subsequent clippings. Very sharp mowers are required to prevent tearing out the young seedlings, and light equipment should be used so that the grass will not be crushed. It is also necessary that the turf be dry when mowed, and all clippings should always be removed.

Tees

High-quality soil and good seedbed preparation are essential on tees. The damage caused by concentrated wear, spike abrasion, and divot scars must heal quickly if good playing conditions are to be maintained. A relatively dry surface is desirable to provide the firm stance needed in making tee shots. These requirements call for seedbed soils that have a high fertility level. Good moisture-storage capacity in the root zone also is necessary, so that the turf can be kept healthy and vigorous with a minimum of irrigation.

Methods of seedbed preparation of tee soils are similar to those used for greens, except that texture modifications with sand and organic materials need not be as extensive. Sufficient coarse sand and peat should be added to produce a soil of the quality of a good sandy loam. The same type of mixing operations and quantities of fertilizer, lime, and other amendments used on greens are suitable for tees.

GRASSES. The types of grasses adapted for use on tees in the various climatic regions and recommended rates and time of seeding are listed in Tables 15 and 16, pages 318 and 320, respectively. These grasses usually have been used alone because of their aggressiveness. In some instances, favorable results have been secured by growing mixtures of Bermuda or zoysia grasses with cool-season grasses such as Kentucky bluegrass. This procedure is still on a trial basis.

Mixtures of Kentucky bluegrass with creeping red or Chewings fescue have been used widely for tees in the Cool Humid region. They are being replaced by colonial and creeping bent because they will not make a tight turf under close clipping and are slow to heal divot scars. The colonial and creeping bents alone or in mixtures can be used in both the Cool Humid and West Central regions where water is available for irrigation. The same proportions and rates of seeding recommended for greens are satisfactory for tees.

In the West Central region it is sometimes necessary to use native grasses for tees because of water limitations. Mixtures of buffalograss and blue gramagrass are desirable, under certain conditions. Where buffalograss is well adapted, there is no advantage in using blue gramagrass in mixtures with it. However, along the borders of the buffalograss area in eastern Montana, central Wyoming, and western Colorado, mixtures of the two species will produce a better sod than either species used alone. Mixture proportions should be approximately 1 part buffalo to 2 parts blue grama. Seeding rates of the mixture should be 1 to 2 lb. per 1,000 sq. ft. where water is not available for irrigation. Rates can be doubled where limited amounts of water can be used during the period of turf establishment.

PLANTING. Methods of seeding tees or of vegetative planting, should conform in general with those outlined for greens. Mulching will reduce surface drying and ensure more rapid and uniform seed germination. It is particularly desirable on banks to prevent washing. Where it is necessary to establish native grasses on tees in the West Central region without supplemental irrigation, seeding methods should be used as outlined for fairways in the following section of this chapter.

Tees should be given the same type of care as greens prior to the first cutting. First clipping heights will vary with the type of grass or mixture used. Kentucky bluegrass and fescues should be permitted to grow to a height of 1½ to 2 in. before being cut for the first time. The clipping height should not be less than 1¼ in. Tees consisting of crested wheatgrass or mixtures containing blue grama or the ryegrasses should be handled in the same way. The bentgrasses, Bermudagrass, and other strongly creeping types can be clipped back to a height of ¾ to ½ in. as soon as they have made an initial growth of 1 to 1¼ in.

Fairways

SEEDBED PREPARATION. Seedbed preparation on fairways is concerned primarily with improvement in the quality of the existing soil. Ordinarily it is not practicable to attempt to modify the physical condition of fairway soils by additions of sand or other texture-improving materials. There have been a few instances where fairway soils have been modified successfully with clay or muck. The cost of such treatments is too high to warrant their general use. Manures and raw sludges sometimes can be used to advantage if they can be obtained and applied at a reasonable

FIG. 18. Meeker harrow. A good tool for seedbed preparation. (*Green Section.*)

cost. When used at heavy rates (30 to 40 tons per acre) they will materially increase the humus and available nutrient content of the soil. If they contain appreciable quantities of coarse or strawy matter, a period of 2 to 3 months should be allowed between application and seeding to permit decay of the coarse material. Occasionally topsoil replacements may be made in construction and grading operations. This is desirable only when topsoil is of sufficiently good quality to warrant the cost of handling. In many instances it is so poor that replacement is not justified. In other cases construction operations are of such a nature that topsoil cannot be saved or is insufficient to cover the areas involved. In such instances, seedbed preparation must be adjusted to the character of soil that is present.

The details of tillage and fertilization will vary depending upon the type of soil. Some soils are of high quality and others are low-value subsoils, poor in texture and fertility. Seedbed preparation for fairways also varies in the different climatic regions. In regions of limited rainfall, preparation methods must conserve a maximum of soil moisture unless irrigation is possible.

Soil-fitting Operations. Plowing to a depth of 6 to 8 in. usually is the most desirable method of breaking up heavy soils in humid regions. Either the moldboard or disk plow is satisfactory for this work. Plowing should be followed by disking and sufficient harrowing to reduce the surface to a fine cloddy condition. Tools like the culti-packer and Meeker harrow can be used to good advantage to further pulverize the soil and firm the seedbed. Rotary tillers can be used when stones do not interfere seriously. Smoothing with a drag or spike-tooth harrow will put the surface into good condition for seeding. Light types of soils can be prepared by thorough disking with a double-disk harrow, followed by a drag or smoothing harrow.

In regions of limited rainfall disking, wherever practicable, is preferable to plowing, especially when vegetative cover is already present. One-way disking will leave a somewhat rough trashy surface that will reduce evaporation and protect the developing grass seedlings from wind scouring. Fitting operations should be completed as far in advance of seeding as is practicable. When only limited supplies of water are available, seedbed preparation should be completed a full season in advance of seeding to accumulate as much soil moisture as possible.

In regions of abundant rainfall seedbed preparation 2 to 3 months in advance of seeding provides an opportunity to kill germinating weeds by disking or harrowing during the fitting operations. Periodic disking or harrowing during this time destroys weeds as they appear. This method is limited to places where erosion is not a factor.

Use of Lime, Fertilizers, and Conditioning Materials. Manures, sludges, or other physical conditioning materials should be applied before plowing or disking and plowed under or thoroughly disked into the soil. If soils are deficient in available phosphate and potash, a 0-20-20 fertilizer can be worked into them in the same operation at rates of 1,000 to 1,500 lbs. per acre. Where only one of these nutrients is needed, a 20 per cent grade of superphosphate or 60 per cent muriate of potash should be used at a rate equivalent to the amounts supplied by the 0-20-20 mixture. Where more than 1 ton of lime per acre is required to adjust the soil reaction, one-half of it should be plowed or disked in and the remainder harrowed into the surface in later fitting operations. If 1 ton or less is required, all of it can be harrowed in after plowing or disking.

Starter fertilizers at rates similar to those suggested for use on greens should be worked into the surface 2 or 3 in. with the smoothing harrow in the final fitting operation. It is particularly desirable that the starter fertilizer for fairways carry part of its nitrogen in slowly available form. The application of fertilizer to seedling grass on large areas is troublesome both because of the labor involved and the danger of burning. The use of slowly available materials will extend the period before additional feeding is necessary.

GRASSES. Practical experience has demonstrated that individual grasses or simple mixtures of adapted species are the most satisfactory for fairway use. Fairway areas should be prepared properly to meet the requirements of the grass that will produce the most desirable type of turf. Attempts to compensate for poor conditions by using less desirable types of grasses because of a wider tolerance to high acidity, poor drainage, low fertility, or other adverse factors will only intensify maintenance problems and will result in chronically poor playing conditions.

SEED QUALITY AND MIXTURES. Tables 16 and 17, pages 320 and 322, give the minimum seed-quality requirements for the various grasses adapted for fairway use. The tables also show the normal seeding rates and optimum seeding times for the different species.

Mixtures should include only those grasses able to persist when grown together under the type of maintenance they are to receive. Three general classes of mixtures are suitable for fairway use. The first of these consists of mixtures of a slow-growing, permanent grass with a temporary type that will produce quick cover. Redtop or domestic ryegrass can be used with Kentucky bluegrass or creeping red and Chewings fescue to provide quick cover until the latter species become established. Mixtures of this type should not contain more than 5 to 10 per cent of redtop or more than 20 per cent of domestic ryegrass. Seeding rates of 75 to 100 lb. per acre of Kentucky bluegrass-redtop mixtures and 125 to 150 lb. per acre of fescue-redtop mixtures are satisfactory.

A second class of mixtures consists of grasses that will persist and form a desirable sod when grown in association with each other. Kentucky bluegrass and creeping red or Chewings fescue can be used in this way in ratios of 1 to 2 parts of Kentucky blue to 3 or 4 parts of fescue. Redtop or domestic ryegrass can be added for quick cover at the same rates as for class-one mixtures by reducing the bluegrass and fescue proportionately. An example of a suitable mixture of this type would be:

Grass	*Per Cent by Weight*
Kentucky bluegrass	30
Creeping red fescue	65
Redtop	5

A good seeding rate for such a mixture would be 100 to 125 lb. per acre. Canada bluegrass is sometimes included where soils are open and droughty. The content of Canada bluegrass should be not less than 10 per cent nor more than 25 per cent of the mixture.

This class of mixtures also includes combinations of the bentgrasses and mixtures of buffalo and blue grama grasses in proportions similar to those recommended for greens and tees. The bentgrasses are often used alone on watered fairways where it may be difficult to maintain good Kentucky bluegrass or fescue turf. Suitable seeding rates of bent mixtures for fairways are 40 to 60 lb. per acre. Seeding rates of buffalo–grama grass mixtures for fairways should not exceed 30 lb. per acre unless irrigation water is available.

A third class of mixtures sometimes can be used to advantage when there are wide variations in soil conditions which cannot be modified adequately by good seedbed preparation. Mixtures of Bermuda and carpet grasses can be used in the southeastern part of the United States on fairways that cut across areas of low ground where water tables are high and drainage installations would be difficult. Under such conditions the Bermudagrass would occupy the higher, drier locations. The carpetgrass would predominate on the low wet areas. Mixtures of this type should contain equal proportions by weight of Bermuda and carpetgrass seed and should be seeded at rates of 75 to 100 lb. per acre. Similar situations may occur in the West Central region where fairways include areas of heavy soils in old lake beds or pockets receiving extra moisture. Mixtures of crested and western wheatgrasses are well adapted to such locations. The crested wheatgrass is best adapted to the drier areas, and the western wheatgrass will occupy the low sections. Mixture proportions should be approximately 2 parts crested wheatgrass to 1 part western wheatgrass by weight. The seeding rate should be 25 to 30 lb. per acre.

The use of the above, and similar mixtures, is justified only when soil variations occur in irregular areas on which it would be impracticable to make separate seedings. In many cases, areas requiring special treatment are extensive and the boundaries are easily defined. In such instances the individual grass best adapted to the location should be seeded alone. This will avoid unnecessary competition with other grasses which may survive temporarily but will not form a permanent turf. Also, it is more economical because of the reduced total quantities of seed required.

The development of mechanical sprigging equipment has made it possible to plant fairways economically with improved varieties of Bermuda and other vegetatively propagated grasses. Several types of planters have been developed, all of which will do an efficient job. The machines can be adjusted to set the planting material in rows of varying width and at different spacing intervals in the rows. When properly operated, a two-row planter can cover 10 to 15 acres per day. The quantity of planting stock required is quite variable, depending on planting thickness and the quality of the material. It may range from less than 50 bu. per acre to two or three times that amount.

METHODS OF SEEDING. Many types of mechanical seeding equipment are suitable for seeding fairways. Mechanical seeders are of two general classes. The first includes those types which drop the seed on the surface but do not cover it. The second class consists of seeders that drop and cover in one operation. Wheelbarrow and cyclone seeders and the various hopper-type distributors are

FIG. 19. A wheelbarrow seeder. (*Courtesy Sewerage Commission, City of Milwaukee.*)

representative of the first class. Grass seed drills and cultipackers with seed-hopper attachments belong to the second group. The type of equipment that is best adapted for a particular job will depend primarily upon the condition of the seedbed and the size and chaffiness of the seed used. The wheelbarrow seeder is suitable for small seeded grasses and where seedbeds are in a somewhat cloddy condition. Its relatively small capacity limits its value for the large seeded grasses that require heavier seeding rates. The large type, tractor-drawn hopper seeders are more satisfactory where bulky seed is used. Cyclone seeders will do a satisfactory job only if a single kind of seed, or a mixture in which all of the seed is of approximately the same size and weight, is used.

If seedbeds are finely pulverized some method of covering the seed must be employed when seeders are used that drop the seed on the surface. A spike-tooth harrow set very shallow, a weeder, or a drag are suitable for this purpose. Firming with a roller or cultipacker should follow the covering operation. If the seedbed is in a cloddy condition, rolling or cultipacking usually is sufficient to secure adequate covering.

Seed drills are suitable for fairway seeding if soils are reasonably firm and they can be set shallow enough to avoid burying the seed too deep. The large seeded grasses usually will not germinate satisfactorily when buried to a greater depth than ½ in. The small seeded types require a covering of ¼ in. or less. Where soils are in a cloddy condition, the cultipacker with a seed-hopper attachment will seed, cover, and firm in one operation. It is not well adapted for seeding large seeded grasses on light sandy soils that are finely pulverized. A separate covering operation usually is required under these conditions.

Mulching of seeded areas is desirable to conserve moisture for good germination and as a protection against erosion. Straw or weed-free hay can be used at rates of 1 to 2 tons per acre. Mulching materials need not be removed from the seedling grass if used in moderate quantities and uniformly distributed. They decay rapidly and should not interfere with turf development. Where wind is a problem the mulch cover can be stabilized and held in place by spraying it with 0.1 to 0.2 gal. per sq. yd. of cut-back asphalt. Special equipment is required for this operation.

The production of good fairway turf of native grasses in the West Central region where supplemental irrigation water is not available requires specialized seeding methods. Seedings can be made directly upon seedbeds that have a good content of organic residues from natural vegetation which has been worked into the soil. When this type of seedbed preparation is not practicable, temporary crop seedings should be made in the season prior to establishment of the permanent turf. The best crops for this purpose are cereal grains and Sudangrass. These should be seeded on a prepared seedbed in the spring and permitted to mature. They are cut in the fall and the straw is removed, leaving a 6- to 8-in. stubble. The permanent grasses are seeded into this stubble the following spring. Best results are secured by this method where seed drills equipped with disk-type furrow openers are used.

Roughs and Nonuse Areas

In constructing modern golf courses it has become a general practice to apply the same methods to the establishment of turf on roughs adjacent to fairways as are used for the fairways. The areas so treated will average 10 to 20 yds. in width, depending upon the details of design. Differences in turf quality required to meet the demands of play are secured by adjustment of the clipping height and other maintenance practices. Seedbed preparation on these areas should be similar in all respects to procedures followed on the fairways.

The extent of preparation required for seeding other sections of the roughs and for nonuse areas will vary with the requirements for cover. They should be seeded with types of grasses that need only a minimum amount of care and have a wide tolerance to the existing soil conditions. The characteristics and soil tolerances of grasses which can be used have been outlined in Chap. 5.

The same basic tillage operations that apply to seedbed preparation on fairways are required to produce adequate cover on roughs and nonuse areas. Fertilizer applications, adjustment of soil reaction, and the extent of other soil treatments depend upon the local soil conditions and the requirements of the grass that is used.

SEEDING METHODS. As noted in the discussion of seedbed preparation, close roughs can be prepared and seeded in the same manner as adjacent fairways. Seeding operations on other sections of the rough and of nonuse areas must be adapted to the type of grasses used. Grasses having a wide range of tolerance to soil conditions are available for all climatic regions, and mixtures are seldom necessary or advisable. The time and rate of seeding for the various species are given in Table 16. Types of equipment and general seeding methods for fairways also can be used for the roughs and other areas.

It is sometimes desirable to make light overseedings on existing vegetation to secure greater density of cover on these areas. Definite improvement of existing turf often can be secured by disking-in moderate quantities of lime and fertilizer and broadcasting seed of an adapted species on this roughly prepared surface. Seeding rates of the various grasses when used in this way should be one-half to one-third of the normal rates listed in the tables.

Turf Nurseries

A small area of one to several thousand square feet of sod may be maintained in a turf nursery for repair purposes on greens. Where greens are to be rebuilt, the full quantity of turf required to replace completely the existing sod sometimes is grown in the nursery prior to reconstruction. In either case soil preparation, planting, and maintenance of the turf should be equal to the treatment given greens.

The seedbed of a sod nursery should be prepared carefully. Since a layer of the nursery soil will be placed on the green when the sod is transferred, it should be of the same quality as the seedbed of the green. Sufficient fertilizer must be applied to keep the turf in vigorous condition. The grass should be clipped at putting-green height and top-dressed when necessary to prevent it from becoming spongy or matted. Weeds should be kept out and disease and insect-control treatments made as required.

7

Turf Maintenance

The primary objective in growing turf on the golf course is to provide suitable conditions for play. Maintenance operations must meet the requirements of the grass when possible but, primarily, must be suited to the demands of the game. At times, practices which are desirable for good turf production must be modified extensively to provide the required playing conditions. Height of cut is an example. Modern golf demands closely clipped fairways. This has become necessary, regardless of the fact that it may be injurious to the type of grass that is present. Similarly, grasses must be kept in an active growing condition throughout the entire season, without opportunity to harden off and mature as they do under natural conditions.

In some cases maintenance practices can be modified to balance the effects of these conflicting requirements for good grass and good playing qualities. When this is not practicable, complete replacement of existing grasses or some other major change must be made, to provide and maintain turf suitable for play.

Turf Quality and Playing Conditions. The surfaces of greens must be firm to avoid footprinting. They must be resilient so that a properly played ball will hold but should not be so soft that the "run" of a poorly played shot is checked. Texture of the grass leaves should be relatively fine. Turf should be dense but free from matting and grain which will destroy putting accuracy. The putting surface must be even and true and should be kept free from ball marks and any other irregularity that influences putting quality.

Turf on tees should be dense and firm. It should be cut close enough so that the ball can be teed up clear of uncut grass at a proper height for the type of shot to be played. Tee surfaces should be reasonably dry and sufficiently resilient to provide a firm stance. The use of fast-growing grasses that are self-healing is desirable, but the turf must be kept free from any tendency toward matting or sponginess. This is particularly important on iron-shot holes where turf is taken in making the shot. Large tee areas will provide better playing conditions. Markers can be moved frequently and areas given sufficient time to heal before further use, thus avoiding the necessity for heavy fertilization and watering to speed up healing of divot scars. This reduces the danger of developing soft grass with a poor root system.

Fairway turf of good playing quality should be sufficiently dense to hold up a ball. It must be firm enough to provide a good stance and the necessary club-head resistance for all types of shots. It must be clipped sufficiently close to provide a good lie. The shot is much more difficult for the average player when the ball rests "in" the grass instead of "on" it. Thin open turf requires closer clipping to provide good lies than when it is dense and firm. Any tendency toward fluffiness, sponginess, or matting is undesirable. Soft grass is especially objectionable. Hard, compact soil covered with weeds and solid patches of clover causes poor lies and seriously affects playing conditions.

The class of players and the extent to which the course is used for tournament play will dictate the type of playing conditions maintained in the roughs. Standards suggested by leading golf professionals include (1) open turf where a ball may be found readily, (2) mowing practices and use of grasses which will provide a minimum penalty of one-half stroke per hole for regular play.

The above is a very brief listing of the more important relationships between the quality of turf on the various areas of the golf course and its "playability." All of these major items are affected to a large degree by maintenance practices. The aim of good management on every golf course should be to produce and maintain turf which fulfills playing requirements.

Maintenance of Greens

Greens-maintenance programs must fit the type of grass that is used. Creeping bent, colonial bent, velvet bent, and Bermudagrass all differ in their response to fertilization, water, top-dressing, and many other practices. Individual strains of these grasses also may require different types of treatment. Vigorous, fast-growing, creeping strains require heavier and more frequent brushing and top-dressing and more careful feeding and watering than slower growing forms. Some are more disease resistant or recover more rapidly following fungus attacks. Others may have a greater tolerance to injury caused by herbicides, fungicides, and insecticides. Because of these differences in the way each grass reacts to maintenance practices it is impossible to establish blanket rules for fertilization, top-dressing, watering, or the many other necessary maintenance operations. If the reasons for and the effects of each one are understood, they can be adjusted to meet the local conditions.

Maintenance practices must be considered on the basis of their effects upon each other. The quantities and rates of fertilizer applications are influenced by the amounts of water used. Fertilizer use affects growth rates and so has a direct bearing on clipping frequency, top-dressing, and similar operations that control putting quality. The frequency and strength of fungicidal treatments for disease control often are dependent upon watering practices and available fertility. These and many similar interrelationships illustrate the necessity for a thorough understanding of how each maintenance practice affects all of the others.

POLING, BRUSHING, VERTICAL MOWING, AND CLIPPING. These practices are closely related. Their immediate function is to maintain a smooth and true-putting surface. Poling, or whipping, breaks up dew and scatters worm casts prior to clipping. It may assist in disease control. Poling is usually done by sweeping a flexible bamboo or steel pole back and forth across the surface of the green with a whipping motion. Rattan brushes, such as those used for street sweeping, accomplish the same results when drawn across the turf. The latter method is slower but has the added advantage of providing a light brushing of the turf before cutting.

Brushing relieves matting and steminess in turf and develops more upright leaf growth. Some of the grasses, notably Bermuda and the creeping bents, produce an excessive number of creeping stems which grow horizontally along the surface of the ground and are not cut off in normal clipping operations. When these stems become too dense, leaf development is restricted and a layered or grainy condition of the turf occurs. This will develop into a spongy mat unless corrected. When the condition is not too severe it is possible to keep it under control with the brush or comb attachments on putting green mowers. Part of the surplus growth will be torn out and the remainder raised so that some of it can be cut off by the mower. This opens the turf and provides a better opportunity for leaf development. Various types of vertical mowing equipment have been developed that can be used in lieu of the mower attachments. They are especially useful where growth has been heavy and an undesirable thatch has developed. The action of brush and comb attachments often is not severe enough to correct this condition.

The basic feature of vertical mowers is a series of knives or blades set perpendicular on a horizontal shaft which revolves at a high rate of speed. The knives cut into the turf, tearing out or cutting off excess growth and accumulated dead material. Such machines have become a standard part of the maintenance equipment on many courses. When used systematically and operated properly, they are very effective in preventing graininess and thatch formation. Proper setting for depth of blade penetration is vital to their successful use, particularly on heavily thatched turf. If set too deep at the time of the first treatment they will scalp and scar the turf severely. Proper procedure is to reduce the thatch gradually by repeated use of the machine, interspersed with light top-dressings to reduce rapid accumulations of new growth and hasten decomposition of the dead organic layer. It is essential to apply only light dressings. Attempts to cover up thatch with heavy applications, before it has been opened up sufficiently for soil to penetrate into it, causes objectionable layering. Creeping bents and Bermudagrasses require frequent verti-cutting and top-dressing, due to their fast growth rate and strong stolon production. The velvet bents become very spongy when neglected and are difficult to renovate because of their fine texture. Extreme care must be used in attempting thatch reduction on them by vertical mowing and top-dressing.

The use of properly adjusted mowing equipment that is in good condition is essential on putting greens. True-putting surfaces cannot be maintained if mowers are dull and tear or pinch the grass leaves instead of shearing them closely. Mowers that have not been leveled properly will produce objectionable streaking because one side is cutting lower than the other. Loose reel bearings will cause rippled surfaces. Where power equipment is used, clutch and transmission gears must operate smoothly and throttle controls must work freely. Sudden starts because of a stiff throttle or faulty clutch will cause uneven operation and irregular clipping heights and will damage the turf by drive-drum slippage. The direction of cut should be changed each time the green is mowed, and numerous directions of cut should be used. This will avoid grooving of surfaces and reduce the tendency of the creeping grasses to grain.

Clipping heights will vary with the season and with the type and growth rate of the grass. Maximum heights for both Bermudagrass and the bents usually should not be greater than 5/16 in. Higher cutting will encourage matting and sponginess and will increase the requirements for top-dressing and brushing. Good-quality creeping and velvet bent turf can be clipped to minimum heights of ⅛ in. without injury. Minimum clipping heights of colonial bents and Bermudagrass should be somewhat higher. The height of cut should never be reduced suddenly. Grass develops a balance between tops and root systems. Upsetting this balance suddenly causes a severe shock to the turf and may result in serious injury. It is less injurious to clip turf frequently than to permit it to grow long and then cut it back severely. Sometimes it is desirable to permit the grass to grow for varying periods without clipping to encourage recovery from disease or other injury. When cutting is renewed, mowers should be set high for the first cutting and lowered gradually over a 2 or 3-week period until the desired cutting level is reached.

The frequency of clipping depends upon such factors as weather conditions, quantities of water and fertilizer used, and other items which influence the growth rate of the grass. The best putting surfaces are maintained when greens are cut every day. Daily cutting is desirable on the slower as well as the faster growing grasses. The growth rates of turf on different areas of a green will vary. They differ, also, for the individual strains that make up a mixed turf, as on old South German mixed bent greens. Frequent clipping reduces the unevenness caused by these variations.

As a general rule it is necessary to remove clippings from putting surfaces. When daily cutting is practiced and growth rates are slow, clippings sometimes can be left on the turf without interfering with putting conditions. During periods when *Poa annua* is seeding heavily, clippings may be left on greens composed of this grass, for reseeding. Where it is desirable to reduce the *Poa annua* population, the clippings should be removed.

FERTILIZATION AND LIMING. The basic principles of turf fertilization are well understood. They can be used as a satisfactory guide in planning a feeding program that is adapted to local needs. Estimates of fertilizer and lime requirements should be made as far in advance of the growing season as practicable. This will permit making necessary budget provisions and the placing of orders in time to ensure adequate supplies of materials when they are needed. Systematic soil testing (see Chap. 3) is the best basis for a sound maintenance fertilization program.

Complete fertilizers should be applied to bentgrass greens in spring and fall. The ratios of phosphate and potash to the nitrogen in the mixture will depend upon the available quantities of these nutrients in the soil, as shown by test. Where levels are high, a total annual application of 2 to 3 lbs. each, of P_2O_5 and K_2O, per 1,000 sq. ft. will be sufficient to supply the needs of the turf. If levels of either nutrient are low and must be raised, annual rates of 6 to 7 lbs. should be used until the deficiencies are corrected.

The source of the fertilizer nitrogen also affects the nutrient ratio that should be used. A few examples will illustrate this. If all of the nitrogen is in quickly available form, and the soil test shows high levels of phosphate and potash, the ratio for both fall and spring should be a 1-1-1, applied at a rate to supply approximately one pound each of the three nutrients per 1,000 sq. ft. If the nitrogen is from a slowly available source, a 2-1-1 or 3-1-1 ratio can be used at a rate to supply one pound each of P_2O_5 and K_2O and proportionally more nitrogen. Where phosphate and potash are low and the nitrogen in the fertilizer is from a quickly available source, ratios of 1-2-2 or 1-3-3 will be needed for each application. These can be narrowed to 1-1-1 when all of the nitrogen is slowly available. Similar adjustments can be made when only one nutrient is deficient; as a 1-2-1 or 1-3-1, if phosphate is low, and a 1-1-2 or 1-1-3, if only potash is short. Here again, adjustments must be made for the type of nitrogen present. If it is from slowly available sources, a 2-2-1 or 3-3-1 should be used for low phosphate and a 2-1-2 or 3-1-3 for low potash (see Chap. 3 for explanation of *ratios*).

The rates of application of fertilizers of various ratios will depend on the actual analysis of the mixture. The rate for any analysis must be adjusted to the amount and kind of nitrogen (quickly or slowly available) it carries. It is seldom necessary or desirable to use more than one pound of actual nitrogen in quickly available form per 1,000 sq. ft. per application. Thus a 10-10-10 analysis (1-1-1 ratio) with only quick acting nitrogen should be applied at a rate of 10 lbs. per 1,000 sq. ft. Since higher rates of slowly available nitrogen (2 to 4 lbs.) are necessary, spring and fall applications of a minimum of 20 lbs. of a 10-5-5 analysis with this kind would supply the same quantity of phosphate and potash as the 10-10-10 above, and double the amount of nitrogen. If a still larger total quantity of nitrogen were needed, an analysis such as a 15-5-5 could be used at the 20 lb. rate.

Normally, it will not be necessary to use additional phosphate and potash between spring and fall applications. Nitrogen must be applied periodically during this time because of rapid consumption by the grass and possible leaching losses. Either quickly or slowly available forms, or mixtures of them can be used. If the latter, adjustment of rates must be made, based on the actual quantity of each form present. If only quick nitrogen is used, applications will be needed at approximately ten-day intervals during the favorable part of the growing season, at a rate of no more than 1 lb. of actual nitrogen per 1,000 sq. ft. They should be reduced during periods of unfavorable conditions and discontinued entirely on cool-season grasses during hot weather. For Bermudagrass turf, rates should be maintained through the summer and tapered-off gradually as cool fall weather approaches.

If slowly available forms are used for supplemental nitrogen applications, the number and rate will depend on whether natural organics or Urea-form compounds are used. If the former, applications normally can be made at approximately monthly intervals at a minimum rate of 2 lbs. of actual nitrogen per 1,000 sq. ft. These also should be reduced on cool season grasses during hot periods. If the nitrogen in the complete fertilizer used for spring and fall applications is predominantly from Urea-form, it is seldom necessary to make more than one additional application of this material during the season. The rate should be from 3 to 4 lbs. of actual nitrogen per 1,000 sq. ft. and the time will vary with the condition of the turf. Normally, it should not be later than early June. Since Bermudagrass has a longer growing season than the cool-season grasses, it may need more than one supplemental application.

Bermudagrass greens that are overseeded with winter grasses require a special fertilizer program. The use of nitrogenous fertilizers on Bermuda turf should be discontinued one month in advance of winter seedings, to reduce the amount of available nitrogen in the soil. No nitrogen should be applied prior to seeding the winter grass or until the new turf has become well established. Liberal preseeding applications of phosphate and potash should be made. These materials can be used at rates of 2 to 5 lb. of phosphoric acid (10 to 25 lb. of 20 percent superphosphate) and 6 to 8 lb. of potash (10 to 15 lb. of 60 per cent muriate of potash) per 1,000 sq. ft. The fertilizer applications should be made 2 to 4 weeks before seeding to prevent injury to seed germination. Nitrogen feeding usually can begin about one month after the winter grass is established. It is very desirable to have soil tests made at this time to determine whether sufficient available phosphoric acid and potash are present to balance nitrogen applications. If these nutrients are low, a complete fertilizer should be used. Ratios can vary from 1-1-1 to 1-2-2, depending upon soil needs. Applications of these ratios should be at the rate of ½ to 1 lb. of nitrogen per 1,000 sq. ft. It sometimes is necessary to make supplemental applications of soluble nitrogen to the winter grass during the cool weather of December and January. These treatments should be limited to a maximum of ½ lb. of nitrogen per 1,000 sq. ft. and must be watered in thoroughly to prevent burning. It should be emphasized that watering practices must be carefully controlled, particularly in the early stages of development of the winter grass. Heavy watering will increase damping-off diseases and cause high nitrogen losses in sandy types of soil.

Fertilization to stimulate the Bermudagrass should start as soon as it begins to come up in the spring. Complete fertilizers with ratios within the same range as those used in the fall should be applied at this time. It may be necessary to repeat this treatment within 4 to 6 weeks, depending upon soil deficiencies of the minerals. Subsequent applications can consist of either slowly or quickly available forms of nitrogen. Differences in periods and rates of application are as outlined previously for greens.

On greens consisting largely of annual bluegrass there is no assurance that it can be kept in good condition by any system of maintenance. If weather conditions are unfavorable, it will die out. Fertilizer practices that are best adapted to it include (1) the limited use of nitrogen (½ lb. or less per month) to prevent excessive succulence, (2) liberal applications of phosphate and potash, (3) a soil reaction close to pH 7.

The suggested programs for the fertilization of greens as outlined above are not foolproof and must be modified to fit local conditions. Good judgment and extreme care in making fertilizer applications is necessary always. Uniform applications and protection against burning are essential. Regardless of whether organic or inorganic forms of nitrogen are used, too frequent and too heavy applications, particularly when soil moisture is kept too high, will result in injury. Quantities used and the frequency of applications must be based upon a careful estimate of turf needs. Grass will show lack of available nitrogen promptly. Applications should be made when indications of nitrogen hunger appear. Conversely, serious nitrogen deficiencies completely upset the nutrient balance necessary for good turf growth. Grass that is weakened by chronically low supplies of available nitrogen usually is more susceptible to disease and recovers very slowly from attacks. It also is less resistant to invasion by weeds and will not compete successfully with those types which can grow well at low nitrogen levels. Annual bluegrass, pearlwort, chickweed, and clover flourish during the cool weather of fall and spring when growth rates of bentgrasses may be checked by low supplies of available nitrogen.

Finally, the nitrogen program should be so adjusted that available quantities are reduced gradually as severe weather conditions approach. This applies equally to the coming of hot weather in the summer and cold weather in the fall. Grass that is soft and succulent will be injured more seriously, both in periods of hot humid weather and when sudden cold spells occur, than when it has had an opportunity to adjust gradually to lower nitrogen supplies and to develop a tough, hard type of growth. The danger of forcing it by liberal use of nitrogen just prior to extended periods of unfavorable conditions cannot be disregarded.

LIME. The use of lime on both bent and Bermuda greens should be based upon soil reaction. Applications should be made whenever tests fall below pH 6.0. (Rates for various pH levels are given in Chap. 3.) Finely ground limestone is the safest and usually the most convenient form. Where soils are low in magnesium (less than 500 lb. per acre by Hellige-Truog test) dolomitic limestone containing at least 20 to 30 per cent magnesium should be used (see discussion in Chap. 9 on use of lime in disease control).

WATERING. The use of water on greens is outlined in Chap. 4, in the section on Water Management.

TOP-DRESSING is used to (1) improve the putting surface, and (2) modify soil conditions under the turf. A third objective must be added where Bermudagrass greens are top-dressed to prepare them for seeding winter grasses.

The need and value of top-dressing must be measured by its

usefulness in restoring turf quality and improving putting conditions. When greens have been subjected to heavy winter play, top-dressings may be essential to restore putting surfaces that have become uneven because of trampling and frost action. In severe cases several dressings may be required to put them in good

FIG. 20. A convenient shed for preparing and storing top-dressing. (*Courtesy Sewerage Commission, City of Milwaukee.*)

condition. Top-dressing is necessary when turf has become thin because of disease, insect injury, or loss of annual bluegrass. Ball marks and other scars heal slowly when turf is thin, and slight surface irregularities have a more pronounced effect upon putting quality. Top-dressing is an essential part of the treatment required to renovate sod that has become stemmy or matted. Where surface compaction is a serious problem because of poor soil texture, a regular program of top-dressing and aeration can be used effectively to build a layer of good soil under the established turf. Such conditions also would indicate need of aerating in connection with top-dressings as noted under Compaction Correction, page 169.

Top-dressing should not be considered as a standard and routine practice that must be used at regular intervals as a part of normal turf maintenance. It requires expensive materials and is time consuming. It is an excellent aid in restoring turf quality when soil conditions are bad or putting surfaces are not true. It is not a pana-

FIG. 21. Steel mat for working in top-dressing. (*Courtesy Sewerage Commission, City of Milwaukee.*)

cea. It will not permanently improve poor turf resulting from bad drainage or other chronic conditions of a similar nature. Good judgment is needed in determining where and when it can be used effectively. Where greens have been well constructed and a good strain of grass has been used, there may be no necessity for top-dressing for long periods of time. Good day-to-day care will keep the turf in satisfactory playing condition.

Top-dressing programs should be adjusted to the specific condition to be corrected. Where repairs to putting surfaces must be made following heavy winter use, top-dressings should be concentrated in the early part of the season. They should be continued until the undesirable condition has been corrected. Similarly, repeated dressings within a limited period are necessary to correct sponginess and matting. Dressings designed to improve the putting quality of thin turf are a necessity whenever surfaces lose

FIG. 22. Rubbing board for working in top-dressing. (*Courtesy Sewerage Commission, City of Milwaukee.*)

their trueness. They may be required at irregular periods throughout the entire season, or they may be needed only in periods when annual bluegrass is lost. Top-dressings to build a better layer of soil under turf should be made at regular intervals. They should be as frequent as the condition of the turf and the demands of play will permit, to establish good soil conditions as quickly as possible.

The quantities of material used and the frequency of top-dressing must be adjusted to the requirements on each green.

They depend primarily upon the kind of grass and the severity of the conditions to be corrected. Quantities may vary from 1/5 to ½ cu. yd. per 1,000 sq. ft. Applications can be made at 10-day to 2-week intervals, if necessary. Colonial and velvet bents will not stand as heavy or as frequent treatments. Particular care must be employed in top-dressing velvet bents. Quantities should be lim-

FIG. 23. Top-dressing preparation. Mixing soil, sand, and peat through a shredding machine. (*Pennsylvania Agricultural Experiment Station.*)

ited to less than ¼ cu. yd. per 1,000 sq. ft., and the material should be well screened, uniformly distributed, and thoroughly worked into the turf. Heavy, uneven applications will cause severe injury. Minimum quantities of material must be used when turf is thin. If a single dressing will not produce the required improvement, treatments should be repeated. Heavy dressings cannot be used because there is not sufficient grass to stabilize the material that has been applied. As previously noted, dressings can be made frequently on heavy creeping bent and Bermudagrass turf. It is seldom practicable because of interference with play to make applications more often than at 3- or 4-week intervals. In sections where summer temperatures are high, top-dressings should be restricted to very light applications or discontinued entirely during the summer months.

The proportions of soil, sand, and organic matter used in the preparation of top-dressing mixtures have been outlined in Chap. 6. The weed-seed content of soil used in the mixture should be determined by testing a small quantity of the soil in a flat or pot for germination of seeds. If noxious weeds are present, most of the seeds can be killed by mixing various nitrogenous materials such as Cyanamid, sulfate of ammonia, or activated sewerage sludge with the top-dressing (see Chap. 8 for a description of this method). Top-dressing mixtures also can be sterilized by the use of chemicals such as Methyl bromide and VPM (see Chap. 8).

Renovation of Greens

Renovation is a specialized form of maintenance. It includes practices and treatments used to improve turf which has deteriorated to such an extent that normal maintenance operations cannot keep it in good condition. Determination of the cause of deterioration is the first step in a turf-improvement program. The principal reasons for poor turf quality on greens are (1) poor drainage, (2) soil compaction, (3) heavy matting and sponginess, (4) development of sand and organic-matter layers, (5) injury due to disease, insects, neglect and accidental causes, (6) unadapted grasses, and (7) tree competition. Adequate correction of these basic causes of poor turf is an essential part of any systematic program for permanent improvement. Complete renovation also is sometimes practiced where the existing turf is to be replaced with another type of grass. This is most common in the South when common Bermudagrass is to be replaced with one of the better putting green varieties.

Early fall is the best time to renovate in northern sections. Growing conditions usually are good at this period, and grass has a better opportunity to become well established before weeds and hot weather become a problem. In the South, early spring is the most desirable time for renovation of Bermudagrass greens.

Drainage Correction. It is a waste of time and effort to attempt to secure permanent improvement by reseeding or any other renovation method unless bad drainage has been corrected. Poor drainage affects the vigor and quality of turf so seriously that improvement in other ways cannot compensate for it. Methods for

Fig. 24. The self-powered light Aerifier with ½-in. spoons for use on greens. (*Courtesy West Point Lawn Products Company.*)

the correction of surface and subsurface drainage on greens are discussed in detail in Chap 4.

Compaction Correction. Compaction in the surface layer of soil can be corrected by the use of suitable aerating equipment. Where it is confined to small areas, the tubular-tine fork can be used for piercing and aerating the compacted layer. When entire greens require treatment, power-operated tools such as the Aerifier and Terforator can be used. The soil cores left on the surface should be removed if compaction has developed because of poor soil quality. If the soil is good, the cores can be broken up by matting or brushing. Lime, fertilizer, and treatments which may be required for insect control can be applied before the cores are removed and worked into the holes in this operation. The turf should be mowed to remove any ragged tufts that may result from the aeration operations. Seedings are made following mowing and covered with a light top-dressing (see Reseeding and Vegetating, page 171. Soils that compact badly because of

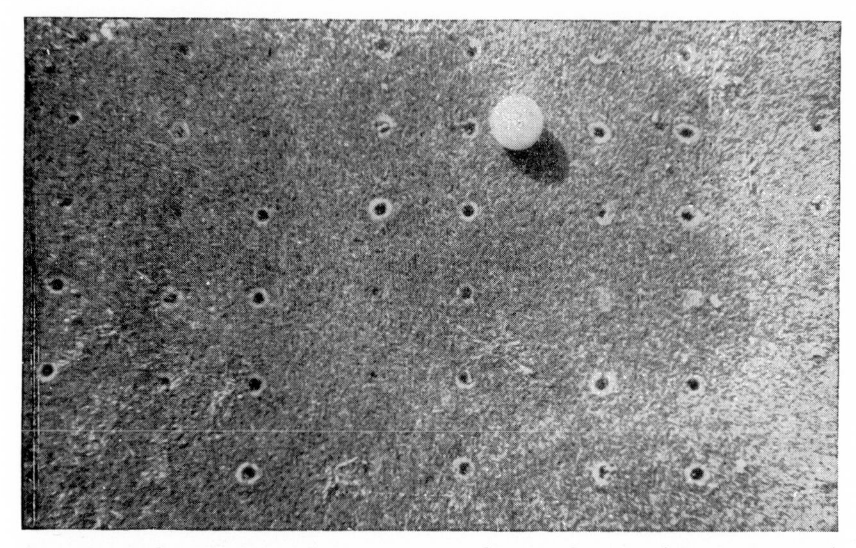

FIG. 25. Holes in green after aeration with a Terforator. (*Green Section.*)

poor physical condition cannot be modified adequately by a single treatment. A regular program of periodic aerations and repeated top-dressings is necessary to secure permanent improvement.

THATCH AND LOCALIZED DRY SPOT CONTROL. Turf that consistently is cut too high or too infrequently will develop an undesirable spongy and matted condition. Matting also may be due to failure of old stems and roots to decay because of unfavorable soil conditions for the activity of the organisms that decompose organic matter. In the latter case the mat may become so dense in certain areas that a watertight surface thatch is formed. This results in the development of localized dry spots. Renovation procedure is similar in both cases. The turf should be thoroughly aerated as previously outlined. Following aeration it should be heavily brushed or raked, close clipped, and top-dressed. Where large sections or entire greens are involved, the use of some type of vertical mower is more efficient than hand work. The quantity of surplus growth that can be removed in a single treatment will depend to some extent upon whether it is necessary to maintain a putting surface during the renovation process. A layer of spongy or matted material should not be covered with a single heavy top-dressing. When the turf is in this condition, it is necessary to repeat light brushing or verti-cutting, and top-dressing applications periodically to secure the desired results. In renovation of this type it is essential that the turf be opened up thoroughly before top-dressings are applied and that lime and fertilizer be used to provide favorable conditions for soil organisms. Top-dressings applied to a heavy turf under acid conditions will serve only to increase mat formation.

WEED, CLOVER, AND ANNUAL BLUEGRASS CONTROL. The removal of weeds, clover, and undesirable grasses is an essential part of any renovation program. It should be emphasized, however, that weed invasions are not basic causes of poor turf. They are the results. They come in as turf weakens or when maintenance is of such a type that they are favored more than the desirable grasses. A renovation program that is limited only to their destruction is of little use. It is effective only when their encroachment is due to superficial turf injury from disease, insects, or accidents. Ordinarily, weed control is only the first part of the renovation program. It provides better conditions for turf development when the basic causes of deterioration have been corrected. Detailed methods for weed eradication are discussed in Chap. 8, Weed Control.

RESEEDING AND VEGETATING. When high turf density is required as quickly as possible, it may be necessary to reseed or replant vegetatively following renovation. Reseeding should be done only after there has been thorough surface preparation to insure good germination and seedling development. Seed planted in heavy thatch will not germinate satisfactorily. Even when it does, the seedlings often die before the roots can reach the soil. Prior to seeding, the green should be thoroughly aerated, followed by some method of scarification such as vertical mowing or spike disking. This will break up the soil cores and open the turf so that the seed can get down to the soil surface. Any needed lime, fertilizer, or pest control treatments should be made before scar-

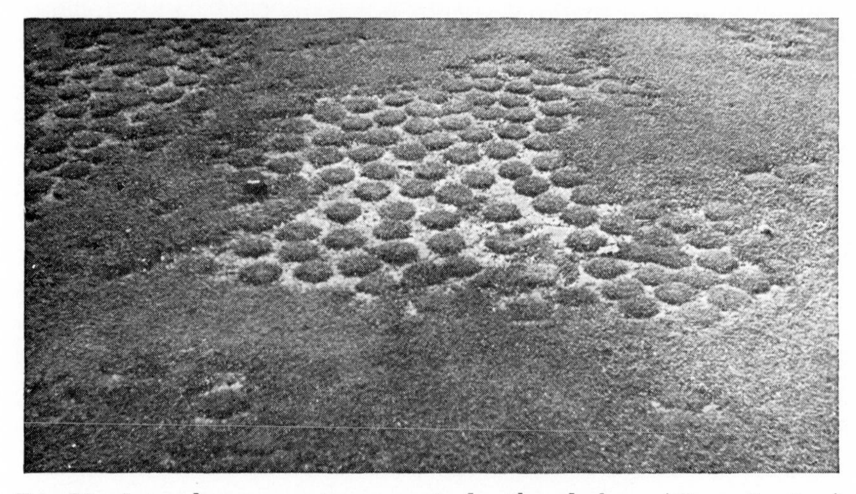

FIG. 26. Injured area on a green repaired with sod plugs. (*Green Section.*)

ification and worked into the soil in this operation. Normally, only ⅓ to ½ of the amount of seed required for new seedings will be needed for renovation overseedings. The seed should be broadcast over the area and covered with a light top-dressing. Light rolling and watering will help to settle the top-dressing and hasten germination.

Various methods can be used to introduce stolons of vegetatively propagated varieties into established turf. They can be plugged in, as illustrated in Fig. 26. They can be cut into the sod by inserting them into narrow slits opened at an angle with a heavy knife or other suitable tool. Or they can be dibbled into aerator holes with a blunt dibble. In extreme cases, where the turf is very thin, they can be broadcast over the area and covered with top-dressing, as for new plantings. Regardless of the method used, the surface should be limed, fertilized, aerated, and the turf opened up as thoroughly as possible before plantings are made.

Where large areas of a green have been injured, it is often more satisfactory to repair it by sodding than to seed or vegetate. The old turf, including thatch, should be cut out of the area and the soil prepared in the same manner as for seeding. Renovation by sodding is justified only when good quality sod is available which has been grown on prepared soil that has the same physical characteristics as the soil on the green (see Chap. 6 for sodding methods).

TREE COMPETITION. Tree roots that penetrate the grass-root zone of greens cause turf to thin out because of excessive competition for nutrients and moisture. Trees also may affect turf by preventing good air drainage. In either case, the source of the trouble must be removed before a satisfactory renovating program can be completed. Competition by tree roots sometimes can be eliminated effectively by the construction of a deep ditch filled with porous material between the tree and green. Cutting tree roots with a power-drawn knife also will check competition by them. Severed roots already in the green will decompose under good conditions of aeration, soil reaction, and fertility. A properly constructed ditch will prevent additional root invasion for a considerable period if the backfill material is coarse and drainage out of the bottom is rapid. Cutting with a power knife is not effective for as long a period. On greens affected by lack of air movement, provision for air drainage by judicious pruning or tree removal is a necessary preliminary to a permanent turf-improvement program.

Apron Maintenance

Apron-maintenance practices should be designed to eliminate surface irregularities, ensure good resiliency, and provide satisfactory turf quality for the specialized type of play on these areas. The elimination of surface irregularities is essential to prevent undue deflection of the ball on approach and run-up shots. Close clipping and good turf density are necessary for the same reason.

CLIPPING. The height of cut on aprons depends upon the predominating type of grass. Where the turf is composed primarily of bent, Bermuda, or other creeping grasses, clipping height should be ½ to ¾ in. or less. When the sod consists primarily of Kentucky bluegrass, fescue, or grasses with similar growth habits, height of cut should not be less than 1 to 1¼ in. On certain holes clipping operations on aprons can be continuous with fairway mowing. In cases where the type of construction is such that excessive turning is required on apron areas, they should be cut separately to avoid compaction.

WATERING. The same general water relationships prevail for aprons as apply to greens. The amount of water and frequency of applications may vary from those required on greens because of basic differences in soil texture and other properties. They must be adjusted to turf requirements and soil conditions.

DISEASE, INSECT, AND WEED CONTROL. Aprons should receive the same insecticide and fungicide treatments as greens. Unless insects and diseases are controlled on these areas, they may become prolific sources of contamination to greens turf. Diseases such as dollar spot and brown patch may develop strong centers of infection in the higher cut turf of aprons. Similarly, such insects as chinch bugs and mole crickets will spread into greens turf rapidly if not controlled adequately on apron areas. Eradication of weeds, particularly crabgrass, is desirable to prevent seed infestation of the green and because of their effect upon playing conditions. Detailed control measures for these pests are outlined in Chaps. 8, 9, and 10.

TOP-DRESSING, AERATION, AND OTHER MAINTENANCE PRACTICES. The use of top-dressing on apron areas usually is limited to leveling of surface irregularities. A good-quality sandy loam soil is satisfactory. Where only poor-quality soil is available a suitable mixture can be made by using ratios of 6 to 10 parts soil, 1 to 3 parts sand, and 1 to 2 parts organic material (peat). Ordinarily, coarser material can be used than would be suitable for greens.

Aprons may become more compacted than fairways because of

the concentrated traffic to which they are subjected. This factor together with frequent clipping and overwatering weakens the grass and brings in clover, annual grasses, and weeds. Periodic aeration, less frequent watering, and the correct use of fertilizer and lime, based on the type of grass present, are essential to maintenance of good apron turf.

Apron areas immediately in front of sloping greens often remain saturated for long periods because of runoff and seepage from the greens. Where designs are not adapted for the quick disposal of this water by surface contouring, a single tile line laid across the front of the green can be used. Tile should be set at a depth of 2 to 2½ ft. and the ditch backfilled with porous material to within 6 to 8 in. of the surface.

Fairway Maintenance

A sound fairway-maintenance program must be based primarily upon the kind of grass that predominates in the turf. The best grasses spread vegetatively by creeping stems which grow either above or below ground. The bents spread by surface runners or stolons, Kentucky bluegrass and creeping red fescue have underground stems or rhizomes. Bermudagrass may develop both above- and below-ground creeping stems. Growth rates and characteristics of the different grasses vary. The bents and Bermudagrass spread much faster than Kentucky bluegrass, the zoysias, and buffalograss. Some grasses develop an upright type of growth, while others form a dense mat of foliage close to the ground. Maintenance practices must consider these differences in growth habits. They must be adapted to differences in the response of the grasses to variations in soil and weather conditions, to disease and insect attacks, and to weed invasion. When it is impossible to maintain satisfactory turf with the grass that is present on a particular fairway, the only satisfactory solution is conversion to one that is better adapted to the prevailing conditions.

MOWING. Mowing practices must meet the demands of play. They may conflict with what is best for the grass. The principal function of green leaves is to convert the raw nutrients absorbed by the roots into finished products for growth. When total leaf surface is reduced by clipping, the process of food manufacture is slowed down. Unless the grass can adjust itself to the height of cut to which it is subjected, it will weaken and eventually die or be crowded out by plants that can tolerate this type of treatment. Kentucky bluegrass, the fescues, and many of the coarser bunch grasses can make only limited adjustments to clipping height. These grasses have an upright habit of growth and produce only a medium number of leaves. Close clipping removes a large proportion of the total leaf area. Their growth rates are not sufficiently rapid to replace losses promptly. New leaf and stem formation is restricted, and the turf becomes thin and weak. It is less able to withstand the effects of compact soil, overwatering, disease and insect attacks, and other adverse conditions. The bluegrasses, except *Poa annua,* fescues, and other slow-growing, erect types of grasses cannot withstand continuous cutting at heights of less than 1 to 1¼ in.

Grasses that form a dense mat of foliage close to the ground or are able to replace losses in leaf area rapidly because of fast growth rates can be cut close. Satisfactory turf of the bent grasses, Bermuda, carpet, centipede, and other low-growing creeping types can be maintained at cutting heights of ½ to ¾ in. under normal fairway-maintenance care. Clipping heights of buffalograss will vary between ¾ and 1 in., depending upon the growth rate. Seasonal regulation of clipping height is sometimes desirable. During the spring and fall when grass is growing rapidly, bluegrass and fescue can be cut closer without injury than during midsummer. Increasing the clipping height of fast-growing grasses such as the bents and Bermuda is not desirable because of the problem of increased matting and sponginess.

Mowing frequency depends upon the growth rate of the turf. Clipping intervals should be spaced so that not more than ¼ to ½ in. of leaf blade is removed at any one time. Close clipping of turf that has been permitted to grow to a height of 1½ to 2 in. between cuttings may cause more severe injury than where clipping to the same height is more frequent.

The modern types of heavy mowing equipment will cause serious compaction and corrugation (washboard effect) when operated repeatedly and at high speeds on saturated soils. These may be avoided to some extent by changing the direction of cut so that the tractor wheels do not follow in the same track repeatedly. This is particularly desirable where turf has a tendency to grain. Cutting in the opposite direction or diagonally to the previous cut will assist in preventing undesirable matting.

FERTILIZATION. The same basic principles of fertilizer use that apply to greens also apply to the maintenance fertilization of fairways. Regular applications of a complete fertilizer should be made annually, unless soil tests show that adequate quantities of an individual nutrient already are present. Annual soil tests to determine levels of available phosphate and potash are particularly important where the turf consists of Kentucky blue or Bermuda grasses, both of which have high requirements for these nutrients. Also, they are essential, especially for potash, on peat lands and on light, sandy soils, where leaching losses of this element are high. When tests show results below medium-high levels, phosphate and potash always should be used.

Where a complete fertilizer is needed it can be used on the cool-season grasses as a single treatment in early fall, or split into fall and spring applications. Split applications always should be made on warm-season grasses, with the first coming in early spring as soon as growth starts. The ratios and rates used will depend on the form of nitrogen in the fertilizer, the kind and quality of turf, and the general fertility level. As in the case of complete fertilizers for maintenance of greens, the ratio of nitrogen to phosphate and potash must be adjusted to the rate of availability of the nitrogen and requirements for the latter nutrients (see discussion of greens fertilization).

Lower total quantities of fertilizer normally are needed on fairways than for greens because of the less intensive management of the former, and because clippings are not removed from them. The total quantity also is affected by the kind of grass and the extent of irrigation. Fast growing grasses like the bents, Kentucky bluegrass, and Bermudagrass, need heavier fertilization than fescues and zoysias. Larger quantities are required on irrigated fairways because of heavier utilization and losses. The total amount used, whether in single or split applications, is determined by the analysis and is based on the quantity and kind of nitrogen in the fertilizer. On unwatered fairways, fast growing grasses will normally need a minimum of 150 to 200 lbs. of actual nitrogen per acre to maintain good growth throughout the season. This would require an annual application of 1,500 to 2,000 lbs. of a 10-5-5 mixture. It could be put on in one or two applications if all or most of the nitrogen was in slowly available form. If most of it was in soluble form, it should be split into four or five applications at monthly intervals. On irrigated turf, rates should be increased to 1½ times these amounts. If the turf consists mostly of slow growing grasses, the above quantities can be reduced by one-half.

When rates as previously outlined are used, and the nitrogen is derived principally from slowly available sources, it seldom is necessary to make supplemental fertilizer applications during the season. Some additional nitrogen may be needed if the original rate proved to be too low, or if abnormal weather conditions should reduce the rate of release to a point where it is not supporting satisfactory growth. If this is a recurring problem, two alternatives are possible. Either the fertilizer formulation can be changed to contain a greater percentage of quickly available nitrogen, or supplemental nitrogen can be applied. If the latter, the quantity of a fast-acting form should be limited to 25 to 50 lbs. of actual nitrogen per acre (50 to 100 lbs. of urea or 75 to 150 lbs. of ammonium nitrate). Extreme care must be taken to water the turf promptly and thoroughly following use of this class of materials. The nitrogen rate should be increased to double the above amounts if a natural organic form is applied, and to three times as much for Urea-form compounds.

Fertilizer applications can be made with various types of distributors. Where drills are used, the shoes should be removed and a baffle board sloping toward the rear should be set directly beneath the tubes from the fertilizer box. The board will distribute the fertilizer and prevent it from being deposited in rows. Several large hopper-type distributors are available commercially that can be used both for fertilizer and lime distribution.

Spreaders should be calibrated to apply the correct quantities. The physical condition of different kinds of fertilizers determines the rate at which they will feed through the distributor. There are various ways of determining the distribution rate at a given set of the machine. A simple method uses a rectangular sheet-metal or wooden pan that is hung directly under the outlet spouts so that it catches the fertilizer as it is discharged. The distributor is operated over a measured area, and the fertilizer discharged in the pan is then weighed. The length of the test strip can be determined by measuring the circumference of the spreader wheel and then counting the number of wheel turns. If the measured area covered was 1/10 acre and 50 lb. of fertilizer was discharged, the rate of application at the particular set used is 10 x 50, or 500 lb. per acre. Table 9 is convenient for reference in measuring areas for use in calibrating fertilizer equipment.

TABLE 9

Hopper length ft.	*Length of strip in feet needed for*		
	1/10 acre	*1/20 acre*	*1/40 acre*
7	622	311	155
8	545	272	136
10	436	218	109

LIMING. The lime requirements of the various types of fairway grasses are shown in Table 2, page 25. Applications of finely ground limestone should be made whenever the soil reaction falls below the optimum range for a particular grass. Usually it is not necessary to apply the full amount of lime required to bring a soil to the neutral point. Table 7, on page 49, Chap. 3 shows satisfactory application rates at various pH levels for different groups of grasses. As noted in the discussions of the use of lime on greens, dolomitic limestone having a magnesium content of at least 25 to 30 per cent should be used where soil tests show magnesium deficiencies.

Lime can be applied at any time of the year. Late fall or winter applications are desirable from the standpoint of economy of labor. Applications at this period also will permit the lime to take effect before phosphates are applied the following season.

WATERING. See Chap. 4 for a discussion of irrigation systems and water management on fairways.

WEED AND INSECT CONTROL. Control methods are presented in Chaps. 8 and 10, respectively.

Fairway Renovation

The development of a sound program for the renovation and improvement of fairways, just as for greens, rests upon a correct diagnosis of the principal causes of turf deterioration. The most common reasons for poor fairway turf are (1) the use of unadapted grasses, (2) poor physical properties of the soil and inadequate drainage, (3) low fertility and unfavorable soil reaction, (4) poor maintenance practices such as overwatering and improper clipping, and (5) injury due to disease, insects, winterkilling, and accidents.

Systematic renovation of fairways located in northern sections is most successful when started in the fall. This applies particularly to areas where crabgrass is a serious problem. In these sections turf that is strong enough to resist reinfestation by this pest can be produced only by utilizing the full fall and early spring growing season. In southern areas where warm-weather grasses are used, renovation programs should begin in the early spring.

The first step in a fairway-improvement program is correction of the conditions responsible for deterioration of the existing turf. Soil compaction or surface thatching of the grass can be broken by thorough aerating. Needed surface or subsurface drainage should be installed where necessary. Where low fertility or soil acidity are the major problems, applications of fertilizer and lime should be made to meet the requirements shown by accepted types of soil tests that have been run carefully and interpreted accurately. If the turf is poor owing to insect attacks, suitable measures for their control must be adopted. Finally, a grass must be selected which is adapted to the soil, climatic, and maintenance requirements of the location. Suitable methods for performing all of the above operations are outlined in the appropriate chapters on these subjects.

Standard materials required for fairway renovation include seed, fertilizer, lime, and herbicides for weed control. Necessary

FIG. 27. The heavy tractor-drawn Aerifier unit with 1-in. spoons.

tools include scarifying equipment, a fertilizer and lime distributor, equipment for application of insecticides and herbicides (where treatments are necessary), and a seeding machine.

A standardized renovation program that is commonly used when fairways have become heavily infested with *Poa annua* which is to be destroyed and replaced with desirable permanent grasses, consists of the following consecutive operations:

1. Drainage correction, if required (see Chap. 4).

2. Destruction of existing *Poa annua* and other weeds in late August by spraying with sodium arsenite at a minimum rate of 40 lbs. in 50 to 100 gals. water per acre. This will severely brown

Fig. 28. The fairway spiker. (*Green Section.*)

Fig. 29. A three-gang fairway Verti-cut machine assembly for excess growth removal and thatch control. (*Courtesy West Point Products Corp.*)

and may kill any scattered bentgrass or fescue that is present. Kentucky bluegrass and Bermuda usually recover.

3. Thorough aeration to open up the turf. A minimum of four to six passes with an aerifier or similar machine will be required.

4. Application of lime and fertilizer as determined by test

FIG. 30. New seeding of Astoria bentgrass seeded on a fairway with a seed drill.

(see Chap. 6). If insects have been a serious problem, control treatments can be made at this time (see Chap. 10).

5. Use of flexible tine harrow, a spike disk, or similar tool, to break up cores and work lime and fertilizer into aerator holes.

6. Area permitted to lie fallow until fall crop of *Poa annua* has germinated. *Poa annua* normally germinates between the last week in August and mid-September. If dry weather occurs and water is available, its emergence can be hastened by irrigating.

7. New crop of *Poa annua* to be sprayed with sodium arsenite at a minimum rate of 25 lbs. per acre. If the kill has not been satis-

factory within a 5 or 6 day period, the treatment should be repeated. (The permanent seeding can be made before this second treatment providing the retreatment is applied before the new seeding has germinated and emerged.)

8. Area dragged with flexible tine harrow or similar tool to loosen surface if it has crusted. Trash accumulations which might

FIG. 31. The mature turf. (*Courtesy Sewerage Commission, City of Milwaukee.*)

prevent seed from coming in contact with the soil should be removed.

9. Seeding. Grasses, seeding rates, and equipment should be as outlined for turf establishment in Chap. 6.

10. Drag with flexible tine harrow, steel mat, or section of cyclone fence, to cover seed.

11. Roll with light roller.

The same general outline should be followed when fairways are heavily infested with crabgrass or clover, except that one treatment with 50 to 60 lbs. of sodium arsenite per acre will kill the crabgrass and check the clover sufficiently to prevent it from interfering with the development of the new seeding. In the event that enough clover survives to be troublesome, it can be treated the following spring (see Chap. 8).

Maintenance of Tees

The maintenance of good turf on tees is a practical impossibility unless the teeing ground is large enough to permit moving of tee markers often enough to give injured turf a chance to recover before the area must be used again. When turf is being injured beyond repair by constant play on restricted areas, tees must be increased in size. If this is not practicable, play from bare ground is the only alternative. There is a limit to the abuse that any turf can stand, and it is reached quickly on small tees which are subjected to iron play.

Tee markers should be moved promptly when the turf shows evidence of serious injury. Divot scars should be filled immediately with a good quality of top-dressing materials and reseeded if required. The necessity for reseeding will depend largely upon the kind of grass present. Fast-growing types such as creeping bent and Bermudagrass will heal rapidly without additional seeding. Where Kentucky bluegrass, fescue, or colonial bent is used, reseeding large scars is desirable to hasten recovery. Domestic ryegrass or redtop can be mixed with the permanent grasses. The seed can be mixed with the top-dressing used to level and fill divot scars.

Tee turf should be maintained at a height that will permit the ball to stand clear of the top of the grass blades without being teed too high. When growing conditions are good, daily cutting of fast-growing types of grasses is necessary. Clipping intervals can be greater in the case of slower growing grasses such as Kentucky bluegrass, fescues, the zoysia grasses and buffalograss. Frequent close clipping is essential for turf that is composed of the bentgrasses and other types that will become spongy at high cutting levels. Periodic top-dressing is required on these grasses for the same reason. Any tendency toward matting or sponginess is highly undesirable because of its effect upon playing conditions. Good-quality sandy loam soil is satisfactory for use as a top-dressing material.

The turf on tees must be kept in a vigorous condition so that it will heal rapidly. Periodic fertilization and the use of lime when required is necessary. Nitrogen must be used carefully, however, to avoid overstimulation and development of soft grass. Where the turf on tees is bent or Bermudagrass the fertilizer program should be essentially the same as for greens maintenance. Tees of Kentucky bluegrass, fescue, and other slow growing grasses, should receive the same basic fertilizer treatment as fairway turf of these grasses. It is essential to avoid overstimulation that will result in soft grass that will be easily injured under the heavy use it receives. Except in cases where quick stimulation is necessary, the nitrogen in tee fertilizers should be from slowly available sources to provide the greatest possible toughness and wear resistance.

Tee watering should be adjusted carefully to playing requirements. Water applications should permit the maximum amount of time between watering and heavy use of the tees. This provides better playing conditions and helps to prevent compaction by heavy trampling on wet surfaces. Water absorption and rate of surface drying can be helped materially by frequent spiking or aerification.

Disease, insect, and weed control should be standard maintenance practices on tees, just as for greens. Detailed outlines for these treatments will be found in the chapters on these subjects.

Tee renovation usually involves reconstruction to provide larger areas. Basic considerations are soil quality, seedbed preparation, types of grasses, and seeding methods. These items are discussed in detail in Chap. 6. The renovation of established turf on tees is a day-to-day maintenance problem. Where it is impracticable to keep the turf in good condition because of chronic problems of poor drainage, poor quality soil, tree competition, or other basic causes, complete reconstruction usually is the most economical and desirable method of renovation.

Maintenance of Roughs

The relationship between maintenance of roughs and the demands of play has been discussed in the first part of this chapter.

The height and frequency of mowing will depend upon the prevailing type of cover and the policy with regard to playing conditions. Where roughs are composed largely of turf-forming grasses and are kept short, the standard types of fairway gang mowers can be used satisfactorily. Sickle-bar, rotary, or large reel-type mowers adapted for high grass must be used on roughs which are cut only occasionally and consist mostly of coarse grasses and weeds.

When a fair stand of the better grasses is present in roughs, it can be improved by the use of moderate quantities of fertilizer and lime. The grasses usually will respond rapidly to fertilizer applications and will help materially in reducing noxious weeds that may spread to fairway areas. In many instances the better grasses will come in naturally when lime and fertilizer are applied. First fertilizer applications should consist primarily of phosphate and potash with only limited quantities of nitrogen. Ratios of 1-3-1 or 1-3-2 can be used at rates to supply a maximum of 10 to 15 lb. of nitrogen per acre. As better turf develops the proportion of nitrogen can be increased.

Roughs often are important breeding grounds for injurious insects and sources of weed seed that spread to fairways and greens. Japanese beetles and dandelions are good examples. Unless they are checked in the rough, they become serious problems on other turf areas.

Maintenance of Traps and Bunkers

The sand used in traps should be similar in texture to that used for seedbeds and top-dressing. These specifications are given in Chap. 6. Washed river, lake, or sea sand is preferable when it can be obtained at a reasonable price. The edges of the particles have been rounded, and it will not pack as tightly and will dry out more quickly. Fine sands that will blow and pack badly are undesirable for these reasons. Sands which contain silt and clay that will cause surface crusting after rains should not be used. A depth of 4 to 6 in. of sand is sufficient over the floor of the trap. It may be necessary to increase this somewhat at the base of long trap faces to keep a sufficient quantity on the slope.

Traps should be raked when surface crusts form or when players have left footprints or other irregularities that would constitute unfair hazards. In raking traps the sand first is pulled up against the face of the trap in a uniform slope that is free from irregularities, then the floor of the trap is raked in a direction parallel to the side of the green which the trap faces. Various types of rakes have been designed for use in traps. Any rake is satisfactory that does not leave deep furrows which are unfair hazards to play.

Grass traps and hollows are used frequently at the back of greens to catch balls that are overshot. Normally, these are considered to be a part of the rough. When so classified they should be maintained at the same mowing height and given the same type of care as close roughs adjacent to fairways. Grassed mounds designed as hazards should be treated in a similar manner.

Aggressive grasses and weeds which frequently invade traps are troublesome because they interfere with play and complicate maintenance. They occur most commonly in traps with shallow depths of sand or where the sand compacts and holds moisture for relatively long periods. Several types of nonselective chemical weed killers are available that can be used to eradicate all undesirable vegetation of this kind completely. Herbicides that are useful for this purpose, together with rates and methods of treatment, are discussed in Chap. 8.

8

Weed Control

Weeds become a major problem in turf when the grass loses its vigor and density and cannot compete with them. Many varieties thrive under conditions that are unfavorable for the grass. For example, clover and knotweed take possession on areas where nitrogen levels are low and soils are heavy and compact. Crabgrass is a serious pest in sections where high summer temperatures check the growth of grass and favor its development. Pearlwort and chickweed invade greens when soils are in poor condition, when weak strains of grasses are used, or following serious injuries by disease and insects. Weed encroachment is the result and not the primary cause of poor turf. Weed eradication will not result in permanent improvement unless the conditions that weakened the turf are corrected and unless grasses are used that are best able to compete with them. A weed-control program must begin with correction of the fundamental causes of poor turf. These include poor drainage, poor soil condition, low fertility, and every other factor that affects turf. These have been discussed in previous chapters.

There are two ways to control weeds. The first is by preventing their invasion. The second is by eradication after they have taken possession. Both methods require a combination of good cultural practices and chemical control measures. (Descriptions of common turf weeds and effective methods for control are given in the Appendix, page 293).

Control by Cultural Practices

Preseeding Control. Weeds can be germinated and killed in the seedbed before the grass is planted. This method of control is useful before sowing seed or planting sprigs or stolons. The seedbed is prepared two or three months in advance of planting and kept fallowed to permit the weed seed in the surface soil to germinate. Light harrowing or cultivating at 2- or 3-week intervals during this period will destroy the sprouting weeds. Patience is required to delay seeding until all the weed seeds have germinated. Seedbeds should be prepared as for immediate planting, except for application of the starter fertilizer and final surface grading (see Chap. 6). The starter fertilizer should be applied prior to the last working. This cultivation mixes the fertilizer into the soil and serves as a final grading operation. Care must be used in this operation not to turn up weed-seed-infested soil for lower depths. Germinating seeds and seedlings can be killed in seedbeds by preplanting treatments with chemicals, as described in the section of this chapter on chemical weed control.

Mowing. Mowing controls weeds in two ways. It reduces seed production. When done properly, it increases the ability of the grass to compete with weeds for moisture and plant food and to shade and smother developing seedlings.

Seeds, or bulblets and nuts that function like seeds, are the principal source of weed infestations. Mowing will prevent seed production by weeds that develop upright seedstalks. It is completely effective in controlling annual weeds of this type, both in established turf and new seedings. Annual weeds grow from seed to maturity in a single season. When the seed heads are cut off, their ability to reproduce is destroyed. Weeds such as lambsquarters, shepherdspurse, and upright growing annual grasses like foxtail can be controlled readily in this way.

Clipping off the seed heads of perennial weeds does not eliminate the plants that have become established in turf. It materially reduces the danger of new infestations that start from seed. This class of weeds lives for several years or more. Once established these weeds are not dependent upon seed production to perpetuate themselves. Seed formation must be prevented to check their spread. Seed of plantain, dandelion, buckhorn, and other perennials that produce upright seedstalks can be destroyed by clipping.

Roughs and nonuse areas may be prolific sources of pollution if they are not mowed until after seed has matured. These areas should be watched carefully, and whenever weeds that may be

FIG. 32. Power mat for use following aerification or for raising crabgrass stems prior to cutting. (*Green Section.*)

troublesome elsewhere begin to develop seed heads, they should be mowed. A safe plan is to cut the heads at blossoming time, because many weed seeds will grow even though they are only partially developed at cutting time.

Some of the creeping types of weeds, such as the crabgrasses, produce seed heads close to the ground. Dragging with a wire mat to raise the seed heads, followed by close clipping, will help reduce seed formation. Vertical mowing with equipment designed for this purpose also is very effective in removing seed heads and checking development of the plants, without seriously affecting the permanent grasses. It is especially useful on Kentucky bluegrass and fescue turf because of their lower density and the greater possibility of injury to them from the close clipping that can be employed on bentgrass, Bermuda, and other creeping types of grasses. Where crabgrass is dense the mowing and matting operations should start with clipping as close as the mowers can be set safely for the kind of grass that predominates in the turf. It should be followed by drastic matting in several directions. Alternate mowing and matting are repeated until the best clean-up possible by this treatment has been obtained. Various types of mats can be used. Heavy woven wire fencing with 6- to 8-in. mesh makes a good drag for raising the seed heads. If vertical mowers are used, they must be adjusted carefully so that they will not scalp and tear out the good turf. It may be necessary to remove alternate knives on the shaft when equipment is used on which they are close set.

These practices, in combination with chemical treatments, are very effective in controlling crabgrass, chickweed, clover, and other species of creeping weeds. Chemical treatments are discussed in the section of this chapter on Chemical Control.

Soils contain large numbers or dormant weed seeds that germinate when conditions become favorable. These seeds come from many sources. Creeping weeds that bear seed heads close to the ground are one source of infestation. Matting and close clipping do not destroy all of the seed which they produce. Seeds also may be carried into the turf by wind, by floods, by birds, on the feet of players, or by maintenance equipment. No practical method has been developed for destroying these seeds before they have germinated. Raising the height of cut will help some grasses to shade and smother out the young seedlings. This method is best adapted for killing crabgrass seedlings in Kentucky bluegrass and fescue turf. Cutting these grasses at heights of 1¼ to 1½ in. improves their density and makes them better able to suppress the seedling plants. It also helps them to compete with the older weeds for moisture and plant food, because the higher cut grass is more vigorous, has a larger root system, and grows faster. Increasing the height of cut of bents, Bermuda, and other creeping grasses is not desirable owing to the danger of matting and sponginess.

FERTILIZING. Weeds take possession when the turf becomes open and thin because of starvation. If they are scattered and do not occur in large solid patches, systematic fertilization will increase the vigor and density of the grass and will eliminate most of them automatically. The kind of fertilizer and the rate of application should be as outlined for maintenance in Chap. 7. Heavy infestations must be destroyed by a chemical herbicide which is effective for the kind of weeds present. Reseeding and fertilization should follow (see discussion of Chemical Weed Control).

Weeds that have peak periods of activity can be checked by timely fertilization to stimulate the grass. Annual bluegrass and chickweed grow best in the cool weather of fall and early spring. Fertilizer applications should be made early in the fall to produce vigorous turf that can compete with them throughout this period. Where annual bluegrass and other cool-weather weeds are present in turf, spring fertilizer applications must be delayed until the turf grasses have started active growth. The quality of the fertilizer used is important. Early fall applications of mixed fertilizers that contain a high proportion of their nitrogen in slow form will provide a nitrogen carry-over for early spring growth of the grass. They are particularly effective for the bentgrasses which grow very slowly in cool weather unless some available nitrogen is present. The residual nitrogen carried over from the fall application usually is sufficient to give them an early start and keep them growing at a reasonable rate. This is a safer program than to apply soluble nitrogen late in the fall and again in early spring.

The same method of fertilization will discourage clover. Clover prefers warm weather. Its growth during the cool weather of late fall and early spring is very slow and sometimes stops entirely. Well-fertilized grass that is growing during these periods will invade solid clover stands and thin them out.

Timely applications of fertilizer containing slowly available nitrogen are effective in reducing infestations of summer weeds such as crabgrass and knotweed. Early spring applications that are made as soon as the grass begins active growth supplement the nitrogen remaining from treatments made the previous fall and produce earlier and more uniform growth. Ordinarily good nitrogen residues from spring applications of slowly available forms carry over into the summer. These produce a uniform rate of growth that will keep the grass dense and vigorous during the period of weed-seed germination and early seedling growth. Readily available inorganic forms of nitrogen are not suitable for this purpose. They cause a quick stimulation, followed by a relatively rapid reduction in growth rate as the nitrogen is exhausted. This type of growth is not effective in keeping out weeds.

WATERING. Water management is important in checking weed-seed germination and seedling growth. Mature turf can tolerate dry soil at the surface longer than germinating seeds and young seedlings. Water should be withheld in periods when maximum germination is taking place until the surface inch or more of soil has become well dried. Sprouting seed will die in this dry soil, and young seedlings that have not developed a sufficient root system to reach moist soil below will be killed. Weeds such as annual bluegrass, knotweed, and the crabgrasses, which have peak germination periods, can be reduced in this way, except in rainy weather.

Many weeds thrive in saturated and compact soils that are unfavorable for grasses. Annual bluegrass, clover, knotweeds, and chickweeds are typical examples. Natural precipitation may cause saturated soils at any time. However, excessive rains seldom occur so often, or last so long, that they cause permanent trouble. Continuous overwatering keeps the soil saturated and is the primary cause of moisture conditions that favor weed encroachment. When overwatering of Kentucky bluegrass and fescue is combined with close clipping and low fertility, these grasses become thin and weeds come in. The most serious losses occur in sections where high summer temperatures check the growth of the grass and favor the weeds.

Water should be used sparingly in the early season to avoid saturated soil. During the summer months the amount should be reduced to the absolute minimum needed to prevent permanent injury by drought. More liberal quantities can be used in the fall if heavier fertilizer applications are made. Watered turf requires more fertilizer, and larger quantities of nutrients are lost from the soil by leaching.

SOIL COMPACTION. Saturated soils compact easily and bake hard when dry. Knotweed, clover, and other weeds that can tolerate these conditions come in as the turf gets thin. The best remedy is thorough aeration in the late summer or early fall followed by fertilization and reseeding when necessary. Grass will respond better to treatment at this time of year. Attempts to control vigorously growing weeds by aeration or scarification are unsatisfactory. The weeds spread into the open areas left by the treatment before the seedling grass can become established.

ADAPTED GRASSES. Grasses differ in their ability to resist weed invasion. In northern regions the colonial and the creeping bents are best able to compete with weeds on watered fairways where close and frequent clipping is required and summer temperatures check the growth of bluegrass and fescue. The growth rate of the bents is faster, and they can maintain better turf density during hot weather. In the South the finer textured dense strains of Bermuda are preferable to the coarse open hay types.

Individual strains of bents and Bermudagrass used on greens differ in vigor and ability to resist weed invasions. Some grow best when fertilized and watered heavily. Others may be injured seriously by the same treatment. Some strains are so poorly adapted to the conditions under which they are being grown that they will not resist weed invasion under any type of management. Conversion of the turf to a grass that is adapted to the location and type of maintenance which it will receive is often the best method of solving the weed problem. The only practical way to determine whether an individual strain will be satisfactory in a particular location is thoroughly to investigate its performance under the same kind of conditions elsewhere or to try it out on a limited scale.

Chemical Weed Control

PRESEEDING TREATMENTS. Many chemicals have been tested experimentally to determine their value for seedbed sterilization to destroy weed seeds or other undesirable growth prior to making permanent seedings. Some of them persist in the soil for only a limited period and their effectiveness is confined to only those seeds which are active at this time. When such materials are used in early spring, they will kill weed seed that is germinating at this time but will not affect crabgrass and other weeds that become active later. Since there is little evidence that they act on dormant seeds, their value for seedbed sterilization prior to seeding is limited to the control of only those species of weeds that are germinating within a period of 2 to 3 weeks after treatment. Cyanamid and 2,4-D belong to this group of chemicals. Both have been used effectively to treat seedbeds known to be infested only with species which have approximately the same germinating period. Rates and methods of application for these chemicals are given in the following pages of this chapter.

A second group of chemicals that are useful for seedbed treatment include those materials which either persist longer in the soil or are effective on dormant seed and living vegetation. Methyl bromide is the most widely used of this class of materials. It will kill most dormant seeds and is extremely toxic to living vegetation such as rhizomes and stolons of bents, Bermuda, and quackgrass. This latter quality makes it particularly useful in eradicating common Bermudagrass on areas where improved varieties are to be planted. Other chemicals of more limited usefulness, either because of lower toxicity or necessary delay in making permanent seedings after application, include VPM, calcium arsenate, Chlordane, Trichloracetic acid (TCA), Amino triozole, and Dalapon. Except Methyl bromide and VPM, all of these materials are of limited value for use as preseeding soil sterilants in seedbeds due to the long waiting period after application before the permanent seeding can be made safely. (See discussion of individual chemicals for rates and methods of use.)

STERILIZATION OF TOP-DRESSING MIXTURES. Soil sterilants also can be used to advantage in treating top-dressing for killing weed seed and undesirable vegetative material. Since this is an expensive and time-consuming operation, the actual necessity for it should be determined before treatments are undertaken. Examination of the soil will serve to determine whether stolons or rhizomes of undesirable grasses or other plants are present. A germination test under optimum soil moisture and temperature conditions will show whether the weeds that are present are likely to be troublesome on greens under the close mowing and intensive management of the turf. The same materials and methods used for preseeding sterilization of seedbeds can be employed for treating top-dressing. These are outlined in the following discussions of the use of individual chemicals.

Chemical Weed Killers for Turf. There are two general classes of herbicides for the control of weeds in established turf. These are the preemergence and postemergence chemicals. Preemergence materials are used to kill the dormant or germinating weed seed in the soil. In general, they are not effective on seedling plants after they have emerged. The possibilities of this type of weed control are very attractive. Some of the chemicals that have been used have been quite effective under certain conditions. Unfortunately, so many factors affect their toxicity, both to the turf and the weeds, the exact relationships of which are not yet fully understood, that results have been very variable. The materials which have shown the most promise are the arsenicals (calcium and lead arsenate), and two complex compounds, Dacthal and Zytron (M-1329). Tests of these materials have been confined mostly to determination of their effects on crabgrass and *Poa annua*. Very little documented information is available on their effect on other species. Also, their toxicity to different kinds of grasses is highly variable. Apparently, Kentucky bluegrass, Bermudagrass, and zoysia, are the least susceptible to them. They may cause severe injury to red fescues and bents. Until more complete information is available, the preemergence herbicides should be used with caution and only on a trial basis.

The most effective postemergence herbicides include the 2,4-D and 2,4,5-T compounds, the methyl arsonates (AMA and DMA), and phenyl mercuric acetate. Sodium arsenite also can be used for selective control, but is most valuable in complete renovation programs because of its relatively low cost and limited persistence in the soil.

All of the postemergence chemicals are specific for certain kinds of weeds. The 2,4-D and 2,4,5-T compounds are most effective on broad-leaf types, such as dandelion, the plantains, clover, and chickweeds. The arsonates and PMA are most toxic to crabgrass and certain other annual grasses. Two other materials (Dacthal and Zytron) have been shown in limited testing to have possibilities for the control of crabgrass, chickweed, and knotweed. (See sections on individual chemicals for control, rates, and methods of treatment with postemergence herbicides.)

Herbicides vary in effectiveness depending upon the time of treatment and soil-moisture conditions. Their selective action in killing weeds without injuring the grass is due largely to differences in susceptibility of the weeds and grasses. When used at heavy rates they will kill the grass as well as the weeds. Their successful use depends upon limiting applications to the recommended dosages and extreme care in securing uniform distribution. The results obtained often depend upon the condition of the turf. If grass is growing rapidly and is succulent, it will be injured more easily than turf with a harder texture. Close-clipped turf usually is less tolerant than that which is mowed higher.

Some herbicides, particularly 2,4-D, seriously injure certain kinds of trees, shrubbery, and flowers. Extreme caution is necessary in areas where spray drift may come in contact with susceptible varieties of these plants.

Amino Triozole. It is specific as a preseeding treatment of seedbeds for the eradication of perennial grasses such as quack and johnsongrass. Spray applications should be made at the rate of 8 lbs. (actual) per acre in the minimum amount of water needed for uniform coverage. The most satisfactory control has resulted from spring treatments applied when the grasses have made 6 to 8 in. of growth. The treated area should be plowed and thoroughly cultivated 10 to 14 days after spraying. A second treatment followed by cultivation sometimes is necessary. Seedings of permanent grasses must be delayed for a minimum period of 6 weeks after the last treatment was made. An alternative method is to apply the chemical in the fall while the grasses to be controlled are still actively growing, followed by plowing in 15 to 20 days. The area should be cultivated as early as possible the next spring. If new growth appears, a second treatment will be necessary, followed by cultivation. Amino Triozole also is specific for the control of poison ivy. A solution concentration of 4 lbs. per 100 gals. of water is sprayed on the plants when in full leaf to thoroughly wet the foliage.

Calcium Arsenate. This is a preemergence herbicide that is highly toxic to germinating seed of crabgrass and *Poa annua.* Practical results with it have been variable, ranging from complete control to less than 60 per cent. It will not seriously affect Kentucky bluegrass and Bermudagrass, but may cause permanent injury to bent, red fescue, and ryegrass. It can be applied at any time before seed germination of the weeds to be controlled and its effects persist from one to three years. Studies at the Indiana Agricultural Experiment Station show that its toxicity is reduced when the soil is high in available phosphates. The most effective rate of treatment is 12 to 16 lbs. per acre of the 73 per cent concentration. Applications can be made dry, using pelleted or granular forms, or as a spray, using the wettable powder in a sufficient quantity of water to insure uniform coverage. Because of the possibility of severe damage to bentgrasses, calcium arsenate should not be used on putting greens when it is desirable to preserve the bent turf, unless the danger of loss is fully recognized. Also, it should not be used as a preseeding treatment in seedbeds unless seedings can be delayed for at least one full season.

Chlordane. This chemical has been used to some extent as a preemergence herbicide for the control of crabgrass. Results with it have been highly variable; seldom showing over 90 per cent control and frequently giving less than 60 per cent. It can be applied at any time before the crabgrass seed has germinated and effects persist for at least one season. No injury to turfgrass has been reported, even from heavy treatments, although it may sometimes cause slight temporary discoloration. It can be applied dry, either in granular form or impregnated on some type of absorbent material, or as a spray, using the concentrated solution or emulsion in sufficient water to secure good coverage. The best results have been obtained at rates of 1½ to 1¼ lbs., actual, per 1,000 sq. ft. Regardless of the formulation used, it always should be watered in thoroughly, immediately after application. It should not be used at the above rates as a preseeding treatment in seedbeds unless seedings can be delayed for at least one full season.

Cyanamid. It is used as a preemergence herbicide for killing germinating weed seed in seedbeds and top-dressing. Under good soil moisture conditions it is toxic for only 15 to 20 days and will affect only those seeds that are germinating during this period. When used for treating seedbeds it should be worked into the top 2 in. of soil at a rate of 75 to 100 lbs. per 1,000 sq. ft. At good soil moisture levels, seedings can be made safely 20 to 30 days after treatment. If applied to dry soil it will be toxic for a much longer period. The Rhode Island Agricultural Experiment Station recommends its use for sterilization of top-dressing by mixing it with the soil at the rate of 13 lbs. per cu. yd. of the top-dressing material. At good soil moisture levels (20 to 30 per cent) weed seeds usually are killed within 4 to 6 weeks.

Dacthal (*Dimethyl 2,3,5,6-tetrachloroterephthalate*). This is an experimental material which has shown definite promise in limited tests for use as a preemergence control of crabgrass. It has been used effectively on Kentucky bluegrass turf without apparent injury. At the New York Agricultural Experiment Station it was found to injure red fescue severely. It should be used with caution and on a trial basis only until more definite information on it is available. The most effective treatment rate has been 4.5 oz. (actual toxicant) per 1,000 sq. ft. It can be obtained as a 50 per cent wettable powder for use as a spray.

Dalapon (*74 per cent 2-2 Dichloro propionic acid*). The principal value of this chemical in the turfgrass field is for the control of perennial grasses in seedbeds prior to seeding. It is used in the same way for this purpose as Amino Triozole. Treatments should be at the rate of 20 lbs. per acre for the fall or first spring application, and 10 to 15 lbs. for any required subsequent applications. New seedings should be delayed for a minimum period of 5 to 6 weeks following cultivation after the last treatment.

Disodium Methyl Arsonate (*DMA*) *and Ammonium Methyl Arsonate* (*AMA*). These are post emergence herbicides that are very similar in their effectiveness for crabgrass control. The Disodium form (DMA) in combination with 2,4-D also will control Dallisgrass in Bermudagrass turf. Both materials will discolor turf severely if applied when the soil is dry and temperatures are above 80 to 85 degrees. The discoloration usually is only temporary and recovery normally is complete within 10 days to 2 weeks.

Two to three treatments with either material at 10-day to 2-week intervals generally are necessary to obtain satisfactory control. Each application should be at a rate of 1.5 to 2.0 oz. (actual) per 1,000 sq. ft. for the Disodium (DMA) form, and 0.6 to 0.7 oz. (actual) for the Ammonium (AMA) form. The DMA should be used at approximately double the above rate for the control of dallisgrass (see Appendix Table 13, page 300).

Methyl Bromide. It is a very effective seedbed and top-dressing sterilant. The liquid quickly vaporizes into a gas when exposed to the air. In this form it is lethal to many kinds of weed seeds, roots, rhizomes, stolons, and some soil insects and disease-producing fungi. Applications are made under gas-tight polyethylene covers which must be sealed around the edges to prevent escape of the gas. Its action is rapid and it is toxic for only a short time after treatment. Seedings can be made 24 to 48 hrs. after removal of the cover from a treated area. Either hot or cold methods of application can be used. The former is more effective when temperatures at the time of treatment are low, due to the quicker vaporization and better dispersion of the gas. In either case, special equipment is required for introducing the chemical under the blanket. Complete directions for making both seedbed and top-dressing treatments are supplied by the manufacturer.

Phenyl Mercuric Acetate (PMA). Its use on turf is primarily as a postemergence herbicide for crabgrass control. It also has fungicidal properties (see Chap. 9). It is most effective when used on young crabgrass seedlings before they have developed beyond the two- to three-leaf stage. It can be used either as a spray or in the dry form. In the latter case it usually is impregnated on an absorbent carrier like Vermiculite. The standard rate of treatment is 5 to 7 pts. of a 10 per cent solution per acre, in a sufficient quantity of water to assure uniform coverage. When used dry, approximately twice as much actual toxicant must be applied as for spraying. It is most effective when soil moisture levels are good and temperatures are moderate. Under these conditions it will not injure the turfgrasses, although it may cause some temporary discoloration. An exception to this is its injurious effect on Merion Kentucky bluegrass. It discolors this variety severely and sometimes causes permanent injury to the turf.

Sodium Arsenite. This chemical has been used successfully for the control of a number of turfgrass weeds. It is effective on both knotweed and crabgrass when a program of repeat treatments is properly timed and is adjusted to soil moisture and temperatures. It will cause severe burning if applied when the soil is dry and temperatures are above 80 degrees. The program of treatments for knotweed control should start with an application of 1 to 1½ lbs. per acre when the knotweed is in the seedling stage. This should be followed by two or three additional treatments at 1½ to 2 lbs. per acre at 10-day intervals. Crabgrass can be checked by the same program of treatments after it has emerged.

Sodium arsenite has found its greatest area of usefulness in killing undesirable vegetation (*Poa annua*, clover chickweed, crabgrass, etc.) preparatory to a complete renovation program (see Chap. 7, Fairway Renovation). It is a nonsystemic poison and will kill only the plant tissue with which it comes in contact. It is not effective for eradicating grasses and other plants with rhizomes. Species like Kentucky bluegrass, Bermuda, and quackgrass, will survive extremely heavy dosages. The bentgrasses are more subject to injury but frequently recover where a dense turf has protected low-growing stolons.

Trichloroacetic Acid (TCA). This is a nonselective killer and soil sterilant that is useful for complete eradication of vegetation along edges of walks, driveways, and parking areas. Its use in sand traps is limited to those where blasting will not deposit sand carrying the chemical on the green. It is highly toxic to all kinds of vegetation and its effect will persist for an entire season. Where entire areas are to be treated, the solution concentration should be at the rate of 75 lbs. per 100 to 150 gals. water per acre. This same concentration can be used for spot treatments. In treating parking areas and other locations from which water run-off is likely to occur, provision must be made to prevent water from the treated areas from washing over turf or other plantings that are to be preserved.

2,4-D (2,4-dichlorophenoxyacetic acid). This is a systemic chemical that is absorbed and translocated by the plant. It is effective for postemergence control of a large group of broad-leaf weeds. Application rates are from ½ to 1½ lbs. (actual) per acre in 25 to 100 gals. water when used as a spray. Dry applications should be at approximately double the rate of spray treatments to obtain the same degree of effectiveness. Dry mixtures with fertilizers and other carriers are commercially available. In using such preparations, rates of application must be adjusted to conform with the actual amount of the chemical needed to insure control of the weeds for which the treatment is made.

Kentucky bluegrass, fescues, Bermudagrass, and other warm season grasses, are highly tolerant to 2,4-D. The bentgrasses may be injured materially by fall treatments. There is little evidence that spring applications at minimum rates will permanently injure actively growing bent turf. (See Appendix Table 13, page 300, for time and rate of treatment for control of individual weeds.)

2,4,5-T (*2,4,5-Trichlorophenoxyacetic acid*). This is a systemic postemergence herbicide effective for control of clover, lawn pennywort, and certain other broad-leaf weeds. It often is used in mixtures with 2,4-D in equal proportions of active ingredients. Treatments for the control of clover are most effective when made in late fall or early spring when the plants are in active growth. Repeat applications often are required and should be made as soon as regrowth has started. Rates of treatment, either alone or in combination with 2,4-D, should not exceed 1 to 1½ lbs. (actual) per acre, with the minimum to be used on bentgrass. As for 2,4-D, bentgrass turf should be treated only in the spring after active growth has started.

2(2,4,5-TP) or SILVEX (*2(2,4,5-trichlorophenoxy) propionic acid*). In trials that have been somewhat limited this chemical has been found to be very effective for the control of all species of chickweeds. It should be applied in the fall or early spring when the plants are active. The recommended treatment rate is 1 to 1½ lbs. (active) per acre (1/3 to ½ oz. per 1,000 sq. ft.). A sufficient quantity of water should be used to insure complete coverage. There is some evidence that the heavier application may injure bentgrass and *Poa annua* turf when treatments are made under conditions unfavorable to the grass.

Weed Control on Greens

Killing Weeds in Top-dressing Soil. The first essential in controlling weeds on greens is to make certain that noxious types are not being seeded in top-dressings. Top-dressing soil taken from waste areas frequently contains many weed seeds, even though the current crop of weeds on the area was cut before the seed matured. There are two simple methods for eliminating weed seeds from top-dressing soil. The first is to plow the soil bed at least one full season before the soil is to be used. The area should be deep cultivated periodically to destroy germinating seeds and young plants. If cultivation is deep and thorough, very few ungerminated seeds will be left at the end of the season.

Soil beds can be treated with chemical herbicides to kill the weed seeds. The same methods used for preseeding treatments of seedbeds are satisfactory. The amount of chemical may be doubled if the soil is not used until 4 to 6 months after treatment. Weed seed also can be destroyed in top-dressing by mixing chemicals with the pile of screened soil as previously described.

Protection Against Other Sources of Infestation. Weeds in roughs and nonuse areas should not be permitted to mature seed. Wind-blown seed from these areas may infest greens. Seed and pieces of living stems also may be carried by water or on the feet of players. Seed production by plants bearing upright growing seedstalks can be controlled by early mowing. Creeping or decumbent plants should be killed with suitable herbicides.

Low-grade bent and redtop seed may be a source of weed infestations on greens. Seed of this quality frequently contains large quantities of weed seeds such as chickweed that are difficult to eradicate when once established. Such seed is expensive at any price and should not be planted.

Soil adhering to stolons coming from a weed-infested nursery may be a source of infestation. Most of the weed seeds can be eliminated by washing the stolons with a strong stream of water over a screen.

Hand Weeding. Hand weeding is a laborious and expensive method of weed control. It is justified on greens only when weeds are scattered and few in number. Crabgrass, plantain, dandelion, and weeds of this type can be cleaned out satisfactorily in this way. Solid patches of clover, pearlwort, chickweed, and similar creepers are best controlled by spotting with slow-acting chemicals, such as arsenate of lead that will check and weaken them, permitting the grass to crowd them out. The materials can be applied with a salt-shaker type can or porous cloth bag. When patches are not too large, they may be plugged or cut out and the bare area sodded with clean turf. If weed infestations are heavy, chemical-control methods are more satisfactory than attempts to hand weed. The slight discoloration or injury sometimes caused by herbicides used in low concentrations will not affect playing conditions any more seriously or for a longer period than the pitting left by wholesale weed removal.

Control by Spotting. Rosette types of weeds such as dandelion and plantain and creepers in solid patches may be controlled effectively when not too numerous by spotting with mixtures of herbicides and fertilizers. Sodium arsenite or 2,4-D (dry formulations) are the chemicals best adapted to this method of control. Mixtures of 4 to 5 per cent sodium arsenite with fertilizer can be applied directly to the weeds in small amounts. From ½ to 1 teaspoon of the mixture is sufficient for single weeds. Larger quantities are required for solid patches. A weed cane that automatically delivers a small amount of material can be purchased commercially.

Dilutions of dry types of 2,4-D at the rate of 1 part 2,4-D to 500 to 600 parts of fertilizer can be used in the same way. The fertilizer included is to stimulate the surrounding grass after the weed has been killed. Pearlwort and other hard-to-kill weeds that develop in solid patches may be spot treated by brushing them lightly with a concentrated solution of 2,4-D. A dilution of any liquid formulation of 2,4-D at the rate of 1 part of the concentrate to 10 or 12 parts of water is suitable. This concentration will kill the grass if it comes in contact with it; so care must be used in applying it not to get it on the turf. 2,4-D is absorbed and translocated to other parts of the plant so that it is not necessary to cover the entire weed with it. Stems that have crept out into the grass will be killed although they have not received a direct application of the chemical.

Spot treatments also may be made by dusting small quantities of inorganic nitrogenous fertilizer, such as sulfate of ammonia, directly on patches of clover, pearlwort, chickweed, and similar weeds, early in the morning when the dew is heavy. Light quantities are sufficient. Heavy amounts will retard recovery of the grass. This will produce a severe burn in a few hours that will severely check the weeds. The patches should be watered after the burn has developed to wash the fertilizer into the soil. The fertilizer will stimulate surrounding grass to grow into the area before the damaged weed can recover.

CONTROL BY BROADCAST CHEMICALS. The use of herbicides on putting greens always should be undertaken with caution and only after full information has been obtained on the possible effect of the chemical on the turf. Many materials which will kill the weeds may be so injurious to the grass that their use is not justified. Some chemicals that can be used safely on mature turf will inhibit or seriously retard germination for varying periods. This limits their usefulness where it is necessary to reestablish a turf by reseeding as promptly as possible. Appendix Table 14, page 304, lists the safety factors and adaptability of a number of herbicides for greens use. It should be emphasized that provision must be made, when herbicides are used, for prompt reestablishment of a turf cover on bare areas resulting from weed eradication. For example, it is poor management to destroy a heavy turf of *Poa annua* with a fall treatment of calcium arsenate or some other effective chemical, without making adequate provision for reseeding or sodding the treated area.

It is essential also that herbicidal treatments be properly adjusted to the period of maximum susceptibility of the weeds to be controlled. If preemergence chemicals are used, they must be applied far enough in advance of seed germination to be effective before emergence of the seedling plant. Postemergence materials vary in their effectiveness on both weeds and turf with such factors as soil moisture, temperature, and age of the plants to be controlled. PMA is very toxic to seedling crabgrass in the two- to three-leaf stage, but is much less effective on more mature plants. Many herbicides injure permanent grasses only when they are used when soil moisture is low and temperatures are high. All of these things must be carefully considered in selecting and applying chemicals to greens turf.

The necessity for proper calibration of applicating equipment to secure uniform coverage at the proper rate cannot be overemphasized. Many herbicides which are highly selective for specific weeds at the recommended rates of treatment may be extremely toxic to the permanent grasses at stronger dosages. In making dry applications with mechanical spreaders the materials must be distributed uniformly by the use of scatterboards or other devices that will prevent concentration of the chemical in rows. Overlapping must be avoided because of the double concentration on lapped areas. In making spray treatments, nozzles delivering a fan-shaped spray are most efficient. The spray boom must be adjusted to the proper height for even distribution, and pressure and speed of travel must be calibrated with the size of the nozzle orifice.

Weed Control on Tees

Where the turf on tees is good with only scattered weeds, periodic light treatments with a herbicide that is effective for the weeds present usually is sufficient to keep down serious infestations (see Appendix Table 13, page 300). Dry applications of chemicals like 2,4-D and the arsenicals, mixed with fertilizer are very useful. The light amount of the herbicide will check weed growth and depress seed formation, and the fertilizer will stimulate the grass and increase its ability to compete successfully. When herbicides are used in this way, treatment rates should be kept to approximately one-half of the standard dosage.

When weed infestations are heavy and complete renovation is necessary, the turf can be reestablished by seeding or sodding. If it is to be reseeded, the same program should be followed as outlined for fairway renovation (Chap. 7). Sodding often is the most satisfactory method of tee repair when weed infestations are heavy. The seedbed should be sterilized before laying the sod to prevent weed development in divot scars. Methyl bromide and VPM are the best materials for this purpose because of their effectiveness and the minimum delay between treatment and laying the new sod. If other sterilizing agents are used, their period of toxicity to new seedings or sod should be checked carefully and the program adjusted to it.

Weed Control on Fairways

The three essential phases of fairway weed control are (1) determination and correction of the conditions that weakened the grass and permitted weed invasion, (2) use of cultural practices and chemical weed killers that will eradicate the weeds, and (3) use of adapted grasses and maintenance practices that will ensure vigorous turf and prevent reinfestations.

THE PRELIMINARY SURVEY. Thin, open turf is the immediate cause of weed invasions. A complete survey should be made to determine the reason for poor turf. This includes a careful investigation of drainage and physical soil conditions and determination of soil reaction and available quantities of the major nutrient elements by reliable tests. The grasses should be identified and an estimate made of the approximate percentages of desirable types that are present. The effects of past maintenance practices, such as clipping height, watering, fertilization, and liming, should be considered. Injury by disease, insects, or other causes of a similar nature that are not directly related to chronically bad soil conditions should not be overlooked. The existing weeds should be identified and the severity of the infestation estimated.

The survey will show the causes for poor turf and weed encroachment. It will indicate the corrective measures needed to provide favorable conditions for the grass. It will supply the necessary information for selecting the best method of weed eradication and for establishing a sound maintenance program to prevent reinfestation.

Drainage. Poor drainage is responsible for invasion by two classes of weeds. The first group comprises those types which can live in saturated soils. Various sedges, undesirable grasses such as sweet vernal and velvet grass, and some creeping weeds like creeping buttercup thrive on wet soils. The second class includes annual weeds that come in on poorly drained, compacted soil that bakes hard when it dries in the summer. Knotweed is an example. In northern regions, ponded water that collects in depressions during winter and early spring because of frozen soil and poor surface drainage kills the grass. Chickweed, clover, and annual bluegrass become serious pests in these spots.

Kentucky bluegrass, fescue, and Bermudagrass cannot compete with weeds under poor drainage conditions. Both surface and subsurface drainage must be corrected if satisfactory turf is to be produced with these grasses (methods for improving drainage are discussed in Chap. 4). Where drainage cannot be corrected because of high water tables, or other causes, a partial solution is the use of creeping bents in northern regions and carpetgrass in the South.

Soil Compaction and Poor Physical Condition. Lack of air in compacted soil weakens the grass by restricting root systems and encourages weeds which can tolerate such conditions. Compaction is caused by trampling, the use of maintenance equipment, or rolling when soils are too wet. It can be corrected by thorough aeration with an Aerifier, or similar tool, that can penetrate through the compacted layer. The work should be done in the spring or fall when grass is growing vigorously and should be accompanied by applications of lime, if needed, and fertilizer. When weeds are scattered and infestations are moderate, the combination of aeration, liming, and fertilization usually suppresses them. Where invasions are heavy and clover, chickweed, or similar weeds occur in solid patches, it will be necessary to use a chemical herbicide.

Lime and Fertilizer. Lime applications should be based on the soil-reaction test (pH) as described in Chap. 3. The quantity of raw ground limestone required for different kinds of grasses at a given pH reaction are listed in Table 7, page 49.

Any of the fertilizers illustrated in the tables in Chap. 3 can be used in a fairway-renovation program. The mixtures with high potash percentages are best on light sandy soils. Rates should be used that supply from 100 to 150 lb. of nitrogen per acre. Lower potash mixtures can be used at the same rate on heavier soils. Where such fertilizers are not available, mixtures of organic and inorganic nitrogen carriers with superphosphate and muriate of potash can be used. Ratios and analyses should be as outlined in Chap. 4.

ADJUSTMENT OF CLIPPING HEIGHT AND WATERING. The proper adjustment of clipping height and watering are important for weed control in Kentucky bluegrass and fescue turf. Both grasses grow slowly during hot weather and are seriously weakened by constant clipping at heights of less than 1 to 1¼ in. Attempts to compensate for close clipping by heavy watering are bound to fail. Overwatering saturates the soil and makes a bad matter worse. The net result is more weeds and clover at the expense of the grass. For detailed suggestions on clipping and water management see the section of this chapter on weed control by cultural practices.

RESEEDING WITH ADAPTED GRASSES. Reseedings will hasten turf coverage on areas where little or no grass remains after the weeds have been killed. They can be used also to introduce a grass which will produce better turf. The quantity of seed required will depend upon the amount of grass that is present. Where a thin sod of Kentucky bluegrass or fescue is to be improved, the amount of seed should be one-half to two-thirds of the quantity required for a new seeding, or approximately 50 to 75 lb. per acre. The rate for bent or Bermudagrass is about 25 to 40 lb. per acre. Where a complete change-over in the turf is to be made, as from Kentucky bluegrass to bent, the bent should be seeded at the full rate of 50 to 75 lb. per acre.

A satisfactory seedbed can be prepared with an aerifier or by cross spiking several times with a fairway spiker. A wheelbarrow seeder or any other standard type of seeding equipment can be used to sow the seed. Renovated areas should be clipped and rolled. Seedings also can be made successfully with a grass-seed drill equipped with disk furrow openers. The disks on these machines are 4 in. apart, and cross seedings should be made to secure good coverage. With either method fertilizer and other soil amendments should be applied before the seeding is made.

CHEMICAL WEED CONTROL ON FAIRWAYS. The selection of a herbicide for use on fairways will be determined by the kind and per cent of permanent grasses present, the type of weeds to be controlled, and the degree of necessity for avoiding discoloration or temporary injury to the turf. Different species of grasses vary materially in their tolerance to various chemicals (see Appendix Table 14, page 304). The degree of this tolerance depends on the conditions under which the treatments are made. The arsenicals and most other chemicals are more severe when soil moisture is low and temperatures high. Also, sprays normally cause more turf discoloration than dry treatments. Serious discoloration often can be avoided by adjusting treatments seasonally. Except for crabgrass and other summer weeds, applications of herbicides for the control of many kinds of weeds can be made in the fall or spring with excellent results (see Appendix Table 13, page 300). Frequently, it is necessary to treat at both periods to secure maximum control, particularly for clover, *Poa annua*, and chickweed. Both fall and spring treatments should be made only when the weeds are actively growing.

When postemergence herbicides are used for control of crabgrass and other summer weeds, some degree of turf discoloration cannot be avoided. It usually is more severe with the arsonates than with PMA. This emphasizes the desirability of early treatment with PMA. Preemergence chemicals also are quite variable in the extent of injury they may cause. Here again, the kind of grass, and time and rate of application of the herbicide are the controlling factors. The limited information available for chlordane, calcium arsenate, Dacthal, and other compounds, show wide variations in their toxicity to both weeds and grasses. As previously noted, the use of such materials should be on a trial basis only, until such time as their effects are better understood.

PREVENTION OF REINFESTATIONS. Prevention of reinfestations by weeds depends greatly upon the use of sound maintenance practices after weeds are killed and fairways reseeded. When reseedings are made in the fall accompanied by a liberal quantity of a complete fertilizer high in organic nitrogen, no further fertilization is required for the remainder of that season. The turf should be fertilized the following spring with one-half to two-thirds of the amount used the previous fall. It is unwise to clip young Kentucky bluegrass or fescue turf closer than 1½ in. during the first season. They should be cut whenever a height of 1¾ to 2 in. is reached. Bent and Bermudagrass may be clipped back to ½ to ¾ in. as soon as they have grown to a height to 1 to 1½ in. The sparing use of water will reduce injury from damping-off and other diseases. Needed water should be applied slowly to avoid saturation of the surface soil. Sufficient water should be used to moisten the soil to a 5- or 6-in. depth. Mowers and other heavy equipment should be operated on the new turf, in so far as practicable, only when the soil is reasonably dry to avoid compaction. Even if insecticides have been applied as a part of the renovation program, the turf should be watched carefully for attacks of insects such as grubs, chinchbugs, and army worms and control treatments made promptly if infestations appear. Weeds in roughs and nonuse areas, which are a potential source of new infestations, should be clipped or treated with herbicides before seeds mature.

Weed Control in Roughs and Nonuse Areas

Applications of lime and fertilizer and the use of adapted grasses often will reduce the weed populations on roughs and nonuse areas. Grasses respond quickly to feeding under the infrequent mowing and clipping usually practiced and will compete strongly with the weeds, sometimes driving them out completely. Liming should be based on the soil-reaction test. A grade of complete fertilizer similar to that used for fairways can be applied annually or at 2- to 3-year intervals, depending upon the original soil fertility. Rates of application can be varied over a wide range, depending upon the amount of good grass that is present and the local soil condition. Minimum quantities of 300 to 400 lb. per acre should be used when weeds are heavy and grass is limited. The rates can be increased as more good grass develops.

Weed control on these areas can be hastened by using chemical weed killers in combination with lime and fertilizer applications. The same program of treatments should be followed as for fairways. By using maximum amounts of such materials as the arsenicals and 2,4-D, the number of treatments needed to secure satisfactory control can be reduced. As noted previously, the rates of dry treatments, either alone or mixed with a carrier, should be approximately double the quantity used for sprays.

9

Turf Diseases and Similar Types of Injury

Almost all of the better turf-forming grasses are subject to serious attacks of disease, particularly when maintained under close-clipped conditions. A knowledge of the characteristics of these diseases, and of the best methods for their prevention and control is an important item in successful turf management.

The Nature of Turf Diseases

The most serious diseases of turf grasses are caused by fungi. A fungus is a low form of plant life without the green coloring matter (chlorophyll) that enables grasses and other higher plants to manufacture foods necessary for growth. Fungi must secure nutrients from dead or living plant and animal tissues. Some types live only on the dead organic matter of soils, but others have the ability to attack living plants. The disease-producing organisms often develop on the dead organic matter in the soil. When moisture and temperature conditions become favorable, they attack the living tissues of grass, causing severe injury or complete destruction. They produce delicate strands (mycelium) similar to the single filaments of a fine spider web. These threads penetrate the leaves and stems, causing the cells to break down and producing eventual death of the plant.

The type of injury caused by the various disease-producing fungi is characteristic for each organism. The size, shape, or color of the scars produced on the turf aid in their identification. For example, the brown patch fungus causes a circular area of injured turf with a characteristic bluish or smoky ring at the outer edge. This may vary from a few inches in diameter to more than 2 ft., depending upon the severity of attack. In contrast, the dollar spot disease produces a scar about the size of a silver dollar. Unless checked promptly, it destroys both leaves and stems in this area and causes a pit in the turf right down to the surface of the soil. The disease known as copper spot causes a similar scar, but the dead grass has a copperish color in contrast with the grayish white color of dollar spot scars.

The time of disease attack also may aid in identifying the casual organism. Thus, snow mold injury occurs in late winter or early spring when temperatures are low. In contrast, brown patch and pink patch, which show the same circular type of injury, develop only during the high-temperature and -humidity periods of midsummer.

Fungus diseases may spread in several ways. When the disease is active, pieces of the fungus threads, or mycelium, may be carried to healthy grass and become new sources of infection. Some fungi produce minute spores that function like seeds of the higher plants. These germinate when moisture and temperature are favorable and produce new plants. The fungus strands also may produce small hard bodies called sclerotia from which new plants develop. The spores and sclerotia can remain dormant for long periods of time, when conditions for germination are unfavorable. They carry the fungus through the winter and are the primary sources of infection during the following season.

In the discussions of individual diseases in the following pages of this chapter the causal organism is listed in *italics* after the common name of the disease.

Conditions Favoring Fungus Diseases

MOISTURE. The fungi that cause turf diseases need liberal quantities of moisture for germination of the spores and sclerotia, and to keep the mycelium strands growing actively. The latter are very delicate and cannot withstand drying out. Saturated soils and high air humidity create ideal conditions for their rapid development. Poor drainage, heavy watering, and excessive rains that keep soils waterlogged for long periods increase the chance of disease infection. Humid air and heavy dews keep the foliage wet and favor fungi growth. Pockets of stagnant humid air that occur where there is poor air drainage aggravate disease attacks.

Excessive moisture produces lush grass and makes it more susceptible to disease. The injurious effects of saturated soils on turf have been noted previously (Chap. 4, Drainage and Irrigation). An added factor is the inability of the grass to recover from injury because of low nutrient availability and shallow restricted root systems, always typical of waterlogged soils.

TEMPERATURE. Excessive moisture alone will not cause fungus attacks. It must be accompanied by temperatures that are favorable for development of the disease-producing organisms. Like every other plant, each fungus has an optimum temperature for growth. The brown patch organism grows best at the relatively high temperatures of midsummer. Snow mold represents the other extreme. It causes the most severe damage in the late winter and early spring when temperatures are close to the freezing point. Diseases such as dollar spot and leaf spot of blue grass will grow over a much wider temperature range than brown patch and snow mold but are apt to be most severe during cool wet periods in the late spring and early fall (see discussions of individual diseases for temperature ranges best suited to the development of each kind of organism).

SOIL ACIDITY. Acid soils favor the development of turf diseases. Most of the disease-producing fungi will grow at acidity levels that weaken the grass. When acidity is high, disease attacks are more severe because the fungi are growing strongly and the grass is less capable of resisting them. High acidity checks the activity of many desirable soil organisms. When soil reaction is near the neutral point (see soil-reaction discussion, Chap. 2), types of soil organisms that keep the disease-producing fungi in check are more active. Because of the above relationships the grass diseases usually cause the most serious injury when soil reactions fall below pH 6.0. It is often practicable to reduce the severity of disease outbreaks on greens by light dressings of hydrated lime at rates of 5 to 10 lb. per 1,000 sq. ft. These can be made at 3- to 4-week intervals during the time when disease attacks are likely to occur. This practice is safe when soil reaction stays below pH 7.0 but will cause iron chlorosis and trace-element deficiencies when the reaction is pH 7.5 and above. Lime should not be used in the semi-arid sections, except occasionally to stop algae.

SOIL FERTILITY. Soil fertility and fertilization indirectly affect the frequency and severity of disease attacks. Grass that has been weakened by starvation or that is soft and succulent because of excessive feeding is damaged more heavily by fungus attacks than when it is healthy and vigorous. Nitrogen is the key element. It is the growth-producing nutrient and must be supplied at a constant and uniform rate to keep turf in good condition. Nitrogen applications must be so regulated that sufficient quantities will be available to meet the normal growth requirements of the grass, without overstimulation. Its use should be as outlined in Chap. 7, Turf Maintenance.

Grass needs phosphate and potash to supplement the nitrogen. Unless it can obtain liberal quantities of these minerals in addition to nitrogen, it cannot maintain healthy normal growth and becomes more susceptible to disease attacks. Good supplies of available potash are particularly important in reducing disease injury. Ordinarily one to two applications per season of a fertilizer containing phosphate and potash will be adequate to meet grass requirements for these minerals. Applications should be at rates to supply 2 to 4 lb. of actual phosphoric acid and 4 to 7 lb. of actual potash per 1,000 sq. ft. Light sandy soils should receive the heavier rates.

MATTED TURF. A heavy mat of spongy turf provides ideal conditions for the growth of disease-producing organisms. It always contains large amounts of dead leaves and stems which absorb moisture readily and remain damp for long periods. This condition is favorable for the growth of fungi and increases the difficulty of securing good control with fungicides. Where turf is heavily thatched, it is often necessary to use so much water to secure adequate penetration of the fungicide into the matted layer that normal treatments are too dilute to be effective. Under such conditions heavier rates of treatment are required that may discolor the turf. The matted grass on higher cut aprons and other areas adjacent to putting surfaces frequently becomes a source of infection from which the disease spreads to the green. The best remedy is thorough aeration of these areas to hasten drying out, and repeated brushing, close clipping, and top-dressing, as described in Chap. 7.

Disease Prevention and Control

The frequency and severity of disease attacks depend upon the weather, soil conditions, and management practices. While it is impracticable to control the weather, it is possible in many cases to modify soil conditions and management practices so that diseases can be prevented or reduced materially. Measures for prevention and control can be grouped into three main classes, namely: (1) cultural practices, (2) resistant grasses, and (3) fungicides.

CULTURAL PRACTICES. The cultural practices discussed in previous chapters that are basic for growing healthy turf will aid in reducing injury from disease. Those which are most useful in preventing serious attacks include:

1. Provision for adequate surface and subsurface water drainage.
2. Good air circulation over greens.
3. Correction of surface compaction with suitable aerating tools.
4. Modification of heavy soils by a program of aerating and top-dressing to build a porous layer.
5. Adjustment of soil reaction to pH 6.0 or higher.
6. Use of the more slowly available nitrogenous fertilizers in quantities that will produce normal growth without overstimulating.
7. Provision for a constant supply of available phosphate, potash, and trace elements.
8. Adjustment of watering practices to provide as long intervals

between applications as practicable. Continuously saturated turf must be avoided.

9. Elimination of matted or spongy turf.

RESISTANT GRASSES. Grasses that are immune or highly tolerant to disease ultimately should provide the best and most simple method of control. Several grasses have shown some evidence of disease

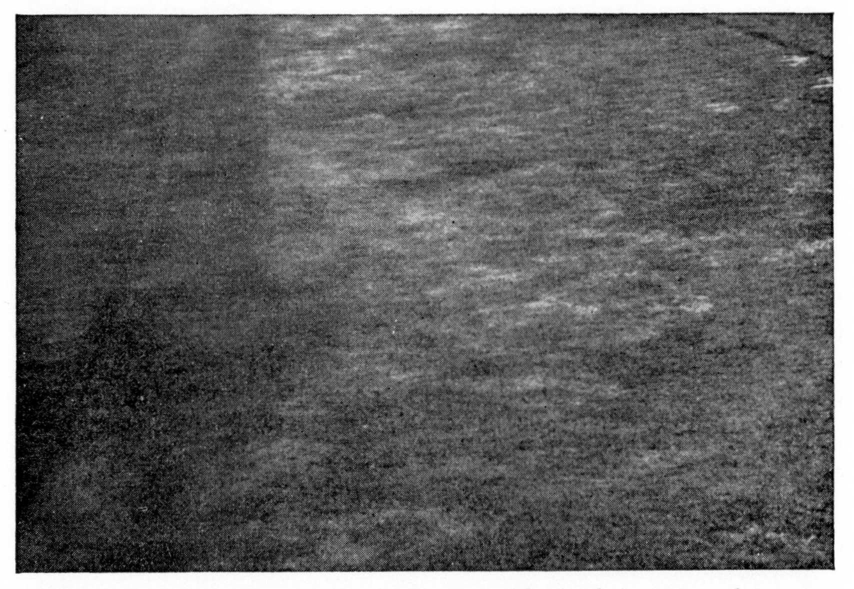

FIG. 33. Disease-resistant (left) and susceptible (right) strains of creeping bentgrass on a putting green. (*Pennsylvania Agricultural Experiment Station.*)

tolerance, but their resistance has been variable under different environmental conditions. It is possible to reduce the frequency of fungicidal treatments and to avoid serious attacks of diseases for which no control measures are known by the use of grasses which have shown some degree of disease tolerance.

Bentgrasses differ in their tolerance to disease. The colonial bents are more resistant to dollar spot and snow mold than the creeping and velvet bents. Seaside bent is very susceptible to both diseases. On the other hand the colonials are highly susceptible to brown patch. Individual selections of creeping bent show differences in susceptibility to snow mold, dollar spot, brown patch, and helminthosporium. Observations made over a wide range of conditions indicate that the Arlington strain (C-1) is attacked less severely by dollar spot and that Congressional is more resistant to snow mold than many other varieties. Observations of the Merion strain of Kentucky bluegrass indicate resistance to the leaf spot disease that is a serious problem on bluegrass turf. Some of the newer fescue strains, such as Illahee and Pennlawn, also show considerable disease tolerance. No disease injury has been observed on the zoysia grasses grown in the United States. The selection and breeding work with Bermuda, Bahia, buffalo, and other turf grasses now under way eventually should provide strains of these grasses that are more resistant to the diseases common to them.

FUNGICIDES. The use of chemicals that will kill disease-producing organisms but do not permanently injure the turf has become an important and widely used method of disease control. Many materials have been tested for their value as fungicides. Some of these that are very effective in killing the disease organism cannot be used because of their injurious effects on the grass. New products constantly are being developed and recommended for the control of a wide variety of diseases. These must be used with caution until their immediate and cumulative effects have been determined.

Some fungicides are specific for the control of only one or a limited number of diseases, while others have a wider range of effectiveness. The latter are called broad spectrum fungicides and usually are composed of two or more compatible chemicals, each of which is specific for certain disease producing fungi. Because of the close relationship of weather (temperature and moisture) to the activity of the disease organisms, practically all fungicidal materials must be applied periodically during periods when attacks are likely to occur to insure protection against serious injury. The following discussions give the general characteristics and usefulness of the various classes of chemicals used for disease control on turf, and the general descriptions of the more prevalent disease producing organisms, with the most effective treatments for keeping them in check. Rates and frequency of treatment with individual fungicides will be found in Appendix Table 20, page 326.

INORGANIC MERCURIALS. The mercury compounds, corrosive sublimate (mercuric chloride) and calomel (mercurous chloride), have been the most widely used fungicidal chemicals for the con-

FIG. 34. Spraying for disease control. (*Courtesy Sewerage Commission, City of Milwaukee.*)

trol of turf diseases. Usually they are applied as mixtures of one-third corrosive sublimate and two-thirds calomel. When properly used they are effective for some of the most prevalent turf diseases such as dollar spot, brown patch, and snow mold. They will not control the helminthosporium (melting out) diseases that seriously injure Kentucky bluegrass, red fescue, *Poa annua,* and some types of bents. Both materials can be applied either wet or dry. Calomel is insoluble and corrosive sublimate only slightly soluble in cold water. When applied as a spray, stock solutions can be prepared by dissolving the chemical in hot water to which a small amount of salt has been added. The salt increases the rate at which corrosive sublimate will dissolve. A convenient method of preparing stock solutions is to dissolve a sufficient quantity of material to treat one green, or a unit of area such as 1,000 sq. ft., in a gallon of hot water and store it in glass jars or jugs for future use. If the sprayer used has a good agitator to keep the material in suspension, the chemical can be applied satisfactorily without dissolving it beforehand. If applied dry it should be mixed with a sufficient quantity of top-dressing, dry sand, or other diluting material to ensure uniform distribution. Wet applications should be washed off the foliage to prevent burning following treatment. Dry applications should be watered in thoroughly. When applied alone, if mixed with an organic material such as Milorganite or Agrinite, it is not necessary to water in dry applications unless the soil is very wet. Treatments may cause temporary discoloration of the grass. The mercury compounds should be used only at a reduced rate, (1 to 1½ oz. per 1,000 sq. ft.) during the hot weather of midsummer because of the danger of permanent injury to the turf.

ORGANIC MERCURIALS. Some of the organic phenyl mercurials have been used successfully for the control of certain fungus diseases. Phenyl mercury acetate (PMAS) is effective for dollar spot and copper spot. Other organic mercury compounds, distributed commercially under the names of Puraturf and Puratized 641, have controlled copper spot, dollar spot, and pink patch. These materials are water soluble and are applied as sprays. Like the inorganic mercury compounds described above, the phenyl mercuries may cause temporary turf discoloration which usually disappears within 1 week to 10 days following treatment. Other mercury compounds, distributed under various trade names such as Semesan, Special Semesan, Fungol and Nu-Green, have been effective in controlling dollar spot, brown patch, and snow mold when used at strengths to supply the same amounts of mercury applied in the corrosive sublimate-calomel treatments.

All mercury compounds are poisonous when taken internally, and care must be used in handling them.

CADMIUM COMPOUNDS. Cadmium compounds comprise a third group of chemicals for control of certain turf diseases. Both inorganic and organic compounds have been used successfully for the control of dollar spot and copper spot. They are somewhat less effective on pink patch and the fusarium type of snow mold. The materials can be applied wet or dry. They usually have a longer period of effectiveness than the mercurials and will not discolor turf as severely when used at recommended rates. They always should be watered in after application.

SULFUR COMPOUNDS. Some compounds containing sulfur have been found to be effective for the control of certain diseases. Inorganic materials, such as copper- and zinc-sulfates, have been used successfully in combination with Dithane for the control of bluegrass leaf spot. Organic sulfur compounds are available commercially under a number of trade names, as Thiram, Tersan, Sportrete, Arasan, etc. They are effective for the control of brown patch and, to a somewhat less extent, snow mold and dollar spot. They have the advantage of causing less turf discoloration when used in hot weather.

ANTIBIOTICS. Many materials of this type have been tested for use in the control of turf disease-producing fungi. The one that has shown the widest usefulness is Acti-dione. When applied correctly, it has proven to be very effective for the control of bluegrass rust and leaf spot. It also will control dollar spot, melting-out, mildew, and brown patch. It has performed best when applied as a preventive treatment prior to the development of infections.

BROAD-SPECTRUM FUNGICIDES. Since individual chemicals often are effective only for the control of one or a limited number of diseases, some manufacturers have combined two or more materials to provide a product which will act on a number of different fungi. Such combinations are called broad-spectrum fungicides. They are satisfactory when chemicals are used in their preparation which are compatible with each other, and when the grasses on which they are used have the same approximate tolerance to each ingredient in them. For example, it would be undesirable to use a broad-spectrum material containing phenyl mercuric acetate to control rust on Merion Kentucky bluegrass, even though the mixture checked the rust, due to Merion's recognized lack of tolerance to this chemical. An added consideration is that usually it is less expensive to apply the fungicide that is specific for the particular disease, where it has been positively identified, than to use a broad-spectrum mixture containing other chemicals which may have little or no effect on it.

Broad-spectrum fungicides offered by different manufacturers may vary materially in the toxicants they contain. They are convenient because they eliminate the necessity for stocking a number of different materials. Their use should be based on a careful check of the materials they contain and the proven effectiveness of these on the diseases to be controlled.

Fungus Diseases and Their Control

Brown patch (*Pellicularia filamentosa,* formerly *Rhizoctonia solani*) is caused by a fungus that grows best during humid weather when temperatures are between 80 and 90°F. It is the most serious disease of turf during the period from June to September in the area from Philadelphia and Washington west to Kansas City and St. Louis. North of this region where temperatures are more moderate it occurs intermittently during hot humid periods but is controlled more easily because weather changes help to check it.

The disease occurs in circular patches that may vary from a few inches to more than 2 ft. in diameter. When the fungus is growing actively, the patch of dead or injured grass has a characteristic smoky ring at its outer edge where the grass leaves have a bluish water-soaked appearance. Grass that is soft and succulent owing to excessive amounts of available nitrogen is more susceptible to injury by brown patch than where it shows slight indications of nitrogen deficiency. In areas where the disease causes serious injury it is good practice to make heavy applications of slowly available nitrogen (2 to 4 lb. per 1,000 sq. ft.) in the spring that will carry the turf through the hot weather without the necessity for additional feeding until late summer or early fall.

Brown patch can be controlled by a number of chemicals. Those most commonly used include inorganic mercury compounds (corrosive sublimate and calomel), organic mercurials (PMA and special Semesan), materials containing organic sulfur, and broad spectrum mixtures containing one or more of the above. The antibiotic Acti-dione also has been used effectively. The best control, with least turf injury, has been obtained by a program of preventive treatments through critical periods. Under favorable con-

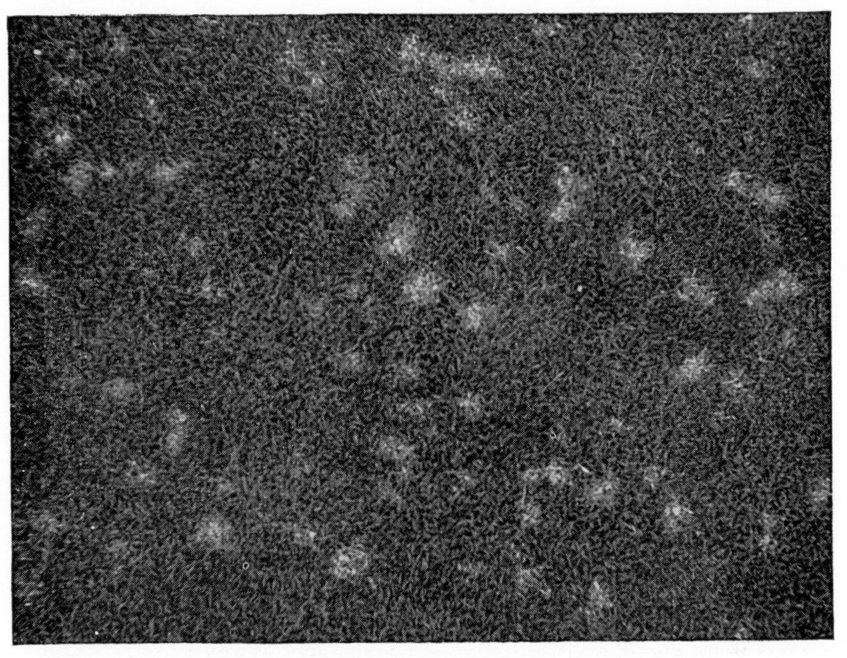

FIG. 35. Dollar spot injury. (*Green Section.*)

ditions the disease develops rapidly and often causes considerable damage before it can be checked, if treatment is delayed until it has appeared. Lighter dosages can be used when a preventive program is followed. This is an important consideration when the inorganic mercuries are used, since the heavier rates needed for control after the disease has appeared may cause injury to the turf in hot weather. At such times, the sulfur and other less toxic materials may be more satisfactory because of the less likelihood of injury by them. The spacing of preventive treatments will vary from 7 to 10 days or more, depending upon how favorable weather conditions are for fungus activity.

DOLLAR SPOT (*Sclerotinia homeocarpa*) causes a characteristic scar on turf cut to putting green height, which is roughly the size of a silver dollar. Injured areas on Kentucky blue and other grasses maintained at higher cuts often are much larger, sometimes reaching a diameter of 3 to 4 in. The disease attacks both leaves and stems, and if not checked promptly, will kill all vegetative tis-

FIG. 36. Heavily matted turf intensifies dollar spot injury. (*Green Section.*)

sue in the infected area. Moderate temperatures with high moisture favor its development and it usually is more prevalent in late spring and early summer, and again in early fall. But outbreaks may occur throughout the season whenever moisture and temperature are favorable.

Good cultural practices are particularly important in preventing serious damage from dollar spot. The disease is much more serious on grass that has been weakened by nitrogen starvation. Conversely, it also will be more severe on turf that is soft and succulent due to excessive supplies of soluble nitrogen. Rates of application of the latter always should be reduced to from ½ to

⅓ of the normally used quantity during periods when the disease may be troublesome. This will help to maintain a better balance between the nitrogen and other nutrients and will result in a harder type of growth that will be more resistant to attack by the fungus. The slowly available forms of nitrogen can be applied in larger quantities at less frequent intervals because of the smaller amounts of available nitrogen released by them at any one time.

A number of fungicidal materials are effective for the control of dollar spot (see Appendix Table 20, page 326). As for brown patch, periodic preventive treatments at moderate rates are better than heavy dosages after the disease has appeared. The normal spacing of treatments is from 10 days to 2 weeks, but this may have to be reduced materially if turf is heavily thatched. Heavy thatching interferes with the penetration of the fungicide in sufficient concentration to kill the fungus. Superficial surface control may be obtained, but reinfections will occur within a period of 2 or 3 days. Under such conditions it always is desirable to open the turf as thoroughly as possible by aerating and verticutting before the control treatments are made.

Snow Molds. (*Fusarium nivale* and *Typhula itoana*). Fusarium patch is the name frequently used to differentiate the injury caused by the *Fusarium nivale* fungus from that produced by *Typhula itoana*, commonly called Gray Snow Mold. In both cases, the type of injury is similar and laboratory identification may be necessary to determine the causal organism. Injury appears as roughly circular spots, a few inches to several feet in diameter. In severe cases these may coalesce to form large, irregular areas. The dead grass in the infected areas is heavily matted and has a silvery gray color.

The fungi attack the grass during mild periods in the winter and early spring when melting snow or heavy rains supply the necessary moisture for their active growth. Damage is not confined to cold climates and snow is not necessary for the development of either organism. Severe injury has been reported in Florida and other sections of the South during periods of cool wet weather in the winter months. Damage always is more severe on greens and other turf areas that are kept in a saturated condition by poor surface drainage, blankets of snow, excessive irrigation, or coverings of straw or other materials. Soils containing excessive amounts of organic matter that retain large quantities of water favor the growth of the fungus. Also, grass that goes into the winter in a soft condition is very susceptible to injury. This often results from late fall applications of quickly available nitrogen.

FIG. 37. Snow mold injury on green. (*Green Section.*)

In common with many other turf disease-producing fungi, the organisms causing snow mold are favored when soil reaction levels get below pH 6.0.

Damage can be prevented or adequately checked by treatment with fungicides. Materials and treatment schedules are the same for both organisms. Mercury compounds (corrosive sublimate-calomel mixtures and organic mercuries) have given the best control. Repeat treatments generally are better than single applications. In the North, the first treatment should be made in late October, before heavy snow may interfere with operations. A second treatment is made in late winter, preferably when the turf is free from snow. In the South, the first treatment is made in the fall as soon as temperatures drop to the range favorable for growth of the fungi. (40 to 50°F.) The spacing of repeat treatments will depend upon when there is indication of fresh infection.

Rates for the first treatment should be at approximately double the strength used for summer control of diseases. Second and later treatments can be at one-half the strength of the first. Critical studies at the Toro Manufacturing Company Research Center, Minneapolis, Minnesota have shown that the fungicidal treatments are most effective when the chemical is mixed with a carrier such as processed sewage sludge or good quality top-dressing. Treatments with dry mixes of these materials were superior to mixes with sand and to spraying with the chemical solution, unless sludge or top-dressing had been applied before the spray treatment was made.

Some grasses are more resistant to the snow molds than others. The colonial bents, as a class, are less susceptible than the creeping bents. A notable exception to this is the Congressional variety of creeping bent, which shows a high tolerance to the disease.

LEAF SPOT, MELTING OUT (*Helminthosporium* spp.). This disease or group of related diseases, attacks many of the turf-forming grasses. One form causes the leaf spot and foot rot of Kentucky bluegrass and red fescue. Injury to these grasses occurs as browned lesions on the leaves which may extend across their entire width, completely killing the portion of the blade above the scar. Lesions also may occur at the base of the leaf sheath, causing the entire leaf to wither and die. This latter type of injury is somewhat more common on the fescues, while the spot injury on the leaf blades is more typical on bluegrass. The most severe infections occur during cool moist weather in the spring and fall, although sporadic outbreaks of the disease may take place during cool wet periods in midsummer. Close-clipped turf on fairways is more severely injured than the higher cut grass of adjacent roughs. Soft grass caused by heavy applications of readily available nitrogen in periods when the disease is active is particularly susceptible to injury.

When bent putting-green turf is attacked, the grass thins out and develops an unhealthy water-soaked appearance. In contrast with helminthosporium infections on bluegrass and fescues, which are most severe in cool weather, injury to bent turf usually occurs during periods of warm moist weather. The rapid loss of annual bluegrass at such times is attributed to this disease.

Cultural practices that have reduced the severity of the disease include the use of slowly available nitrogen fertilizers and thorough drying out of infected turf whenever possible. Some varieties of grasses are more resistant than others. Merion Kentucky bluegrass has a very high tolerance to the specific fungus that causes severe injury to common Kentucky bluegrass and other varieties of this species. Similarly, the Pennlawn and Improved Illahee varieties of creeping red fescues are more resistant than common creeping red and Chewings fescues. There are wide differences in susceptibility of varieties of creeping bent to the species of the fungus that attacks this grass, although all of them may be injured to some degree when severe attacks occur.

Only a limited number of fungicides have proven effective for control of the various species of the fungus which attack the different grasses. Among these, the ferrated type of the antibiotic, Acti-dione, has given good control. Organic mercury compounds, either alone in broad spectrum preparations, also have materially reduced infections. All of these chemicals have been more effective when used periodically as preventive treatments than when applied after the disease has appeared.

COPPER SPOT (*Gleocerospora sorghi*) disease causes areas of injury that are roughly circular in outline and 1 to 3 in. in diameter. The injured grass in the patches has a copperish color due to the masses of fungus spores covering the leaves. Infections occur only in periods of high temperature and high humidity. The velvet bents are most susceptible, but other bents also have been attacked occasionally. The cadmium fungicides used at the recommended rates have given the most complete control.

PINK PATCH OR RED THREAD (*Corticium fuciforme*) damages turf in areas that range from a few inches to several feet in diameter. The grass blades in the injured regions are matted together by the pinkish-colored mycelium of the fungus. The disease requires the same general weather conditions of high humidity and high temperatures that are favorable for brown patch. The velvet bents are reported to be more susceptible than the colonial and creeping bents. Both mercury (organic and inorganic) and cadmium compounds have given satisfactory control.

GRAY LEAF SPOT (*Piricularia grisea*) causes serious injury to St. Augustine grass in the South. The fungus penetrates the plant tissues producing grayish colored lesions which eventually spread across the entire leaf and kill it. Prevention of infection by chemical treatment is the best method of control. Both mercury-containing and broad-spectrum fungicides are effective in reducing injury, if used as preventive treatments before infection has occurred. After the fungus has entered the plant tissue it cannot be killed by chemical treatment. In warm humid weather, when the disease is most active, it will be necessary to treat every 7 to 10 days to provide adequate protection against injury.

RUST (*Puccinia* spp.) attacks many grasses to some extent. The Merion variety of Kentucky bluegrass is highly susceptible to it. The disease is characterized by yellowish-orange to black, raised pustules on the surface of leaves and stems. Badly infected turf has a yellowish, rusty appearance. The most severe attacks occur during periods of dry hot weather from mid-July to late September.

Good cultural practices are very effective in preventing severe rust infections. These include maintaining levels of available nitrogen adequate for normal growth, regular watering, and mowing at frequent intervals. Regular fungicidial treatments every week to ten days, starting when the first infection occurs, also will control the disease. Both antibiotics and Zineb are effective in preventing the spread of infections.

PYTHIUM OR GREASE SPOT (*Pythium* spp.) is a fungus that causes severe damage to closely clipped bent turf on greens under conditions of high temperatures and high humidity. Its occurrence usually is limited to areas where soils are saturated and where water collects temporarily on the surface. It is most serious when temperatures are approximately 90°F. or higher. First symptoms of the disease appear as small damaged areas of turf similar in appearance to injury caused by dollar spot except that they tend to develop in irregular streaks. These enlarge rapidly until large irregular scars are formed that follow the general outline of the saturated area. When the fungus is active, a dense growth of mycelium covers the grass and has a somewhat dark smoky appearance. The dead grass in the injured area has a rusty brown color in contrast with the grayish color of the dollar spot and the reddish brown color of copper spot.

Good surface contouring of greens to avoid concentrations of water during periods of excessive precipitation in hot weather will help to reduce the severity of attacks. Also, creation of favorable conditions for rapid drying out of saturated soil by aeration will check the spread of the disease. Treatment with broad-spectrum fungicides containing mixtures of Acti-dione, mercury, and cadmium compounds have materially reduced injury, but have not given complete control. When weather conditions are favorable for development of the fungus, re-treatments with the fungicide must be made at frequent intervals (3 to 7 days) to keep it in check.

FAIRY RINGS are caused by a number of fungi that produce mushrooms, puffballs, or toadstools. The injured turf occurs in circular bands immediately above the soil area where the fungus is active. The fungus produces a dense mass of mycelium in the soil that traps the air and keeps out water. In periods of dry weather the soil moisture in infected areas is reduced to such a low point that the grass wilts and dies. Grass just inside or outside the circular band where the fungus is active is stimulated to rapid growth and has the dark-green color typical of liberal supplies of available nitrogen. Fairy ring circles may vary in size from 1 or 2 ft. to a mile or more in diameter. Chemical control is difficult because the fungi grow into the soil so deeply that lethal concentrations of the fungicide often do not penetrate to centers of infection. The Washington Agricultural Experiment Station has obtained good results with organic mercury compounds when used with a wetting agent. The following procedure is recommended:

1. Prepare a solution of ½ oz. of PMA in 100 gals. of water, to which has been added 1 lb. of a laundry detergent.

2. Thoroughly aerate the infected area, including at least 2 ft. outside of the green ring of grass. This can be done by hand-forking or with a power aerator. The soil should be opened as deeply as possible (5 to 6 in. minimum depth).

3. Apply prepared solution as a drench at the rate of 40 gals. per 100 sq. ft.

FIG. 38. Injury caused by fairy ring fungus. Note fruiting bodies. (*Green Section.*)

4. Repeat treatments at monthly intervals. If recommended concentrations discolor the turf, the strength of repeat treatments should be reduced by one-third.

Note. PMA cannot be used safely on Merion Kentucky bluegrass. Where this variety is to be treated, a solution of ½ oz. of mercuric chloride or ⅛ oz. of cadminate per 100 gals. of water will provide partial control with deep aeration and re-treatment.

MILDEW (*Erysiphe graminis*) produces a grayish-white powdery growth that coats the leaf blades and later causes dry blotched areas where the fungus has penetrated the tissue. It seldom kills the plants, but the turf is weakened and its growth is checked when infections persist for extended periods. The disease occurs during cool wet periods in the spring and fall and attacks Kentucky bluegrass more severely than the other turf grasses. It can be checked by treatments with the bichloride of mercury-calomel mixture applied at standard rates. Damage is seldom severe enough to warrant the use of fungicidal control measures.

DAMPING-OFF is caused by many different types of soil-inhabiting fungi. Some attack the seed before germination causing it to rot before the seedlings emerge from the soil. Others infect the young seedlings, penetrating the plants just above the surface of the ground and causing them to shrivel and die. The most severe damage from damping-off occurs during wet periods when temperatures are cool to moderate.

Chemical treatments for control of damping-off organisms have not proven to be very effective. Because of the danger of injuring the young seedlings, fungicides can be used only at reduced rates which should not exceed more than one-half of the recommended concentrations for mature turf. This may check the disease to some extent but seldom fully controls it. The use of seed treated with one of the seed disinfectants, such as Thiram or Captan, has been found to increase seedling survival by 15 to 25 per cent where damping-off has been a problem.

Good cultural practices will help to reduce the amount of injury. Seedling grass should not be permitted to grow so tall before clipping that it breaks over and forms a mat which retains excessive amounts of moisture. This provides ideal conditions for fungous growth. Light clipping whenever the grass reaches a height of 1¼ to 1½ in. is effective in preventing matting and will hasten drying. The clippings should be removed or scattered whenever practicable. It is sometimes possible to prevent serious injury when damping-off infections occur by permitting new seedings to dry out thoroughly. When it is necessary to water, it should be applied in the early morning so that the maximum amount of time is available during the day to permit the grass to dry off.

SLIME MOLDS. A number of slime mold fungi occasionally occur on grass in periods of humid weather. They first appear as grayish-white or yellowish jellylike masses that often completely cover the leaf blades. Some of them later turn black when they begin to form spores. They can be washed off easily at this stage. They mar the turf temporarily because of their color and slimy appearance but do not produce serious injury.

ALGAE, or green scum, is not a turf disease. It is a dense growth of minute single-celled plants that develops on thin or bare areas in hot humid weather when soils are saturated with moisture. It usually is more prevalent on greens than on other areas because more water is used on the greens and soils stay wet for longer periods. Algae, like grasses, manufacture their food from air, water, and the minerals they obtain from the soil. They require sunlight for this process. A dense turf checks their development by excluding light. The scum of plants develops only when the grass becomes thin and admits light to the surface of a wet soil. When the soil dries out the plants die and turn black, forming a tough crust that seals the soil and excludes air and moisture.

When the green scum first appears, a light dusting of hydrated lime at 2 to 5 lb. per 1,000 sq. ft. will kill the algae plants. After the black crust forms, the best method of treatment is thorough aeration of the affected area. A rake, spike disk, or some other suitable method of scarification should be used, following aeration, to break up the crust completely. Reseeding and top-dressing can be done as soon as the soil has dried out.

Other Causes of Turf Injury

There are many other causes of turf injury that produce scars which are similar to and are often mistaken for the damage caused by diseases. These include (1) winter injuries, (2) summer injuries, (3) chemical injuries, (4) mechanical injuries, and (5) insect injuries. The first four are described in the following discussion. Insect injuries are discussed in Chap. 10.

WINTER INJURIES. The most important types of winter injury to turf are desiccation (dehydration) and freezing out. Excessive drying out (desiccation) is common in regions where there is limited rainfall and soil moisture is low during the winter months. It is aggravated by dry cold winds. The dry soil and dry air draw so much moisture out of the dormant or semidormant grass plants that they shrivel and die. Injury of this type occurs on both greens and fairways and is most severe on knolls and other exposed areas that are blown free of snow. The damaged grass first has a dull brown color which may bleach out to grayish white by spring. The best method of avoiding winter injury by desiccation is to moisten the soil thoroughly to a depth of 5 to 6 in. late in the fall. Where it is necessary to shut off water because of danger of early freezes, some clubs have rigged tanks for late watering of greens. Late fall watering of fairways must be carefully planned when pipe lines are shallow and must be drained early because of the danger of freezing. It is common practice in northern dry areas to place tree branches and brush on wind-swept greens to collect and hold snow during the winter.

There is good evidence that where desiccation is a serious problem on greens it can be reduced substantially, and often eliminated completely, by protecting them with polyethylene blankets. In trials at the Toro Manufacturing Company Research Center at Minneapolis, Minnesota, clear polyethylene (4-mil Polyfilm) has been used successfully for this purpose. The blankets are placed after the turf has become dormant in the fall and removed shortly after active growth has started in the spring. The soil under the polyethylene film warms much faster and growth starts earlier than where no cover is used. In contrast, insulated blankets (2-in. balsa) hold the frost in the ground longer and delay the start of active growth. When protective covers are used it is essential that greens be treated for snow mold control prior to covering them in the fall.

Winter injury of turf due to freezing out, as distinct from desiccation, is caused primarily by poor surface or subsurface drainage. It is often aggravated by the use of poorly adapted grasses and by management practices that weaken the turf and make it less tolerant to adverse conditions. Poor surface drainage causes water to collect in depressions. The frozen soil prevents it from draining out even when its physical condition is satisfactory. Accumulations of snow and ice may produce the same result by damming back the water. The alternate freezing and thawing of such pools causes winterkilling of the grass. This type of injury is more common on greens but may also occur on fairways and tees.

Freezing out of turf takes place when soils go into the winter in a saturated condition. Wet soils are subject to heaving and honeycombing which cause serious damage to the grass. Injury of this type always is most severe on seepage areas where soils stay wet for long periods.

The first essential in preventing injury by freezing out is to provide good surface drainage. Where freezing out occurs regularly each year on certain areas because water ponds on them, the only permanent remedy is recontouring to eliminate the surface depressions. In regions where heavy snows result in damming the water and formation of ice sheets, many clubs have found it necessary to follow a systematic program of snow removal. This is done as soon as possible when thawing starts in the spring.

Injury to turf by frost action on poorly drained soils and seepage areas is most common in regions where alternate freezing and thawing occurs during the winter. Heaving and honeycombing of the surface soil lift the plants. Roots are torn off and crowns are killed by exposure to low temperature without any soil protection. Methods of providing good subsurface drainage are discussed in Chap. 4.

A good program of turf maintenance during the growing season often prevents or reduces winterkilling. The use of grasses that are cold hardy or adapted to the conditions under which they must be grown is an important factor. For example, when Kentucky bluegrass is destroyed because of saturated soils on spring seepage or ponded areas, colonial or creeping bentgrasses should be used. The bents are more tolerant of wet soils and will survive longer under such conditions. The various kinds of bents differ in cold tolerance. Some of the newer vegetative strains such as Toronto and Old Orchard are more resistant than other types. Seaside is very susceptible to freezing injury.

Sound fall fertilization reduces winter injury. Applications of fertilizer containing nitrogen in slowly available form in early September at rates to supply 2 to 4 lbs. of nitrogen per 1,000 sq. ft. will produce a tough grass that is less susceptible to winter damage. Soluble nitrogen fertilizers will materially increase the danger of overgrowth and development of soft grass that is highly susceptible to winterkilling. Reduced watering also helps to harden off the turf and put it in good condition for the winter.

SUMMER INJURIES. Turf is subject to many types of injury during the growing season that may be mistaken for disease attacks. These may be due to unfavorable weather and soil conditions or to inadequate maintenance. Scald is a common trouble of this kind. It occurs as irregular areas of discolored turf on poorly drained soils during periods of excessive rainfall or when the grass is watered heavily in hot weather. Injury usually is most severe in depressions on a green or where surface water concentrates in restricted runoff channels. The soil remains saturated for excessive periods on such areas. The grass develops an unhealthy yellow color and dies within a few days. Algae usually occupy the areas where the grass has scalded out. Thorough aeration of the damaged areas to hasten drying and permit air to get down to the roots is a temporary remedy and may save some of the turf. The only permanent remedy is to provide adequate surface and subsurface drainage.

Poor air drainage is an important contributing factor to summer scald. High humidity favors the development of many turf diseases. The air at the surface of the ground absorbs moisture constantly from the soil and from the dew or moisture on the turf. Without good air circulation the lower atmosphere becomes saturated, creating ideal conditions for the growth of disease producing fungi. Stagnant air also prevents normal drying of the surface soil after rain or watering and thus aggravates compaction.

Pockets of dead air are most likely to occur over greens and tees surrounded by trees or tall shrubbery, or when located in coves or on the floors of small valleys. It is easy to establish the lack of adequate air movement in such locations. Dews are heavier and evaporate more slowly. The turf and soil remain saturated for longer periods following rains or irrigation than on similar areas in the open. Soil compaction is more serious and disease attacks are more frequent and severe. In Northern regions, areas with poor air drainage and high humidity in summer become frost pockets in winter.

Poor air circulation caused by trees and shrubbery often can be improved materially by judicious thinning and pruning. Channels should be opened through the growth in the direction of the prevailing winds. Sometimes the removal of a single tree is all that is required to provide adequate air flow over the turf. Where poor air drainage is due to the character of the terrain, the only permanent remedy is to relocate the green or tee. In some instances, where this has not been practicable, artificial circulation has been attempted by the use of powerful fans constructed from airplane propellers. Such devices have been used only with indifferent success.

Localized dry spots may develop on greens and fairways where the turf suffers from lack of moisture, even when irrigated regularly. Examination of the soil on these areas will show that water is not penetrating into it and it is dry and powdery. This condition may be caused by excessive surface compaction or because of the accumulation of a dense felt of undecomposed dead roots and stems through which water cannot penetrate. Felting or thatching occurs when soils are poorly drained and develop excess acidity that checks the activity of organisms which cause the decomposition of organic matter. Localized dry spots should be thoroughly aerated and lime and fertilizer added to hasten organic-matter decay. They should be watered regularly until normal soil moisture has been restored.

In regions subject to high temperatures and hot dry winds turf may be seriously injured because of wilting. Wilting takes place when the grass roots cannot absorb moisture from the soil as fast as it is lost from the leaves. The first indications are the development of a dull bluish green color and severe footprinting of the turf. Wilted turf recovers very slowly, and in serious cases the leaves may shrivel and die. Injury can be avoided by frequent light sprinkling (syringing) of turf (two to three times daily) to provide readily available moisture to reduce turf and soil temperatures. This type of watering cannot replace normal irrigation to replenish the moisture supply throughout the root zone.

Turf may lose its vigor and thin out because of tree-root competition. The presence of troublesome quantities of tree roots in the grass-root zone can be detected readily by examination of plugs from the injured areas. As noted in Chap. 7 tree-root competition can be eliminated by ditching between the green and trees that are sources of trouble or by the periodic use of a deep running single-blade root cutter.

CHEMICAL INJURIES. Many kinds of fertilizer will cause severe scorching of turf. Injury is most serious when they are applied on wet grass. Materials like sulfate of ammonia will burn turf even though the foliage is dry, unless they are washed off of the leaves immediately following application. They absorb water from the air rapidly and cause droplets of concentrated solutions to form on the leaves. All of the soluble nitrogen compounds will burn turf in a similar manner. In addition to sulfate of ammonia these include nitrate of soda, ammonium nitrates and phosphates, urea, cyanamid, and ammonia liquids. Mixed fertilizers containing these compounds also cause scorching, although the severity of the injury is reduced where mixtures contain liberal quantities of organic materials. Fertilizers containing muriate of potash will burn turf severely. Hydrated lime applied at rates above 5 to 10 lb. per 1,000 sq. ft. also may scorch the grass. Superphosphate will not burn unless applied at very heavy rates. Raw ground limestone and organic fertilizers can be used at any time without danger of injury.

Turf may be injured or killed by chemicals used as herbicides, insecticides, and fungicides. Mercury compounds (corrosive sublimate, calomel, and organic phenyl mercury compounds) often cause a temporary yellowing and check the growth of grass for a period of 1 week to 10 days following treatment. Discoloration and injury are more severe in hot weather, and dosages should be reduced or treatments discontinued during midsummer. Heavy applications of arsenicals (sodium arsenite and arsenic acid) when made in warm weather, will cause a severe scorch that is similar in appearance to burns caused by fertilizer. Insecticidal and herbicidal materials dissolved in oils should be tried out on a small scale before being used. Many oils injure grass, particularly when applied in hot weather. Selective herbicidal materials, such as 2,4-D, will damage or kill grass when used in heavy concentrations. Treatments must be limited to recommended dosages to avoid danger of injury.

FIG. 39. Border injury on green due to wear by mowing equipment. (*Courtesy Sewerage Commission, City of Milwaukee.*)

MECHANICAL INJURIES. The most common turf injuries due to mechanical causes are (1) damage due to soil compaction by trampling and the use of heavy equipment when soils are wet, (2) scalping by close mowing, and (3) divots.

Soil compaction causes turf to thin out and develop a weak unhealthy condition that does not respond to fertilization, liming, and similar corrective measures. Root systems are restricted and shallow, and the grass does not grow normally, even when weather conditions are favorable. The presence of clover, annual bluegrass, knotweed, and other weeds that can tolerate compact soils often is a good indication of this cause for poor turf. Remedial measures for compaction correction have been fully discussed in Chap. 7

Turf is sometimes injured by too close cutting. When this occurs, the cause of damage usually is self-evident. It happens most frequently on fairways with sharp bumps and ridges and around greens, tees, and traps with abrupt shoulder slopes. Scalped turf has a grayish-white appearance due to removal of practically all of the leaves. The upright growing grasses such as Kentucky blue and fescue are injured most severely, but bent and Bermudagrass on greens also can be damaged by too close cutting. The obvious remedy is proper mower adjustment. Sometimes it is practicable to change the direction of cut so that mower bed-knives do not ride the crest of ridges or other irregular areas. It is often possible to reshape areas where scalping cannot be avoided so that power equipment can be used on them without injuring the turf.

Divot scars on fairways will heal rapidly when there is good fertilization and maintenance. On tees, the scars may be repaired by plugging or by reseeding when tees are top-dressed.

10

Control of Insects and Other Pests

Insects and animal pets damage golf-course turf in two ways. (1) They may destroy the grass by feeding on its foliage or roots. Injury caused by grubs, sod webworms, and chinch bugs is typical. (2) Turf also may be affected by insects or animals that do not feed on the grass but live in the soil under sod and seriously interfere with its playing qualities by their activities. Earthworms, moles, ants, gophers, mole crickets, and crayfish are examples of this class. Appendix Table 19, page 324, lists the most effective insecticides and rates of treatment for the various insect pests.

Three groups of insects directly damage grass by feeding on it. These include (1) those that attack the roots, such as grubs of the Japanese beetle, June beetle, and many other soil-inhabiting insects; (2) those that feed upon the foliage, like sod webworms, army worms, and cut worms; and (3) the sucking insects that suck the plant juices from leaves and stems. Chinch bugs are the most serious offenders in this group. Successful control of each kind depends upon several factors. Insects vary in their tolerance to different insecticides and to different concentrations of the same material. They vary, also, in the peak periods when they are most serious and when control treatments are most effective. To obtain adequate control before serious injury occurs, the early stages of activity must be recognized and the effective insecticide and proper dosage required in each case must be used. Individual insects and control measures are discussed in the second section of this chapter.

Insecticides and Methods of Use

ALDRIN is effective for the control of beetle grubs, earthworms, sod webworms, and mole crickets. It is available as a 2.5 per cent dust and a 2.0 per cent granular formulation for dry application. The dust can be applied directly with a duster. The granular form should be mixed with an appropriate carrier such as fertilizer or screened soil. It is available also as a 25 per cent wettable powder and an emulsifiable concentrate containing 2 lbs. of toxicant per gal. for use as a spray. Regardless of whether the dry or wet form is used, treatments should be watered into the soil thoroughly immediately following application.

ARSENATE OF LEAD is a fine dry powder that is highly insoluble in water. The best grades are 96 to 98 per cent pure. The commercial product usually has a distinctive pink color. Many producers include a deflocculating material to hold the insoluble powder in suspension. A deflocculating agent is not necessary when arsenate of lead is to be applied as a dust. Lead may be applied dry with a mechanical duster or mixed with a diluent, such as finely screened top-dressing material, sand, or certain types of fertilizers, and applied with a fertilizer distributor. It can be applied as a spray, when it contains a deflocculating agent that will keep it in suspension.

The action of lead arsenate on soil-inhabiting insects is dependent upon how rapidly the material penetrates into the soil. Ordinarily its movement is relatively slow. In tests on Japanese beetle grub control conducted at the Moorestown, New Jersey, laboratory a dosage of 25 lb. of actual DDT per acre was found to be 2½ times faster than 1,000 lb. of lead arsenate, while 10 lb. of actual Chlordane was approximately 2½ times faster than 25 lb. of DDT. The rate of penetration can be increased materially by thorough aeration of the soil with an Aerifier or similar tool.

CHLORDANE, a chlorinated hydrocarbon, is one of the most useful of the newer insecticidal materials because of its effectiveness on a wide variety of insects. It is available commercially as wettable dusts that vary in concentration from 2 to 50 per cent of actual Chlordane. Emulsifiable liquids varying in concentration also are on the market. The dusts can be applied dry with a duster or as a spray. The standard rate of application for grubs and many other turf insects is 10 lb. of actual Chlordane per acre (500 lb. of 2 per cent dust, or 20 lb. of 50 per cent wettable powder). Some insects, such as mole crickets and ants, are killed by dosages as low as 1 to 2 lb. of the actual toxicant per acre. Precautions should be taken against inhaling excessive quantities of the dust. Hands and other exposed portions of the body should be washed thoroughly following its use to avoid possible skin irritation.

D.B.C.P. (Nemagon EC-2, Fumazone 70-E). These materials are approximately 70 per cent emulsions of the same active toxicant for nematode control. When used on established turf they should be mixed with a sufficient volume of water to insure uniform coverage. At least 1 in. of water should be applied immediately after treatment to insure that the material is washed into the soil thoroughly.

DDT is an effective insecticide for the larva (grubs) of the Japanese beetle and many other kinds of soil beetles. It controls chinch bugs, sod webworms, cutworms, and army worms and is useful for checking flies on porches and other parts of the clubhouse. It is available commercially as dusts, wettable powders, and liquid sprays in a wide variety of concentrations. The dusts and wettable powders of higher concentration (50 per cent) are most satisfactory for use on turf. Liquid sprays containing 2 to 10 per cent actual DDT are satisfactory for use around buildings for flies and other pests. Concentrations for use on turf vary with the individual insect to be controlled. Treatments range from 10 to 25 lb. of actual DDT per acre. One hundred pounds of the 10 per cent dust or 20 lb. of the 50 per cent wettable powder contains 10 lb. of actual DDT. Similarly, 250 lb. of 10 per cent dust and 50 lb. of 50 per cent wettable powder supply 25 lb. of actual DDT. Dusts and wettable powders should be used on turf. In some cases the liquid sprays have been injurious to grass because of the oil used as a solvent for the DDT. In applying DDT precautions should be taken not to inhale the dust or to permit excessive quantities to be deposited on the skin.

DIELDRIN can be obtained as a 1.5 per cent dust or a 5.0 per cent granular formulation for dry application. The methods of use of these formulations are the same as for Aldrin. A 50 per cent wettable powder and an emulsifiable concentrate containing 1½ lbs. of toxicant per gal. can be obtained for use as a spray. It is effective for the control of grubs, ants, earthworms, chinch bugs, sod webworms, army- and cutworms, mole crickets, chiggers, and ticks. The rates of treatment vary for different insects (see Appendix Table 19, page 324). It should be thoroughly washed in immediately after application.

HEPTACHLOR can be obtained as a 2.5 per cent dust or granular formulation for dry application, or as a 25 per cent wettable powder and an emulsifiable concentrate containing 2 lbs. of toxicant per gal. for use as a spray. It is most useful for the control of grubs, ants, earthworms, sod webworms, army- and cutworms, and mole crickets. Dry applications and wettable powders are more desirable than emulsions because of the danger of burning the turf with the latter. Thorough watering-in immediately after application is essential for maximum results.

MALATHION is available as a 5 per cent dust for dry application, and as a 25 per cent wettable powder and an emulsifiable concentrate containing 5 lbs. of toxicant per gal. for spraying. It is used primarily for the control of aphids, chiggers, ticks, and leaf hoppers and scales. It is very toxic and special precautions should be taken to avoid inhalation and skin contact. Thorough washing with soap and water after use and before eating or smoking is essential.

MILKY DISEASE is a spore powder prepared from infected grubs of the Japanese beetle. It is specific only for the control of this insect. The powder is spread on the turf and the disease spores infect the beetle grubs which eventually die. Usually, material reductions in beetle populations are not obtained in less than a 3- to 4-year period. Since only one treatment is required, the milky disease has been most useful in eventually reducing infestations in parks and other large areas. It does not act fast enough to be dependable on areas where quick control is needed.

PARATHION is a complex organic thiophosphate. The Connecticut Agriculture Experiment Station obtained excellent results in controlling Japanese beetle grubs with 1 lb. of the actual toxicant per acre. It is available commercially in dusts and wettable powders that vary in concentration from 1 to 25 per cent of the toxicant. When used as a dust it is recommended that the material be washed into the soil thoroughly. Because of its high volatility it loses its strength in soil rapidly at high temperatures. Best results are secured when it is used in cool weather. It is a deadly poison, and extreme care must be used in handling it to avoid inhaling fumes or direct contact on the skin. Although the indications are that Parathion is a powerful insecticide, its poisonous properties and effects must be more thoroughly understood before it can be recommended for general use. Atropine sulfate is a recommended antidote for parathion poisoning.

POISON BAITS. Many specific poisons are mixed with various food materials attractive to insects and rodents. The poisons used include such materials as arsenic and strychnine for mice, ground squirrels, moles, and gophers. Poison baits also are effective for ants, cutworms, mole crickets, and similar insects. Materials and methods of preparing bait mixtures are discussed under control measures for individual insects in the latter part of this chapter.

Control Methods for Individual Insects and Other Pests

Success with insecticides depends on the correct use of the right material for the specific insect to be controlled. Since many insecticides will kill only certain insects, correct identification and a working knowledge of the life cycle and habits of the various pests are essential. These are outlined in the following sections of the chapter. Recommended materials and treatment rates are given in Appendix Table 19, page 324.

Caution. Many insecticides are poisonous when taken internally or may cause skin or eye irritation. The following precautions should be observed to insure safe handling and use:

1. Label all containers clearly.
2. Keep away from children and pets.
3. Follow manufacturer's label directions and observe listed precautions.
4. Avoid inhaling and skin contact.
5. Keep out of eyes.
6. Wash thoroughly with soap and water after use.
7. Clean spray and dusting equipment after use.
8. Avoid treating turf when it is in use.
9. Do not apply when drift might cause injury to people or animals.
10. Keep children and pets off turf until the material has been washed in thoroughly and the grass has dried.
11. Avoid contamination of streams, lakes, or ponds, to protect fish and wild life.

JUNE BEETLES (*Phyllophaga* spp.). More than one hundred species of these beetles are found in the northeastern and north-central part of the United States. The adult beetles are light to dark brown in color and roughly rectangular in shape. They vary in length from about ½ to more than ¾ in. The larva are commonly known as white grubs. The grubs cause serious injury to turf by feeding on the grass roots.

The life cycle of the beetles extends over a 2- to 3-year period. They occur in definite broods, designated as A, B, and C. The term Brood A has been applied to the grub infestation that occurred in 1909 and at 3-year intervals since that time. Similarly, infestations that occurred in 1910 and at subsequent 3-year intervals has been designated as Brood B, and infestations that occurred in 1911 and at 3-year intervals, Brood C. The adult beetles emerge in May or June. After mating they deposit their eggs in the soil at depths of 1 to 8 in. The eggs hatch in 3 to 4 weeks, and the young grubs immediately begin to feed upon organic material and living grass roots in the soil. The fine succulent roots of the bentgrasses seem to be particularly attractive to them. The young grubs feed during the remainder of the first season and burrow deep into the soil over the winter. They come up into the root

FIG. 40. Turf injury caused by June Beetle grubs. (*Courtesy Sewerage Commission, City of Milwaukee.*)

zone in the spring of the second season and feed during the entire summer and early fall. When infestations are heavy, some damage may occur during the late summer of the first season. Ordinarily severe injury occurs beginning in June or early July of the second season. The grubs feed for a short time in the spring of the third season and then pupate, emerging as adults the following spring.

The first evidence of grub injury appears as isolated spots where the grass is brown and dying due to heavy concentrations of grub activity in these areas. Such spots should be examined immediately by lifting the sod. The grubs will be found at a depth of 1 to 3 in. First-season grubs usually are ¼ to less than ½ in. long. Second-season grubs are ¾ to more than 1 in. in length. They are grayish to creamy white in color and curl up when disturbed.

JAPANESE BEETLE (*Papillia japonica*) averages a little less than ½ in. in length. Its head and thorax (shoulders) are greenish, and the hard wing covers are greenish bronze. There are two characteristic white spots on the rear part of the abdomen not covered by the wing covers. The larva or grubs look very much like small grubs of the June beetle. Full-grown specimens average about ½ in. in length. They are grayish-white in color and have a relatively thick body. The head is brownish. The adult beetles lay their eggs in the soil in early July. The eggs hatch in a short time (10 days), and the young grubs immediately start to feed on decaying vegetation and live roots. They continue to feed throughout the remainder of the summer and until freezing temperatures occur in the fall. They winter in the grub stage and feed again in the spring before pupating and emerging as adult beetles usually about mid-June. The adult beetles are strong feeders on many kinds of green foliage. They eat the fleshy parts of the leaves, leaving a lacy network of veins.

Japanese beetle grubs are voracious feeders on the grass roots, and damage to the turf increases rapidly as they develop during the late spring and early summer. Treatments in fall and early spring are the most effective times for preventing serious injury.

ANNUAL WHITE GRUB (*Ochrosidia villosa*) is the larva of a brown beetle that is very similar in appearance to the brown June beetles with 2- to 4-year broods, except that it is somewhat smaller. The adult beetle deposits its eggs in the soil in June and July. The eggs hatch in 19 days, and the grubs are almost full grown by fall. They hibernate deep in the soil over winter and begin feeding in late April or early May. They pupate in late June, and the adult beetles emerge within a few weeks. Control treatments should be applied in late July or early August to kill the young grubs before they cause serious damage.

MOUND-FORMING BEETLES. Two types of beetles are troublesome on greens because of the soil that they throw out of the burrows made by the grubs or adults. The first of these is the southern green June bug (Catinus nitida). They are most numerous in the South but may cause trouble as far north as southern Pennsylvania, Ohio, Indiana, and Illinois. The grubs of this beetle are almost 2 in. long when full grown. They do not feed on living grass roots but on the partially decayed organic matter in the soil. In their search for food they open large burrows and throw mounds on the surface that may be up to 3 in. in diameter. The grubs are easily recognized because of their habit of crawling on their back with the aid of stiff hairs. The adult is a velvety green beetle larger than the brown June beetles. This beetle completes its life cycle in one year. Adults lay their eggs in July, and the grubs hatch out in about 3 weeks. They are active from August to cold weather and again in the spring until May when they pupate.

Mounds also are formed on greens by a small brown beetle (*Bolbocerosoma paretum*) that tunnel into the soil throwing out a small mound of earth similar to an anthill. Its active period usually is limited to a few weeks in midsummer, and it seldom becomes so numerous as to cause serious trouble.

CHINCH BUGS (*Blissus hirtus mont.*) are sucking insects, feeding on the juice from the base of the grass leaves and stems at the crown of the plant. They concentrate in limited areas, adults and young bugs feeding on the same plants until all the available juice has been extracted from the grass in one spot. They work outward from these centers of infestation, destroying the grass as they advance.

The bugs are small and very active. Adults seldom exceed one-fifth of an inch in length. They are brownish-black in color with a pale band across the body. The wings are white and folded over the back in the form of an X. There are two forms, which can be distinguished from each other by the length of the wings. The one has wings that extend to the rear end of the body. The wings of the second form are much shortened, only partially covering the body. The latter type, known as the hairy chinch bug, is the one which causes serious injury to turf in the eastern states. Their average life cycle is 50 days, and there may be from two to five broods depending upon the length of the season. The adult bugs winter in dry grass and other debris that offers protection. Newly hatched bugs are wingless and yellow in color turning to a bright red a few days after hatching. Shortly before changing to the adult form they develop the brownish-black color.

Chinch bugs develop best in dry weather, and injury always is more severe in hot, dry summers. They prefer high, dry locations exposed to direct sunlight. Damage first appears as browning of the grass in localized areas, which is often mistaken for dry-weather injury. They multiply rapidly, and if their presence is not detected early and prompt control measures taken, the grass will be completely killed in constantly expanding areas. The bugs seldom become a problem on greens and other closely clipped and watered areas. Heavy rains also check them. The young chinch bugs die quickly when submerged in water. It may also interfere with egg laying and hatching.

In making spray treatments, sufficient water must be used to insure thorough penetration through the turf to the surface of the soil. When dusts are applied they should be watered sufficiently to get the material down to the base of the leaves and stems where the bugs are feeding. One application of any of the recommended insecticides is sufficient to control the insects for at least one full season.

LEAF HOPPERS (*Cicadellidae* spp.). Several kinds of leaf hoppers infest turf and at times may develop in such large numbers as to cause serious injury. They are small green or brownish insects that average less than one-fifth of an inch in length. They have broad triangular heads, and the body tapers sharply to the tips of the wings in the shape of a wedge. The eyes are prominent and bulge from the sides of the head. Their rear pair of legs is strong and powerful like those of a grasshopper and enables them to make long leaps. Leaf hoppers are sucking insects and damage grass by sucking the juices from leaves and stems. When heavy infestations occur on new seedings, they may cause such serious injury that complete replanting is necessary. They seldom produce serious injury to established turf, but they are suspected carriers of fungus diseases. The damage which they cause often is mistaken for injury by disease, dry weather, or other causes. Turf that is attacked heavily becomes discolored. The leaves have wilted or discolored blotches and sometimes curl or are misshapen. Where infestations are so heavy that control measures are required, treatments with DDT or Chlordane at a rate of 10 lb. of actual DDT or Chlordane per acre are effective.

SOD WEBWORMS (*Crambus* spp.) are the larva of medium to small moths that are brownish gray to dull gray in color. There are between 60 and 70 kinds of webworms in the United States. Only about a dozen of these occur in such large numbers that they cause serious injury to grass. The first flight of moths usually occurs in May. Successive generations occur at irregular periods, depending upon environmental conditions and the species of moths that are present. The eggs are dropped into the grass by the moths while on the wing. They hatch into small worms in 1 week to 10 days. The young worms begin to feed on the grass leaves immediately. They construct tunnels covered with pieces of grass and their own excrement and lined with silk. There may be three or more generations or broods in a season. It is not uncommon to find worms of various sizes as well as adult moths in the same area.

Webworms produce injured spots on the turf that are similar in appearance to the dollar spot disease and which are sometimes mistaken for it. During periods of dry weather when unwatered turf is brown and dormant the moths tend to concentrate over the succulent grass on greens and drop their eggs in it, so that large numbers of worms develop in such areas.

The tunnels constructed by the worms protect them from the effects of insecticides that are watered-in immediately after application. The best control is obtained when treatments are made in the late afternoon and the turf is not watered for at least 24 hrs. Precautions in the use of poisonous insecticides as outlined on page 248 should be observed.

CUTWORMS (*Phalaenidae* spp.) are the larval stage of night-flying moths. Several kinds are troublesome pests on golf greens.

The full-grown worms average about 1½ in. in length. They vary in color from a greenish-brown to dark brown on the back, with the underside usually a lighter shade. The moths lay their eggs and the young worms hatch in late summer. They feed until cold weather and burrow into the soil to hibernate during the winter. They emerge the following spring and feed until early summer when they pupate and change to the adult moths. Usually, there is only one generation of worms per season in the North. In the South two generations, and sometimes three, are common.

Cutworms hide in burrows in the turf during the day and feed at night. They damage the turf by cutting off the grass stems and leaves close to the surface of the ground. Injury usually occurs in semicircular scars that are 3 to 4 in. long and 1 in. or more wide. If these areas are carefully probed with a knife blade, the worms often can be found in their burrows.

When either wet or dry treatments are made, the turf should not be watered until the poison has been on the leaves for one, or preferably, two nights. Late afternoon is the best time for making the treatments. Since the material is not washed off of the leaves, it is important that the precautions in the use of poisonous insecticides, as listed on page 348, be fully observed.

ARMY WORMS (*Phalaenidae* spp.) are a species of cutworms. They develop in great numbers under favorable conditions and move over infested areas in large masses, eating the succulent grass or other vegetation as they advance. They are the larva of night-flying moths that tend to concentrate on restricted areas to lay their eggs. The full-grown caterpillars are almost naked (without hair) and are similar in size and appearance to cutworms, except somewhat thinner bodied.

The fall army worm causes serious damage to turf in the South during late summer and fall when grass is greener and more succulent than other vegetation. Although the insect does not survive the winter north of Florida, the moths migrate northward during the summer and produce successive generations progressively farther north. They may cause serious damage to turf in late August as far north as Maryland.

Control materials listed in Appendix Table 19, page 324, can be used either as sprays or dusts. The dusts may be applied alone or mixed with fertilizer. Where the worms are to be controlled on large areas it sometimes is possible to check them by applying the insecticide in a 10- to 20-ft. strip ahead of and across their line of advance.

MOLE CRICKETS (*Scapteriscus* spp.) cause serious injury by feeding on the grass roots. Where infestations are heavy, they can destroy large areas of turf in a short time. They are warm-climate insects, the most serious damage occurring in the South Atlantic states. The full-grown cricket is approximately 1¼ in. long and is brown in color. The body is slender, and the front feet are broad and shovellike for digging. They have well-developed wings and can fly swiftly. The adult cricket lays its eggs in the soil at a depth of about 2½ in. in late July and early August. The eggs hatch in approximately 3 weeks into young crickets (nymphs) that closely resemble the adult except that they are much smaller and are wingless. The nymphs have ravenous appetites and feed voraciously on living grass roots and other organic materials in the soil.

ANTS are troublesome because they make mounds that spoil the putting surface on greens and destroy the grass roots and leaves around the hills. There are many different species, varying in size, activity, and food habits. The mounds which they construct consist of the soil excavated from the subterranean tunnels in which they live. Each colony has a complete social organization consisting of a queen and the workers. The latter gather food for the egg-laying queen and the larvae in the nests. Effective control measures must be designed to kill the queen and larvae which will develop into queens, so that egg laying and perpetuation of the colony will be eliminated.

All of the insecticides recommended for grub control also are effective for ants. Where only a few scattered colonies are present they can be eradicated by spot spraying or dusting the material on the hills and watering it into the nests. If many hills are present, the best method is a broadcast application over the entire area, followed by immediate watering to wash the material down. Treatments usually are effective for periods of 4 to 6 weeks, after which reapplications will be necessary. If all areas surrounding greens are treated, including traps, aprons, fairways, and roughs, for a minimum distance of 50 ft. from the edge of the green, re-infestations can be prevented for reasonably long periods.

EARTHWORMS aid in aerating the soil and thus are beneficial to turf. However, the casts which they deposit on the surface of greens interfere with play to such an extent that worm eradication is necessary.

The same materials used for grubs will control the common species of earthworms (*Lumbricus* spp.). Treatment rates should be approximately double the rates used for grubs. If the soil is dry, the area should be watered thoroughly before the treatment is applied. Water also should be applied after treatment. If infestations are heavy and quick relief is needed, temporary control can be secured by spraying with corrosive sublimate at a rate of 1 to 2 oz. per 1,000 sq. ft. This treatment will be effective only if the area has been well watered beforehand so that the worms will be close to the surface. Treatments are most effective when made in the early morning of a cloudy day.

The tropical earthworm (*Pheretima hupeinsis* Michaelson) is a serious pest on some golf courses in the Northeastern states. Other common names are stinkworm, eelworm, African earthworm, and exotic earthworm. It is smaller than the common earthworm and each body segment has a continuous ring of minute bristles. It is most active during periods of warm moist weather and deposits casts on the greens almost continuously at such times, making constant poling or brushing necessary. The worms are much more difficult to control than the common kinds of earthworms. Treatment rates of toxic materials must be approximately double the quantities used for the common species and it often is necessary to make repeat applications within a week to ten days following the initial treatment to secure adequate control.

FRIT FLY (*Oscinella frit*) is a small insect about 1/16 in. long and one-third as wide that causes occasional damage to turf in the Northeastern and Northcentral sections of the country. It works in the crowns of the grass plants and when infestations are heavy, may cause turf to have a chlorotic and weak appearance, as though suffering from drought or disease. Its presence is easily detected, as it seems to be attracted to white and will light on a golf ball within seconds after it comes to rest. Insecticides that are effective for sod webworms and chinch bugs will control it. Since several broods may be produced over a season, repeat treatments may be necessary if heavy infestations occur.

SCALES (Bermudagrass, Rhodesgrass, and Ruths). The adult forms of these insects are from 1/16 to ⅛ in. in diameter. The body usually is dark colored and covered with a whitish secretion. They concentrate at the joints of runners and the crowns of plants and also may be found in loose surface soil. They are sucking insects and when once attached to the vegetation, do not move. They infest a number of species of grasses but are most common on Bermudagrass and Rhodesgrass. Infested turf turns yellow and, if the insects are not controlled, may eventually be killed.

GROUND PEARL (*Margarodes* spp.) are scale insects that may vary from sand grain size to 1/16 in. in diameter. They are roughly cylindrical in shape, with a whitish covering. In this stage they attack the grass roots, sucking the juices from them. They occur most commonly on centipedegrass but will attack many other species. The first evidence of injury is a yellowing of the turf, followed by browning and eventual death. Damage is particularly severe on turf suffering from drought. No insecticide has given effective control. Good cultural practices, including regular watering in drought periods, and liberal fertilization, enable the grass to grow ahead of serious injury.

NEMATODES are wormlike organisms that are very small to microscopic in size. A number of species have been found to be parasitic on grasses, attacking the small feeder roots and causing various types of damage. The condition known as Yellow Tuft of bentgrasses has been traced to nematode infestation. This is characterized by the development of chlorotic masses of dwarfed growth at the joints of stolons. Damage also may appear as a gradual loss of vigor. The turf thins out and will not respond to watering, fertilization, and other normal maintenance practices designed to stimulate growth. As damage progresses serious wilting occurs and both foliage and roots deteriorate or die off completely.

Since nematode injury is similar in many instances to damage from other causes, diagnosis often is extremely difficult. If infestations are suspected it is suggested that a sample of soil from the injured area be sent to a competent authority for examination. In sampling soil for this purpose, several cores should be taken to rooting depth from different locations immediately bordering the region of heaviest injury. The composite sample should consist of at least a pint of soil with a good moisture content. It should be packaged for shipment in such a way that it will not dry out in transit.

Soil sterilization prior to seeding in areas found to be infested with injurious species of nematodes is an effective method of control. The Florida Agricultural Experiment Station has reported good results with several sterilizing materials: Methyl Bromide, D.D., Chloropicrin, and E.D.B. These chemicals also are effective for sterilizing top-dressings and composts. The manufacturer's directions should be followed carefully in making treatments. Injury to established turf has been reduced materially by chemical treatment. The most effective materials have been the proprietary compounds Nemagon and Fumazone. Treatment rates are given in Appendix Table 19, page 324.

CONTROLLING ANIMAL PESTS ON THE GOLF COURSE. In addition to insects that destroy grass by feeding upon it, various kinds of small burrowing animals create ridges, mounds, or similar structures that seriously affect the maintenance and playing quality of turf. The most troublesome members of this group are moles, mice, ground squirrels, and gophers. Turf also is damaged by a second group of animals that tear it up in search of insects that form a large part of their food. Skunks, armadillos, and birds destroy turf in this way in their search for grubs and worms.

Moles make unsightly ridges in turf areas by tunneling through the soil just below the surface of the ground in their search for worms and grubs on which they feed. If there are no worms or grubs in the turf, the moles go elsewhere in search of food. One of the most effective means of control is elimination of the insects on which they feed.

Mice work beneath the snow in winter, making long runways and numerous holes in the turf. When these occur on greens and tees, it is often necessary to do extensive patching and repair work the following spring to true the surfaces and make them satisfactory for play.

In some sections small ground squirrels burrow into the soil under turf, opening holes and sometimes building unsightly and troublesome mounds of earth.

The pocket gopher is a serious pest in the western and south-central states. They construct runways in the soil that usually are 4 to 8 in. below the surface. They work out from the main runways in short laterals, throwing up mounds of earth that destroy the grass, obstruct play, and seriously interfere with mowing and other maintenance operations.

Skunks and armadillos dig into the sod, scarring and tearing it up in search of grubs and other insects on which they feed. As in the case of moles, the best method of eliminating injury by these animals is to eradicate the insects on which they feed.

Trapping and poisoning are the methods in most general use for eradicating troublesome animal pests. Trapping must be adjusted to the kind of animal and its habits. Many types of traps have been devised, such as the harpoon trap for moles and the Macabee gopher trap. Trapping ordinarily is effective only when infestations are light. Where the animals occur in large colonies, as with mice and ground squirrels, poisoning is more effective.

A poison bait that is suitable for both mice and ground squirrels can be prepared as follows: Mix 1 tablespoonful of gloss starch in ½ teacup of cold water to make a thin paste. Mix 1 oz. of powdered strychnine (alkaloid) with 1 oz. of baking soda and stir into the starch to make a smooth creamy paste. Stir in ¼ pt. of heavy corn sirup and 1 tablespoonful of glycerine. Apply to 12 qt. of whole wheat or oats or to 20 qt. of crushed whole oats and mix thoroughly to coat each kernel. The whole grain is better for ground squirrels and the crushed oats for mice. The bait is placed in poison stations that are easily accessible without exposing it to the weather. The stations can be constructed with square pieces of 8-in. boards separated by two side walls or 1½-in. strips so that a shallow box open at opposite sides is formed. The bait is placed inside the box on the bottom board. Glass jars or drain tile also can be used as stations. This bait also is effective for gophers. It should be dropped through a hole made in the main runway which is closed after the bait is introduced.

Moles, gophers, and squirrels sometimes may be exterminated by forcing various kinds of lethal gas into their runways or burrows. Cyanogas has been used successfully for this purpose. It is forced into the runways at 5- or 6-ft. intervals with a special type of foot pump. Cyanogas is a deadly poison, and care must be exercised not to breathe the fumes. A teaspoonful of carbon bisulfide poured into the openings of burrows or into holes made in the runways at 5- or 6-ft. spacings sometimes is effective. Carbon monoxide fumes from the exhaust of an automobile may be introduced into runways by attaching a length of hose to the exhaust pipe and inserting the opposite end into the mouth of the burrow or in holes made in the runways. Gassing is most effective when the soil is moist and prevents rapid diffusion out of the burrows.

11

Golf Course Operation

Successful operation of a golf course consists essentially of (1) effective organization and sound budgeting of available funds, (2) efficient management of labor and equipment, and (3) maintenance of accurate records of costs and operations. The plan of management is identical for any part of the country, whether the course is private, daily fee, municipal, college, or industrial. Differences occur only in the details of operation. These are due to variations in course design, standards of quality, available funds, and length of the playing season.

Organization for Management

THE PRIVATE COURSE. The private-club course usually is operated by a green committee, through a superintendent. The green committee is an elected or appointed group of club members, ordinarily five to seven in number. It is directly responsible for the club's interest in the golf course. The chairman customarily is a member of the board of directors of the club. A green-committee chairman should always have an understudy in training to take his place. The golf course superintendent is a paid employee of the club. His chief responsibility is to plan and direct the operations necessary for maintenance and improvement of the course.

The green committee is the unit in the club organization that is accountable to the membership for course operation. One of its important functions is to ensure the budgeting of sufficient funds for adequate maintenance. It determines policy in matters relating to course improvements or where extraordinary and unforeseen expenditures are involved. A functioning green committee is alert to just complaints and suggestions for improvement of playing conditions, by the members. It is in a position to keep the membership informed on the necessity for maintenance operations that may temporarily interfere with play or the reason for other abnormal conditions on the course. Occasionally, through long experience, the chairman of a green committee will obtain considerable practical knowledge and consult closely with the superintendent in the day-by-day management of the course. Such a combination is greatly to be desired, but it is generally well to guard against inexpert interference with the technical work of the superintendent. Course management is an exacting and complicated profession, and when a trained and competent superintendent is employed the green committee would be well advised to give careful consideration to his recommendations and to leave the management of the course in his hands.

Where sufficient funds are available, complete responsibility for course management should be placed in the hands of a full-time superintendent, always subject, of course, to the direction of the green committee. Maintenance of the modern golf course requires a wide range of knowledge and experience. This demands the services of a trained man. The superintendent is a specialist in golf-course management. His qualifications include good executive ability and a thorough working knowledge of the technical phases of growing turf to meet the requirements of golf. He must be able to handle labor, to prepare budget estimates, and to maintain adequate operating schedules and necessary records. The good superintendent has a faculty for the orderliness and neatness that are essential in the well-kept course. He has a fair knowledge of mechanics and is capable of keeping expensive equipment in repair at a minimum cost. He understands the requirements of the game and is alert to foresee impending trouble before playing conditions are impaired. It is his responsibility to maintain the best playing conditions possible on all areas of the course throughout the playing season, economically and efficiently. A broad knowledge of all the phases of turf culture is essential. He has acquired this by experience and by keeping abreast of new developments through published information, attendance at turf conferences, and professional meetings where turf problems are discussed.

On some courses it is sometimes the practice, because of budget limitations, to combine the positions of golf professional and course superintendent. The individual so employed should be competent in both fields and should be provided with sufficient assistance; two widely different fields of activity are involved. Obviously, one individual cannot provide the same complete type of professional service and high degree of course excellence as where separate competent supervision is provided in each field. Thus, an individual doing both jobs should have had sound training in both lines and exceptional managerial ability. A good course superintendent does not necessarily make a good golf professional, and vice versa.

DAILY-FEE COURSE. Fundamentally, there is little difference between the private-club golfer and the patron of other golf courses. Each desires a golf course which will provide a fair test of golf under good playing conditions. Both want the best that can be provided for a reasonable and specific expenditure. Organization for management of the daily-fee course must consider that patrons will choose the course which furnishes the most attractive combinations of construction and playing conditions.

The general organization necessary for the management of a daily-fee course is usually much more simple than for any other type. A fee course is almost always a business operated for the purpose of profit. The level of maintenance is determined by the potential income. Since golf is the only activity which is considered, there is no necessity for pressures from groups with other interests such as are sometimes found in private clubs. Consequently, the management problems of a fee course are much less involved. The superintendent usually is completely responsible for setting up an organization which can produce satisfactory playing conditions that will attract the maximum number of golfers and will produce sufficient revenue for a reasonable return plus maintenance and improvement costs.

MUNICIPAL, COLLEGE AND OTHER COURSES. Sound organization for operation of courses of these types should be the same as for private and daily-fee courses. Management should be in the hands of a competent superintendent. He should be given full responsibility for operation within the limits of general policy formulated by the municipality or institution. All too often these courses are managed by remote control from an office that has little knowledge of requirements for good playing conditions. The situation is further aggravated when policy with regard to expenditures, labor, and other matters is based on expediency, rather than on actual needs. Courses of this kind will improve in quality and provide more enjoyable golf only when a competent superintendent is given complete authority to operate within an adequate budget. Good maintenance is impossible when a course must be operated on a day-to-day basis with no assurance that necessary labor, supplies, and equipment will be provided.

Budgets

The preparation of the annual operating budget is an important function of course management. No set formula can be used for all golf courses. The problems and requirements vary between different courses and on the same course in different years. The first consideration in setting up a budget is how much can be spent in any particular year for course operation. If funds are limited, the time of budget preparation is the time to decide what degree of excellence of playing conditions can be obtained with the funds available and what operations must be neglected or omitted. In such instances, the superintendent, in preparing a tentative budget, must use good judgment in retaining items of fundamental importance, while omitting those of less basic value. Provision always should be made for unforeseeable items which may be caused by unusual weather conditions, unexpected prevalence of disease or insect damage, or other factors.

Individual items of the budget should be easily interpreted and should be consistent from year to year, to permit comparisons. They may be listed in detail or consolidated. While there is some variation from course to course, certain items normally appear in all budgets. The most important of these are presented in the following discussion to emphasize the various details which must be taken into consideration, both in budget preparation and in course operation.

A. Supervision
  1. Golf-course superintendent's salary. Add allowances for expenses such as car expense, turf conferences, association meetings, short courses, subscription to trade journals, etc.
  2. Assistant superintendent's or foreman's salary, if any.

B. Labor
  1. Number of regular workers required with some itemization of their individual assignments to duty, their established or suggested wage rates, and total estimated cost for the year. Permanent key employees of long standing or particular merit, whom the superintendent hopes to hold, should be listed individually by name.
  2. Supplementary workmen employed on a part time or seasonal basis or for special improvement jobs should be listed at their total estimated cost per year.

C. Equipment
  1. Maintenance and repair of existing equipment
     a. Parts (including any additional mechanic's or laborer's time for overhauling not included in "labor" above). This item could be further broken down under the headings of various types of equipment. Major items of repair such as complete overhauling of trucks, tractors, or mowers should be listed in individual amounts.
     b. Painting.
     c. Gasoline, oil, grease, electric current for operating motors, lights, water system, etc.
     d. Contingency allowance for unforeseen items of repair, maintenance, or replacement.
     e. Maintenance, repair, and replacement of tee and green equipment: flags and poles, cups, tee markers, fairway markers, tee benches, ball washers and soap, tee towels, trash receivers, water coolers or drinking fountains, sprinklers, hose, etc.

2. Replacement of existing equipment and funds for new equipment.
   a. Depreciation allowance for each piece of major equipment. The probable life of each item should be estimated and allowance made for the proper amount of depreciation per year based on current replacement costs. By this method, a yearly sinking fund for an orderly replacement of equipment can be set up so that replacement can be made when it is economically feasible to do so or when improved equipment is available.
   b. New equipment recommended. Each major item should be listed separately with a concise statement as to the need for it. This may be further amplified by discussion with the chairman of the green committee or other responsible individual.
   c. Small tools and miscellaneous items of small equipment.

D. Maintenance and repair of buildings and structures. List here all foreseeable items of maintenance and repair and proposed additions, if any, to any and all buildings and structures used in course operation, such as equipment barns, shelters, bridges, steps, retaining walls, fences, etc.

E. Supplies. This item should be broken down into such items as top-dressing materials (if these are purchased), sand for traps, itemized lists of kinds, quantities, and estimated costs of required seeds, fertilizers, lime, insecticides, fungicides, weed-control chemicals, etc. A further breakdown is often desirable, showing the estimated amounts, rate, and number of applications on greens, tees, fairways, roughs, and other areas under maintenance. Detailed estimates of these items are necessary in any case, to enable the superintendent to arrive at the required total amounts. Their inclusion in the tentative budget is desirable to inform the green committee and membership how the various items are to be used and why the suggested supplies are necessary.

F. Maintenance of club grounds and landscaped areas. It is usually advisable to list separately the cost of labor, materials, equipment, and similar items necessary for the maintenance of the club grounds, landscaped areas, ornamental plantings, tennis courts, and swimming pools. These costs often are high and do not constitute a legitimate charge against the cost of course operation.

G. Course improvements, major repairs or changes, and extraordinary items. This section should include itemized costs of proposed improvements and other extraordinary items approved by the green committee or other responsible officials.

Management of Labor and Equipment

LABOR. Labor for golf-course maintenance operations is a major problem because of the acute shortages of trained workmen that exist in all parts of the country. Course superintendents and club officials should make a determined effort to attract a better class of steady workmen. Work requirements on courses should be analyzed carefully so that a minimum crew of reliable workmen can be maintained permanently at wages and with other benefits commensurate to other forms of employment in the locality. This skeleton crew of trained permanent workers can be augmented when necessary by students or part-time laborers of a less permanent nature.

It is difficult to set up any general standard as to how many men are needed to maintain the average 18-hole golf course properly. Much depends upon the design and physical characteristics of the course in relation to adaptability to efficient maintenance with modern mechanized equipment. Other variable factors are the number and extent of sand-trap areas to be maintained and the degree of excellence of playing conditions which the particular membership expects and for which funds are available.

High-quality maintenance on the golf course depends upon the carefulness, interest, common sense, and knowledge of each individual workman. Training and supervision of the workers is the superintendent's responsibility. It is one of his most important jobs. He must be able to evaluate the capabilities of his men and assign each to the duties for which he is best qualified or can best be trained. For example, one or more of the men with mechanical ability should be trained to care for all motorized and mechanical equipment.

In assigning duties to the labor crew it is best to assemble the entire group at the start of the day. The day's routine should be outlined to the entire group so that each man knows the general program as well as his individual duties and is informed about special details such as golf parties, weather forecast, etc., which may influence the working schedule.

EQUIPMENT. The equipment required to maintain a golf course properly and efficiently with a minimum of hand labor will vary somewhat from course to course, depending upon the topography, architecture, and physical conditions. The following list includes those items which ordinarily are required on a golf course where a high standard of maintenance is essential.

GENERAL MAINTENANCE EQUIPMENT

1	Truck (usually a dump truck)
2–3	Tractors (mowing)
1	Power sprayer
1–2	7-gang fairway mowers
1	7-gang rough mower
1	30- to 36-in. power scythe
3–4	Power green mowers
1–2	Power tee mowers
1–2	Power mowers (general purpose)
1	10-ft. fertilizer distributor (tractor drawn)
1	3-ft. fertilizer distributor (hand)
1	Rotary hoe-type cultivator
	Cup cutter, cup setter, soil profile cutter, bamboo or steel poles, sufficient shovels, rakes, brushes, sod lifters, and edgers, etc.
	Drag mats (hand for greens, larger for tractor use)
1	Seeder (wheelbarrow, hopper, or drill)
1	Sod cutter
1	Soil aerator (green)
1	Soil aerator (fairway, 3-gang)
1	Vertical mower
1	Soil shredder
1	Power screen

SHOP EQUIPMENT

Hoist
Mower grinder
Air compressor
Bench grinder
Electric drill
Welding equipment
Paint spray equipment
Plumbing equipment
Carpenter equipment
Mechanical equipment
Tree-trimming equipment

SPECIAL EQUIPMENT

Irrigation System

Pumps and motors
Water lines with connecting valves
Sprinklers
Hose
Well or water-supply equipment
Drinking fountains or water coolers

Drainage System

Tile
Manholes
Catch basins

Golf Equipment

Green flags
Green poles
Tee markers
Ball washers
Tee benches
Hole cups

Superintendent's Office

Desk
File
Typewriter
Adding machine
Record books
Record forms

EQUIPMENT MAINTENANCE AND REPAIR. The maintenance and repair of equipment is one of the most important items of golf-course operation, particularly in this day of widespread use of power mowers and other mechanized equipment. It is imperative to have one or more men on the course with some mechanical ability who can be made responsible for the everyday care and maintenance and for the overhauling of all equipment. Each mower and tractor operator should be held responsible for the cleaning, lubrication, and everyday care of the equipment he uses, but few are competent to make repairs and adjustments of mowers or motors. The necessary adjustments, mower settings, and repairs should be the responsibility of the mechanic or of the superintendent. Personal interest and pride of the workers who regularly operate the equipment is the best insurance for economical and efficient upkeep. Numerous operators for any one machine results in loss of interest in the machine and divided responsibility for its care. Frequent painting helps greatly to keep pride alive.

Where equipment dealers are not close at hand, an adequate stock of the most needed replacement parts should be kept on hand at the course and a regular check up made of the parts inventory to keep it up to date. Good care of equipment is even more important in areas where year-round operation occurs and the slack winter season is not available to overhaul and rehabilitate the equipment completely.

The primary factors to be considered in maintaining all equipment are inspection, cleaning, lubrication, adjustment, operation, and storage.

Repairing should be done with regard to the following factors: Worn or broken parts should be replaced when needed. A major repair program should occur during the off season where possible. A major portion of repairs should be done by regular employees to promote familiarity with the machines.

Equipment Replacement. It is false economy to operate machinery beyond its period of usefulness. Replacement of parts is always costly, and when a machine reaches the point where it must be continually repaired and adjusted to keep it in operation it is more economical to discard it and replace it with a new unit. A machine which continually breaks down during the day's assignment is doubly expensive, as in addition to the repair cost it fails to accomplish the needed work. The economy of good equipment can be readily demonstrated by cost records of repairs and loss of time. If yearly depreciation on all major equipment units is properly set up in the budget and this amount is reserved for replacements, the problem can be greatly simplified.

Records and Accounts

Records of Day-to-day Operations. Various methods of keeping accurate daily records of course operations are used by efficient superintendents. Such records are important for the part they play in acquainting the green committee and the membership with the problems of course maintenance. It provides a good picture of operation activities and costs. Accurate records greatly simplify the preparation of a comprehensive budget and report. They provide a continuing check on the efficiency of each worker and tend to eliminate the possible neglect of important day-to-day operations. They constitute an itemized record of expenditures for the entire season. Substantial economies often can be worked out by a careful study of these daily records and their summaries. In sections or during periods where maintenance is routine and does not change to any marked extent from day to day, weekly spot checks usually will supply sufficiently accurate records of operations.

While many methods have been used with varying success, some sort of printed form showing the usual operations should be provided and filled out each day by all workmen. In some instances the same form can be used as a time sheet. A workman's daily time sheet form, designed by the United States Golf Association Green Section, is illustrated on page 272. This may be summarized for each day on a form such as the one shown on page 273. With necessary changes to conform with established bookkeeping systems, they can be used as a guide for the development of forms to meet any particular case.

RECORDS OF COURSE CONDITIONS. In addition to these records, the superintendent should keep records throughout the year of the dates, amounts, and areas of all applications of fertilizers, topdressings, seedings, fungicide, insecticide, and weed-eradication treatments. These records should be correlated with periodical evaluations of the condition of greens, tees, fairways, etc.

COST ACCOUNTS. Maintenance of adequate cost accounts will greatly simplify preparation of budgets and seasonal and annual reports. Accurate, businesslike records often, more than anything else, contribute to the status of the superintendent in the viewpoint of the club executives and membership. Records are of value only when used. To make them worth the time required to keep them, the superintendent must continually attempt to interpret them in terms of trying to reduce costs and improve methods. Various methods are in use for keeping records of course operations and costs. These usually are condensed from daily records on some type of monthly form which summarizes all operations. They may be broken down further to show labor and equipment operation on separate sheets. The summaries should cover the same items carried on the daily time cards and show the totals for each day of the month.

WORKMAN'S DAILY TIME SHEET

Date____________________

Name ____

Hrs.	Operation	Hrs.	Operation
	Greens		Rough
	____*Mowing*		____*Mowing*
	____*Poling*		____*Trimming*
	____*Irrigating*		____*Weed control*
	____*Change cups*		____*Other*
	____*Fertilizing*		Woodland
	____*Cultivating*		____*Brush control*
	____*Vert. mowing*		____*Tree care*
	____*Topdressing*		____*Mowing*
	____*Spraying*		____*Other*
	____*Other*		Swampland or bog
	Green collars		____*Drainage*
	____*Mowing*		____*Weed control*
	____*Irrigating*		____*Other*
	____*Fertilizing*		Nursery—Grass
	____*Spraying*		____*Planting*
	____*Cultivating*		____*Mowing*
	____*Other*		____*Trimming*
	Green aprons		____*Spraying*
	____*Mowing*		____*Irrigating*
	____*Irrigating*		____*Fertilizing*
	____*Cultivating*		____*Other*
	____*Spraying*		Nursery—Trees, etc.
	____*Fertilizing*		____*Planting*
	____*Other*		____*Spraying*
	Fairways		____*Irrigating*
	____*Mowing*		____*Fertilizing*
	____*Irrigating*		____*Cultivating*
	____*Fertilizing*		____*Other*
	____*Cultivating*		Water hazards
	____*Spraying*		____*Trimming*
	____*Other*		____*Weed control*
	Tees		____*Other*
	____*Mowing*		Bunkers—Sand
	____*Irrigating*		____*Raking*
	____*Fertilizing*		____*Weed control*
	____*Repair*		____*Trimming & edging*
	____*Cultivating*		____*Other*
	____*Spraying*		Bunkers—Grass
	____*Ball washers*		____*Mowing*
	____*Other*		____*Other*
	Tee slopes		Misc. maint.
	____*Mowing*		____*Equipment*
	____*Irrigating*		____*Roads*
	____*Fertilizing*		____*Service bldgs.*
	____*Spraying*		____*Benches, shelters*
	____*Cultivating*		____*Other*
	____*Other*		

Workman's Daily Time Report

Date ____________________

Name ____

Operation	Labor, hr.	Remarks
Greens		
Tees		
Fairways		
Rough		
Traps		
Landscaping		
Clubhouse		
Clubhouse grounds		
Equipment		
Structures		
Water system		
Drainage		
Construction		
Miscellaneous		
Total hours		

Gasoline and Oil Report

Date
Equipment No.
Gal. gasoline

Qt. oil
Serviced by
Remarks:

SEASON SUMMARY. At the end of each year a summary can be prepared from the monthly records to give a complete picture of at least the high lights of the season's operations and costs. This should be kept to a workable minimum. Summaries can be condensed to totals of labor and equipment operation on the various course areas, as greens, fairways, etc., or they can be further itemized for the various types of activities, such as mowing, watering, etc.

The items of cost account summaries should conform to those of the budget. They usually cover the following:

Salaries and wages
Materials
Repairs
Services (power, water, telephone, etc.)
New equipment

Cost account summaries are very useful as a guide in preparing annual budgets for course operation. The totals will vary widely for different courses, depending on the maintenance standards, physical character, and bookkeeping system of each. Unless these are identical, cost comparisons between different courses are not valid and can lead only to unfair and often dangerous interpretations of operating efficiency.

Appendix

Glossary of Fertilizer, Liming and Soil-amendment Materials

(*Definitions published by permission of Association of Official Agricultural Chemists from "Official and Tentative Methods of Analysis")

*Acidulated fish tankage (acidulated fish scrap) is the rendered product derived from fish and treated with sulfuric acid. (Contains 4.0 to 6.5 per cent nitrogen and 3 to 6 per cent phosphoric acid.)

*Activated Sludge. Raw sewage, mixed with about 25 per cent by volume of the current make of activated sludge, is distributed to large aeration tanks in the bottom of which are placed porous plates through which air is forced to produce a continuous stream of tiny bubbles. After about 6 hr. contact, the action of the aerobic (living in air) organisms causes the organic matter to coagulate. This mixture of sewage and activated sludge (mixed liquor) then passes the settling tanks in which the coagulated sludge settles to the bottom and the purified effluent flows out at the top. The sludge can be digested in tanks to reduce bulk and be disposed of; or it can be filtered, dried, screened, and sold as fertilizer.

Dried activated sludge is a nitrogenous material of good quality and shows satisfactory availability by both the neutral and the alkaline permanganate methods.

Approximate analysis:

Nitrogen (N)	4.1–6.4%
Phosphoric acid (P_2O_5).........	2.5–4.0%

Dried activated sludge is produced in marketable quantities by the Sewerage Commission of the City of Milwaukee and sold for direct use under the trade name Milorganite (which see). It is also being produced by the Sanitary District of Chicago and sold under the name of Nitroganic to fertilizer mixers. A limited quantity is made and sold by the city of Houston, Texas, under the trade name Hu-Actinite.

The AOAC has adopted as official the following definition: "*Activated sewage products* are made from sewage freed from grit and coarse solids and aerated after being inoculated with microorganisms. The resulting flocculated organic matter is withdrawn from the tanks, filtered with or without the aid of coagulants, dried in rotary kilns, ground and screened."

ALUMINUM SULFATE (Alum, $Al_2(SO_4)_3 \cdot 18H_2O$). Made by treating bauxite with sulfuric acid. Sometimes used to acidify soils for azaleas, rhododendron, and other acid-loving plants.

AMMONIA (NH_3). A gas containing 82.25 per cent nitrogen and 17.75 per cent hydrogen. Produced as a by-product of coke ovens and gas plants. Prepared by absorbing the gas in water (ammonia liquor) or by combining it with sulfuric acid (sulfate of ammonia). Made in large quantities by combining nitrogen of air with hydrogen under high pressure and temperature.

AMMONIA LIQUOR (NH_4OH). Ammonia gas absorbed in water contains 25 to 30 per cent ammonia (approximately 20 to 25 per cent Nitrogen).

*AMMONIATED SUPERPHOSPHATE. The product obtained when superphosphate is treated with ammonia or with a solution containing free ammonia and other forms of nitrogen dissolved therein.

AMMONIUM CHLORIDE (Sal-ammoniac, NH_4Cl). Ammonium salt made by evaporating a solution of ammonia and hydrochloric acid. Contains approximately 26 per cent nitrogen. Leaves a chlorine residue in the soil.

AMMONIUM CITRATE [$(NH_4)_3C_6H_5O_7$]. Salt of ammonia and citric acid used to determine "available" phosphoric acid in fertilizers. The water-soluble plus the citrate-soluble phosphoric acid in a fertilizer is regarded as the portion which plants can use.

AMMONIUM NITRATE (NH_4NO_3). The salt of ammonia and nitric acid. Contains both ammonia and nitrate nitrogen. The pure product contains 35 per cent nitrogen. It absorbs moisture rapidly and will cake rapidly unless coated with a suitable protective material. Used in mixtures with dolomite and in solutions with ammonia and water.

AMMONIUM PHOSPHATE. (Monoammonium phosphate, $(NH_4)H_2PO_4$; Diammonium phosphate, $(NH_4)_2HPO_4$). Prepared by mixing the proper amounts of phosphoric acid and ammonia or of phosphoric acid, sulfuric acid, and ammonia and evaporating the solution. The commercial product (Ammo-Phos) is available in two grades, containing 11 per cent nitrogen and 48 per cent phosphoric acid or 16 per cent nitrogen and 20 per cent phosphoric acid, respectively.

*Ammonium Sulfate [$(NH_4)_2SO_4$]. Commercial ammonium sulfate is composed chiefly of ammonium sulfate. It shall contain not less than 20.5 per cent nitrogen. (It is water soluble, and the nitrogen quickly becomes available for plant use. It leaves an acid residue in the soil which must be corrected by lime to prevent development of excess soil acidity which may injure turf.)

Ammo-Phos. See Ammonium Phosphate.

Arsenicals. Compounds of arsenic with various elements. Lead arsenate and calcium arsenate are insecticides, and sodium arsenite and arsenic acid are used for weed control.

*Basic Lime Phosphate. A superphosphate to which liming materials have been added in a quantity at least 6 per cent calcium carbonates equivalent in excess of the quantity required to convert all water-soluble phosphate to the citrate-soluble form.

*Basic Phosphate Slag. A by-product in the manufacture of steel from phosphatic iron ores. The product shall be finely ground and shall contain no admixture of materials other than what results in the original process of manufacture. It shall contain not less than 12 per cent of total phosphoric acid (P_2O_5), not less than 80 per cent of which shall be soluble in 2 per cent citric acid solution according to the Wagner method of analysis.

Beet-sugar Residue. A liquid produced by combining the residual liquor remaining after beet sugar has been extracted, with phosphate rock and sulfuric acid. It contains 3 to 6 per cent nitrogen and 8 to 10 per cent potash.

*Blood. Dried blood is the collected blood of slaughtered animals, dried and ground, and containing not less than 12 per cent nitrogen in organic form. (Dried blood breaks down rapidly in the soil and releases its nitrogen quickly.)

Blood and Bone. A mixture of dried blood and ground bone. It varies widely in analysis, averaging about 6 per cent nitrogen and 12 per cent phosphoric acid.

Bone Ash. Residual ash from burned bones. Contains 30 to 38 per cent phosphoric acid.

BONE BLACK. Bone charcoal used in various manufacturing processes. The spent material is used as fertilizer. It contains about 15 per cent nitrogen and 30 to 36 per cent phosphoric acid.

BONE MEAL (raw). Ground animal bones. Contains 2 to 6 per cent nitrogen and 14 to 27 per cent phosphoric acid.

BONE MEAL (steamed). Produced by grinding bones that have been steamed to remove the nitrogenous organic matter which is used in the manufacture of glue. Steamed bone meal contains from 2.0 to 4.0 per cent nitrogen and 16 to 40 per cent phosphoric acid.

BONE PHOSPHATE (Bone phosphate of lime). A tricalcium phosphate that occurs in nature in bones, rock phosphate, etc. It is insoluble and is treated with sulfuric acid to make the phosphoric acid available. When added to the soil it supplies phosphoric acid very slowly as it is converted to soluble form by the action of soil acids on it.

BORAX (Sodium tetraborate). Contains the element boron which is sometimes deficient in soil. Used only in very limited quantity.
BORON. See Borax.

CALCIUM. Does not occur pure in nature. Combined with carbon and oxygen it forms limestone. When combined with oxygen it forms calcium oxide which is burned lime. When water is added to burned lime, it slakes and hydrated lime is formed. Calcium also forms compounds with many other elements that are valuable as fertilizers. See following definitions.

CALCIUM CARBONATE. Occurs in nature as limestone, oyster shells, marble, etc. Produced artificially as by-products of various manufacturing processes. Artificial product is usually known as "plant lime."

CALCIUM CYANAMIDE. A compound of calcium, carbon, and nitrogen. Made commercially by passing nitrogen over heated calcium carbide. Sold under the trade name Cyanamid. The AOAC specifies that it shall contain not less than 21 per cent nitrogen. It contains 10 to 15 per cent calcium oxide.

CALCIUM HYDRATE (Hydrated lime, slaked lime). Prepared by adding water slowly to burned lime. Air-slaked lime is hydrated lime produced by permitting burned lime to absorb moisture from the air.

*CALCIUM METAPHOSPHATE. A glassy product that is composed chiefly of the phosphate indicated by the formula $Ca(PO_3)_2$. It shall be of such fineness that 90 per cent will pass a 20-mesh sieve, and its content of available phosphoric acid equivalence shall be stipulated. For example, calcium metaphosphate = 60 per cent available P_2O_5.

CALCIUM NITRATE. A compound of calcium and nitric acid. Commercial calcium nitrate contains approximately 15 per cent nitrogen and 28 per cent water-soluble lime. It absorbs moisture readily and must be shipped and stored in airtight containers.

CALCIUM OXIDE (Burned lime, quicklime). Product resulting from heating the various forms of calcium carbonate (limestone, oyster shells, etc.) to a high enough temperature to drive off all of the carbon and part of the oxygen as carbon dioxide gas.

CALCIUM PHOSPHATE. See Bone Phosphate.

*CALCIUM SULFATE (Gypsum, land plaster). Gypsum, land plaster, or crude calcium sulfate are products consisting chiefly of calcium sulfate. They may contain 20 per cent of combined water. (They do not neutralize acid soils.)

CAL-NITRO. Trade name of a fertilizer material consisting primarily of ammonium nitrate and pulverized dolomitic limestone. Contains 16 to 20 per cent nitrogen that is half in nitrate and half in ammonia form. It is prepared in pellet form to permit easy distribution. Contains approximately 35 per cent carbonate of lime.

CASTOR POMACE. Residue left after oil has been extracted from castor beans. Contains 4.0 to 6.5 per cent nitrogen, 1 to 2 per cent phosphoric acid, and 1 to 1.5 per cent potash.

CEMENT DUST. By-product of cement manufacture. Contains from 6 to 9 per cent potash.

CHILE SALTPETER. See Nitrate of Soda.

CITRATUS. A dicalcium phosphate containing 37 to 40 per cent available phosphoric acid.

COCOA-SHELL MEAL. Finely ground husks of cacao bean. Contains about 2.5 per cent nitrogen, 1.0 per cent phosphoric acid, and 2.5 per cent potash.

*COLLOIDAL PHOSPHATE. Soft phosphate with colloidal clay is a very finely divided low-analysis by-product from mining Florida rock phosphate by hydraulic process in which the colloidal materials settle at points in artificial ponds and basins farthest from the washer and are later removed after the natural evaporation of the water. (Usually contains the equivalent of 20 per cent phosphoric acid, which is only slightly available.)

Cottonseed Meal. The meal produced by grinding the press cake left after the oil has been extracted from cottonseed. Contains approximately 6.5 to 7.5 per cent nitrogen, 2 to 3 per cent phosphoric acid, and 1.5 to 2.0 per cent potash.

Cyanamid. See Calcium Cyanamide.

*Dissolved Bone. Ground bone or bone meal that has been treated with sulfuric acid. Contains 1.5 to 4.0 per cent nitrogen and 14 to 24 per cent phosphoric acid.

Distillery Waste. Residual material after distillation of molasses and other products. Contains some nitrogen and potash. Distillers' grains is the residue from distillation of alcohol and liquors from corn, rye, and other grains. It contains about 3.5 per cent nitrogen, ½ per cent of phosphoric acid, and a trace of potash.

*Dolomite. A mineral composed chiefly of carbonates of magnesium and calcium in substantially uni-modal (1 to 1.19) proportions.

Double Superphosphate. Produced by treating phosphate rock with phosphoric acid. Contains 2½ to 3 times as much available phosphoric acid as superphosphate.

Ferric Phosphate. Found in varying quantities in raw phosphate rock. Its phosphoric acid is highly unavailable unless treated with a mineral acid, as sulfuric. Makes superphosphate sticky when present in large amounts.

Ferrous Sulfate. Salt of iron and sulfuric acid. Formerly used as a weed killer. When applied in small amounts, it will correct chlorosis due to iron deficiency in highly alkaline soils.

*Fish Scrap (Fish tankage, dry ground fish, fish meal). The dried, ground product derived from rendered or unrendered fish. (Contains 6 to 10 per cent nitrogen and 4 to 8 per cent phosphoric acid.)

*Garbage Tankage. The rendered, dried, and ground product derived from waste household food materials. (Contains about 3 per cent nitrogen, 2 to 5 per cent phosphoric acid, and 0.5 to 1.0 per cent potash.)

Grape Pomace. The residual cake after the juice is pressed from the grapes. Contains about 1.0 per cent nitrogen and small quantities of phosphoric acid and potash.

GRASS CLIPPINGS. Clippings removed from greens or other turf. Contain 2.0 to 4.5 per cent nitrogen, about 0.5 per cent phosphoric acid, and 2 to 3 per cent potash.

GREEN MANURE CROP. Term applied to crops like rye, clover, cowpeas, and soybeans that are plowed or disked into the soil while still green to improve its organic-matter content and fertility. Can be used on golf courses to improve topsoil beds for use in building greens and tees and for top-dressing.

*GROUND LIMESTONE. The product obtained by grinding either calcitic or dolomitic limestone so that all the material will pass a 10-mesh sieve and at least 50 per cent will pass a 100-mesh sieve. [Pulverized limestone (fine-ground limestone) is ground to a fineness so that all the material will pass a 20-mesh sieve and 75 per cent will pass a 100-mesh sieve.]

*GROUND SHELLS. The product obtained by grinding the shells of mollusks so that not less than 50 per cent shall pass a 100-mesh sieve. The product shall also carry the name of the mollusk from which said product is made.

*GROUND SHELL MARL. The product obtained by grinding natural deposits of shell marl so that at least 75 per cent shall pass a 100-mesh sieve.

GUANO. Deposits of excrement and dead bodies of birds and bats in localities where there is little or no rain. Varies widely in plant nutrient content and should be purchased on the basis of analysis. May contain less than 1 per cent to over 13 per cent nitrogen, 10 to 35 per cent phosphoric acid, and up to 4 per cent potash.

GYPSUM. See Calcium Sulfate.

HAIR. Hair from tanneries and packing houses. Not suitable as a fertilizer unless processed. Is used in making wet-base goods and nitrogenous tankage. Contains 8 to 10.7 per cent nitrogen.

HARDWOOD ASHES. Ashes produced by burning hard woods. Unleached ashes contain 2 to 8 per cent potash. Leached ashes have a much lower potash content.

*HOOF AND HORN MEAL. Processed dried and ground hoofs and horns. Contains 10 to more than 15 per cent nitrogen in slowly available organic form and 1 to 2.5 per cent phosphoric acid.

HUMUS. A brownish-black amorphous substance resulting from the decay of organic matter in the soil.

IMHOFF SEWAGE SLUDGE. See Sludge Sewage.

IRON SULFATE. See Ferrous Sulfate.

*KAINIT. A potash salt containing potassium and sodium chlorides and sometimes sulfate of magnesia with not less than 12 per cent potash.

KELP. A species of seaweed that is used to a limited extent as fertilizer after proper processing. Dried kelp contains 1.6 to 3.3 per cent nitrogen, 1 to 2 per cent phosphoric acid, and 15 to 20 per cent potash. It also is rich in iodine.

LAND PLASTER. See Calcium Sulfate.

*LANGBEINITE. A natural salt of magnesium and potassium that occurs in large deposits in New Mexico and Texas. It is purified by washing with cold water, and the material containing potash magnesia sulfate is prepared by drying and grinding. Contains 25 per cent potash and 25 per cent sulfate of magnesia.

LEAF MOLD. Partially decomposed leaves. Useful as a source of organic matter for use in preparing top-dressing. May contain 1 to 3 per cent nitrogen and traces of phosphoric acid and potash.

LEATHER. Scraps and shavings of leather that are used in making base goods and nitrogenous tankage. Sometimes ground. Contain 5 to 12 per cent nitrogen that is very slowly available because of resistance to decay.

LEUNAPHOS. Trade name for concentrated fertilizer materials containing ammonium phosphate, ammonium sulfate, and sometimes ammonium nitrate. Various grades are produced that vary in composition from 16 to 20 per cent nitrogen and 16 to 49 per cent available phosphoric acid.

LEUNASALTPETER. A trade name for a product containing approximately 26 per cent nitrogen. About one-fourth of the nitrogen is present in nitrate form and three-fourths in the ammonia form.

*LIME. The word lime when applied to liming materials means either calcium oxide or calcium and magnesium oxides. Agricultural liming material is material whose calcium and magnesium content is capable of neutralizing soil acidity (see Calcium Carbonate, Calcium Hydrate,

Calcium Oxide, Magnesium Oxide; also Ground Limestone, Ground Shells, Ground Shell Marl.)

LIME NITRATE. See Calcium Nitrate.

LINSEED MEAL. The ground cake produced when flaxseed is processed to extract linseed oil contains approximately 6 per cent nitrogen, 2 per cent phosphoric acid, and 1 per cent potash.

MAGNESIA (Oxide of magnesium). Often associated with calcium in lime. Heaviest concentrations in dolomitic limestone.

MAGNESIUM SULFATE (Epsom salts). A white water-soluble salt. May be mixed with fertilizers to supply readily available magnesium.

MANGANESE. A soft metal that occurs most commonly as the oxide or carbonate. Forms water-soluble manganese sulfate with sulfuric acid. Manganese is essential for plant growth and is deficient in some light sandy soils, particularly in parts of Florida.

MANURE. See Green Manure, Mushroom Soil.

The approximate content of moisture, nitrogen, phosphoric acid, and potash in various kinds of manures is shown in Table 11.

TABLE 10

ANALYSIS OF MANURES

Kind of manure	*Moisture,* %	*Nitrogen,* %	*Phosphoric acid,* %	*Potash,* %
Barnyard (mixed cow and horse)	72.0	Trace–1.5	Trace–1.0	0.5–1.0
Cow (dry, ground)	44.0	1.5–2.0	0.5	1.5
Poultry (fresh)	65.0	1.0–2.5	0.5–2.0	0.5
Poultry (dry)	5.7	2.0	1.5	1.0
Poultry-house litter	12.5	Trace–1.0	0.5–1.0	Trace–1.0
Horse	53.0	0.5–1.0	Trace–1.5	0.5–3.0
Horse (dry, ground)	8.5	2.5	2.5	2.0
Sheep (fresh)	44.5	1.0	1.0	1.0
Sheep (dry, ground)	7.9	2.0–4.0	1.5–2.5	1.0–3.0

*MANURE SALTS. Potash salts containing high percentage of chloride and 20 to 30 per cent of potash.

MARL. Unindurated or soft rock deposits high in calcium carbonate. The quantity applied to correct soil acidity is based on the calcium carbonate content of the material used.

MEAT MEAL. Dried and ground cooked meat. Contains very little bone. Average analysis is 10.0 to 11.5 per cent nitrogen and 1 to 5 per cent phosphoric acid.

MILORGANITE. Trade name for activated sludge manufactured by the City of Milwaukee (see Activated Sludge).

*MONOAMMONIUM PHOSPHATE. A commercial salt made by combining phosphoric acid with ammonia. It shall contain not less than 10 per cent of nitrogen and not less than 46 per cent of available phosphoric acid.

MOWRAH MEAL. The ground cake remaining after the oil is extracted from seeds of the bassia tree (India). Contains about 2.7 per cent nitrogen in slowly available organic form, 1 per cent phosphoric acid, and 1 per cent potash and is used for earthworm eradication. Deteriorates when exposed to the air.

MULTIPLE SUPERPHOSPHATE. A name applied by some manufacturers to double superphosphate (which see).

*MURIATE OF POTASH. A potash salt containing not less than 48 per cent of potash, chiefly as chlorides.

MUSHROOM SOIL (Spent mushroom soil). Discarded manure mixed with casing soil from mushroom beds. Contains 17 to 25 per cent partially rotted manure. Useful on golf courses as an ingredient of top-dressing. Contains about 1 per cent nitrogen, 0.5 per cent phosphoric acid, and 1.0 per cent potash.

MUSTARD MEAL. Ground residue after oil has been extracted from mustard seed. Contains about 5 per cent nitrogen, 1 per cent phosphoric acid, and 1 per cent potash.

NEBRASKA POTASH. Highly alkaline salts obtained by the evaporation of brines found in Nebraska. Contain 20 to 30 per cent potash in carbonate and sulfate form.

NITRATE OF AMMONIA. See Ammonium Nitrate.

NITRATE OF LIME. See Calcium Nitrate.

NITRATE OF POTASH. See Potassium Nitrate.

NITRATE OF SODA. Sodium salt of nitric acid. Natural nitrate of soda from

Chilean deposits may be obtained in crystalline and granular (pellet) form. The salt is water soluble and quickly available. It contains approximately 16 per cent nitrogen. Commercial Chilean nitrates contain small quantities of many other elements, such as boron, magnesium, manganese, copper, and zinc. Nitrate of soda (Arcadian) is produced synthetically by combining ammonia (oxidized to nitric acid) with soda ash (sodium carbonate). It contains 16.0 to 16.5 per cent nitrogen.

*NITRATE OF SODA AND POTASH. A commercial product containing nitrates of sodium and potassium. It shall contain not less than 14 per cent of nitrogen and 14 per cent of potash.

NITRATES. Combinations of nitrogen and oxygen in the proportion of NO_3 with metals and alkalies such as sodium, potassium, calcium, and ammonia. Derived from deposits of nitrate of soda in Chile or produced by converting the nitrogen of the air into nitric acid and combining it with a base such as soda ash, ammonia, or lime.

NITROGANIC. Trade name for activated sewage sludge produced by the Pasadena, California, sewage-disposal plant. Contains approximately 5.3 per cent nitrogen, 2 per cent available phosphoric acid, and 0.3 per cent potash.

NITROGEN. A colorless, odorless, highly inert gas that constitutes about four-fifths of the air. It is found in combination with other elements as natural deposits of such salts as nitrate of soda. It is obtained from the air by several different processes of combining it with other elements. Three general groups of fertilizer materials contain nitrogen. These are (1) nitrates (nitrate of soda, potassium nitrate, etc.), (2) ammonia salts (sulfate of ammonia, ammonium phosphate, etc.), and (3) organic materials (sludges, manures, tankages, seed meals, etc.). The materials in groups 1 and 2 are water soluble, and the nitrogen which they contain is quickly available to plants. Organic nitrogenous materials must be decomposed by microorganisms before the nitrogen becomes available.

*NITROGENOUS TANKAGE (Process tankage). Products made under steam pressure from crude inert nitrogenous materials, with or without the use of acids, for the purpose of increasing the activity of the nitrogen. These products shall be called "process tankages" with or without further qualification. The water-insoluble nitrogen in these products should test at least 50 per cent active by the alkaline or 80 per cent active by the neutral permanganate method.

PEANUT-HULL MEAL. Ground peanut hulls or shells containing 1.5 to 2.5 per cent nitrogen and trace amounts of phosphoric acid and potash.

PEAT. Partially decomposed organic matter resulting from decay of reeds, sedges, mosses, and other aquatic plants under water. Composition varies widely depending upon conditions under which formation took place. Peats are high in moisture-absorptive capacity, varying from 200 to more than 1,000 per cent. Used on golf courses as physical soil conditioners. Organic matter content varies from 70 to 95 per cent. Contain 1.5 to 2.5 per cent nitrogen, which is very slowly available, and small amounts of phosphoric acid and potash. Charred peat has been artificially dried at a temperature that causes partial decomposition.

*p*H (Hydrogen-ion concentration). Arbitrary scale of values expressing the degree of acidity of solutions, soils, or compounds. The neutral value is pH 7.0. Values above pH 7.0 denote alkalinity, and those below 7.0 denote acidity. The higher the number above 7.0, the greater the alkalinity. The lower the number below 7.0, the higher the acidity.

*PHOSPHATE ROCK. A natural rock containing one or more calcium phosphate minerals of sufficient purity and quantity to permit its use, either directly or after concentration, in the manufacture of commercial products. (Commercial phosphate rock contains 66 to 78 per cent equivalent of tricalcium phosphate.)

PHOSPHATES. Salts of phosphoric acid formed by combining phosphoric acid with a metal or alkali. Phosphates of soda, potash, ammonia, and lime are used as fertilizers.

PHOSPHORIC ACID (P_2O_5). A compound of phosphorus and oxygen. Never used alone as fertilizer. The phosphorus in fertilizers usually is in the form of phosphoric acid combined with hydrogen and some metallic element such as calcium and sodium or combined with ammonium. It is the practice to state the amount of phosphorus in any fertilizer in terms of the amount of phosphoric acid which it contains.

PHOSPHORUS. One of the essential elements for plant growth. It is not used alone as a fertilizer but occurs in many fertilizers in combination with other elements (see PHOSPHORIC ACID).

POTASH (Potassium oxide, K_2O). A compound of potassium and oxygen. It is never used alone as a fertilizer as it is a strongly corrosive alkali. As used in fertilizers it usually is in the form of potassium chloride (muriate of potash) or potassium sulfate and sometimes potassium carbonate or potassium nitrate. In the fertilizer trade the term potash designates the equivalent amount of potassium oxide in the various potash salts.

POTASSIUM. A soft metal which resembles lead. It oxidizes readily when exposed to the air and combines with water to form caustic potash. It is never used as a fertilizer in its pure form, but its salts are in general use. The potassium content of fertilizers is expressed as the potash equivalent of the potassium salts which they contain (see Potash).

POTASSIUM CHLORIDE. See Muriate of Potash.

*POTASSIUM METAPHOSPHATE. A product represented by the formula KPO_3. It shall be of such fineness that 90 per cent will pass a 50-mesh screen, and its phosphoric acid and potash equivalence shall be stipulated. For example, potassium metaphosphate = 58 per cent P_2O_5, 32 per cent K_2O.

POTASSIUM NITRATE. The potassium salt of nitric acid. Small natural deposits occur in various parts of the world, but most of it is manufactured from nitrate of soda and muriate of potash. The commercial grade should contain a minimum of 12 per cent nitrogen and 44 per cent potash.

*POTASSIUM SULFATE. Commercial potassium sulfate is a potash salt containing not less than 48 per cent of potash chiefly as sulfate and not more than 2.5 per cent chlorine.

POULTRY MANURE. See Manure.

*PRECIPITATED BONE PHOSPHATE. A by-product from the manufacture of glue from bones and is obtained by neutralizing the hydrochloric acid solution of processed bone with calcium hydroxide. The phosphoric acid is chiefly present as dicalcium phosphate. Contains approximately 40 per cent available phosphoric acid.

*PRIMARY FERTILIZER COMPONENTS are those at present generally recognized by law as necessary to be guaranteed in fertilizers; namely, nitrogen, phosphoric acid, and potash.

PROTEIN. The term referring to the nitrogen-carrying portion of livestock feed. To determine the total nitrogen in a feed such as cottonseed or soybean meal that is to be used as a fertilizer divide the percentage of crude protein by the factor 6.25.

RAPESEED MEAL. The meal produced by grinding the residual cake after the oil has been pressed from rapeseed. It contains approximately

5.0 to 6.0 per cent nitrogen, 1.5 to 2.0 per cent phosphoric acid, and 1.0 to 1.5 per cent potash.

SALT. The product of the chemical combination of an acid and an alkali. Many common inorganic fertilizer materials are salts produced either naturally or artificially. For example, when the alkali caustic soda reacts with nitric acid the salt nitrate of soda is formed, or when the alkali ammonium hydroxide reacts with sulfuric acid the salt ammonium sulfate is produced. Common table salt (sodium chloride) is formed when caustic soda or sodium bicarbonate is treated with hydrochloric acid.

*SECONDARY FERTILIZER COMPONENTS. Fertilizer components other than "primary fertilizer components" that are essential to the proper growth of plants and that may be needed by some soils. Some of these components are calcium, magnesium, sulfur, manganese, copper, zinc, and boron.

All fertilizer components with the exception of potash and phosphoric acid, if guaranteed, shall be stated in terms of the elements.

SHEEP MANURE. See Manure.

SILICA. The oxide of the element silicon. One of the most abundant of the earth's ingredients. Quartz and sand are common forms of silica. It combines with alkalies to form silicates, most of which are insoluble in water and weak acids. Large quantities of potash are present in many soils in the form of insoluble silicates that are unavailable to plants.

SLUDGE—SEWAGE. An organic product resulting from the treatment of sewage. There are four principal types depending upon the method of treatment: (1) primary sludge, settled or digested; (2) Imhoff tank sludge; (3) chemical-precipitation sludge; (4) activated sludge, digested or dried.

Primary sludge is produced by settlement of the solids in sewage. The solids may be dried and disposed of, but they are more commonly digested in tanks. During this process a portion of the solids are gasified and liquefied. The remaining solids are collected on drying beds and contain 50 to 80 per cent moisture, depending upon the detention period and weather conditions. They are no longer nuisance producing or a health menace. The sludge can be disposed of as fill or in the local market as a low-grade fertilizer.

Approximate analysis on moisture-free basis:

Nitrogen (N) 1.5–2.5%
Phosphoric acid total (P_2O_5) 1.0–1.5%

Imhoff sludge is produced by anaerobic (living in absence of air) organisms in tanks. Part of the sludge is liquefied, and the rest settles to the bottom of the tank. The sludge has about the same analysis as primary digested sludge. This method of sewage treatment is less important now than formerly.

The addition of chemicals to sewage, principally iron salts and lime, for the purpose of precipitating the solids produces chemically precipitated sludges. It is commonly filtered, dried, and incinerated. From the fertilizer standpoint it is a variable product which may contain 1½ to 3 per cent nitrogen on a dry basis and about 1.5 per cent phosphoric acid.

SMIROW TANKAGE. Trade name for a nitrogenous tankage containing 8 to 10 per cent nitrogen.

SODIUM. A soft metal that oxidizes readily in air—forming sodium hydroxide (caustic soda). It is widely distributed and combines with acids to form salts such as sodium chloride, sodium nitrate, sodium carbonate, etc. It sometimes reacts in the soil to liberate potassium from insoluble compounds.

SOOT. Deposits from the smoke of coal or wood. It is composed almost entirely of carbon. At one time it was used extensively on golf courses but has been replaced by more efficient fertilizers. May contain 1 to 6 per cent nitrogen, about 1 per cent phosphoric acid, and a trace of potash.

SOYBEAN MEAL. Produced by grinding the cake remaining after the oil has been extracted from soybeans. Contains about 7 per cent nitrogen, 1.5 per cent phosphoric acid, and 2 per cent potash.

SULFATE OF AMMONIA. See Ammonium Sulfate.

SULFATE OF POTASH. See Potassium Sulfate.

*SULFATE OF POTASH-MAGNESIA. A potash salt containing not less than 25 per cent potash, not less than 25 per cent of sulfate of magnesia, and not more than 2.5 per cent chlorine.

SULFUR. A yellow crystalline material that is produced commercially in a high degree of purity (99.5 per cent). It forms sulfur dioxide when burned in air, which can be combined with hydrogen and oxygen by suitable processes to form sulfuric acid. Sulfur is essential for plant growth. It is present in most soils in sufficient quantities to meet plant

TABLE 11

ANALYSIS OF WASTE MATERIALS

Material	*Nitrogen,* %	*Phosphoric acid,* %	*Potash,* %
Brewers grains (wet)	1.0	0.5	Trace
Cocoa-shell dust	1.0	1.5	2.5
Cotton waste	1.0	Trace	Trace
Distillery waste	3.5	0.5	0.5
Feathers	15.0	...	...
Felt-hat factory waste	14.0	...	1.0
Sweepings from powder mills	10.0	...	34.5
Hair	8.0–16.0	...	...
Hare and rabbit waste	7.0	1.5–3.0	0.5
Leather waste	5.0–12.0	Trace	Trace
Oyster-shell mound siftings	Trace	10.0	Trace
Peanut shells	1.0	Trace	0.5
Picker waste from cotton mills	1.0	0.5	1.5
Powder-works waste	2.0– 3.0	...	16.0–18.0
Raw sugar residue	1.0	8.0	...
Shoddy and felt	4.0–12.0	...	...
Silk waste	8.0–11.0	...	...
Silk-mills by-product	8.0	1.0	Trace
Silkworm cocoons	9.5	1.5	1.0
Soot	1.0– 6.0	1.0	Trace
Tobacco stems	1.0– 5.0	0.5–1.0	1.0–10.0
Wool waste	2.0– 6.0	Trace–4.0	Trace– 3.0

requirements. When deficient, it can be added to the soil in superphosphate, sulfate of ammonia, and other sulfates.

SULFURIC ACID. See Sulfur.

SUPERPHOSPHATE. The material commonly used for supplying phosphoric acid in fertilizers. Prepared by mixing finely ground phosphate rock and sulfuric or phosphoric acid. Superphosphates contain 15 to more than 50 per cent available phosphoric acid, depending upon the method of preparation. Those containing the higher percentages (over 20 per cent) are called double or treble superphosphates. The definition of superphosphate by the AOAC requires that the "grade that shows the available phosphoric acid shall be used as a prefix to the name." Example: 20 per cent superphosphate.

TANKAGE. Material prepared by pressure cooking refuse from slaughterhouses, dead animals, or other animal matter. It is pressed, dried, and ground after fats and other products have been extracted. The analysis

TABLE 12

NUTRIENT CONTENT AND EFFECTS ON SOIL REACTION OF VARIOUS FERTILIZER MATERIALS

Material	*Nutrient content, %*			*Effect on soil reaction*
	Nitrogen	*Phosphoric acid*	*Potash*	
Ammonium sulfate	19.5–21.2	...	...	Increases acidity
Nitrate of soda	15.4–16.5	...	...	Decreases acidity
Potassium nitrate	12.6–13.5	...	42.9–45.2	Decreases acidity
Cyanamid	21.0–23.7	...	...	Decreases acidity
Urea (pure)	46.0–46.2	...	...	Increases acidity
Ammonium phosphate (1)	10.4–11.7	48.0–52.6	...	Increases acidity
Ammonium phosphate (2)	15.8–16.8	20.0–22.8	...	Increases acidity
Calurea	34.0	...	...	Increases acidity
Calcium nitrate	13.0–15.5	...	...	Decreases acidity
Animal tankage	5.5–10.0	5.0–18.0	...	No effect
Dried blood	6.0–14.0	...	...	Increases acidity
Fish scrap	6.5–10.0	5.0– 8.0	...	No effect to slight increase
Cottonseed meal	5.3– 7.5	...	...	Increases acidity slightly
Castor pomace	4.0– 7.0	2.0– 3.6	...	Increases acidity slightly
Sewage sludge, activated	4.9– 7.5	2.0– 4.0	...	Increases acidity slightly
Bone meal, raw	4.5– 5.3	17.0–23.0	...	Decreases acidity
Bone meal, steamed	0.7– 1.0	20.0–30.0	...	Decreases acidity
Ureaform	37.0–39.0	...	...	Increases acidity
Superphosphate	...	13.5–22.0	...	Decreases acidity
Double (or treble) phosphate	...	40.0–50.0	...	Decreases acidity
Precipitated phosphate	...	37.0–42.0	...	Decreases acidity
Muriate of potash	...	...	47.0–61.5	No effect
Sulfate of potash	...	...	47.0–52.0	No effect
Cotton-hull ashes	...	...	20.5–34.8	Decreases acidity
Tobacco stems	1.3– 1.6	...	4.4– 5.4	Decreases acidity
Guano, natural	1.0–12.0	10.0–25.0	...	Decreases acidity

varies from 5 to 10 per cent nitrogen and from 8 to 30 per cent bone phosphate.

TOBACCO STEMS. Ground tobacco stems and other waste tobacco products which may or may not have been extracted for nicotine. Contain approximately 1 to 5 per cent nitrogen, 0.5 to 1.0 per cent phosphoric acid, and 1 to 10 per cent potash.

TREBLE SUPERPHOSPHATE. See Double Superphosphate.

TUNG-OIL POMACE. The dried ground residual cake from extraction of the oil from tung seeds. Contains approximately 6 per cent nitrogen, 2 per cent phosphoric acid, and 1 per cent potash.

URAMON. A form of urea prepared by coating semigranular urea with a material that reduces the rate of moisture absorption. It contains 42 per cent nitrogen as urea (see Urea.)

URAMITE. Trade name for Urea-form (which see).

UREA. A crystalline product prepared synthetically by combining ammonia and carbon dioxide. The commercial material contains 46 per cent nitrogen which is water soluble and quickly available. The nitrogen is in synthetic nonprotein organic form.

UREA-AMMONIA LIQUORS. Various solutions of urea in aqueous ammonia. Contain varying amounts of nitrogen from approximately 20 to 30 per cent in the form of free ammonia and approximately 9 to 15 per cent in water-soluble organic form.

UREA-FORM. Material prepared by mixing urea and formaldehyde under conditions that will ensure the reaction of more than one molecular equivalent of urea per mole of formaldehyde. The plasticlike material formed by the reaction, when finely ground, releases nitrogen at a rate comparable to the rate of release from organic nitrogenous fertilizers. The nitrogen content varies from 36 to 39 per cent.

VEGETABLE POTASH. Material prepared from distillery water containing approximately 33 per cent potash in the form of muriates, sulfates, and carbonates.

WASTES. Wastes and by-products from many types of manufacturing plants often contain materials that have fertilizer value. Some are used by fertilizer manufacturers for mixing with other materials in making commercial fertilizers. Some can be used directly as fertilizers. They usually are bulky and may be of value only when obtainable locally to eliminate excessive transportation costs. The low-cost materials sometimes can be used to advantage as a source of organic matter in the preparation of top-dressing.

Table 11 gives the approximate analysis of some waste materials having fertilizer value.

Descriptions of Common Turfgrass Weeds

(See Appendix Table 13, page 300, for chemical control)

Annual bluegrass (*Poa annua*), also known by its botanical name *Poa annua,* is a winter annual. Leaves are similar to Kentucky bluegrass in shape but are lighter green in color. Individual plants have an upright habit of growth and do not produce rhizomes. Plants flower and seed profusely during late spring and early summer. Seed heads form and produce viable seed irrespective of cutting height. Annual bluegrass grows luxuriantly in spring and fall when the weather is cool and moist. It usually dies in hot weather.

Annual bluegrass makes an excellent putting-green, fairway, and tee turf when it is growing vigorously. It is a very uncertain grass because of its annual habit and quick disappearance during hot humid weather. It has other serious objections on greens. Growth is rapid when weather is too cool for the bentgrasses to grow. Bent will be crowded out by it in spring and fall when the infestation is heavy and uniform over the entire green. When infestations occur in scattered clumps, the green becomes rough and bad for putting by midafternoon, even though it was mowed in the morning.

In the cooler parts of the Northern region, annual bluegrass makes an excellent grass for shaded tees provided it is fertilized generously and given enough water. It does better than any other grass under these conditions and renews itself quite rapidly even under heavy play.

Maintenance practices best adapted for its control are as follows: (1) Fertilization of the bent turf should be made in late summer and early fall before the annual bluegrass has reestablished itself. Fertilizers high in organic nitrogen should be used to provide a carry-over into the late fall that will keep the bent active. Spring fertilizer applications should not be made until the bentgrasses have started active growth. (2) Water should be used sparingly in late summer and early fall when annual bluegrass seed is germinating and the new plants are becoming established. This will permit the mature bentgrass to compete with it. (3) Good soil aeration will encourage vigorous growth of bents and other desirable grasses at the expense of annual bluegrass.

Where attempts are made to hold annual bluegrass throughout the summer, it should be kept well watered without soil saturation. Nitrogen should be used sparingly, soil reaction should be kept near the neutral point, and liberal quantities of phosphate and potash should be applied.

Black medic (yellow trefoil) (*Medicago lupulina*) is an annual legume. The plant develops many branches from a single taproot. Under close clipping these flatten down and produce seed heads close to the ground. The yellow flowers grow in small clusters similar in shape to white clover blossoms. The leaves have three lobes but are smaller and narrower than those of white clover. Trefoil is tolerant to droughty conditions because of its deep taproot. It is apt to become established in dry periods when the grass is injured or checked by lack of moisture.

Buckhorn (*Plantago lanceolata*), or narrow-leaved plantain, is a rosette-type perennial with long narrow lance-shaped leaves and a coarsely fibrous root system. It thrives on soil of low fertility and appears quickly when turf becomes thin. The seed heads are borne on a thin wiry upright stem. Timely mowing, before blossoming, will reduce seed formation and check infestations in roughs and nonuse areas. The mature seeds develop a sticky coating when wet and adhere readily to players' shoes and equipment.

Buttercup (*Ranunculus repens*). Creeping buttercup occurs chiefly in the eastern part of the Cool Humid region from Maine to Virginia. It is a long-lived perennial and spreads by long slender creeping stems that root and produce new shoots at the joints. It prefers moist soil of good fertility and frequently invades approaches to greens that receive heavy applications of water and fertilizer.

Catsear (*Hypochoeris radicata*), or false dandelion, is a perennial rosette type of weed that has the same general habit of growth and leaf shape as the true dandelion. It reproduces entirely by seed. The yellow flowers are borne on upright branched stalks and bloom from June to September. When plants occur in roughs, seed production can be checked by timely mowing.

Chickweeds. The two varieties of chickweed most common in turf are the common (*Stellaria media*) and the mouse-ear (*Cerastium vulgatum*). The common chickweed is an annual. It blooms and sets seed throughout the entire growing season. The foliage is a light green color. it is very hardy, and plants that develop late in the fall will live over winter and seed very early the next spring. Eradication is difficult because the stems root at the joints. Kill must be complete;

otherwise new plants will develop from the surviving joints. The mouse-ear chickweed is a perennial. It blooms and sets seed through the warm weather of summer. It can be distinguished from common chickweed by its more oblong leaves, its dark bluish-green color, and the downy hairs that cover the entire plant. Chickweeds are shallow rooted and become established easily wherever soils are so heavily compacted and saturated with water that desirable grasses are weakened. They often occur on greens, forming solid patches where turf has been injured by disease and insect attacks.

CINQUEFOILS (*Potentilla* spp.), also called five-finger and false strawberry, are perennials that spread by runners that produce new plants at the joints. The plant looks and grows very much like the strawberry. The yellow flowers are produced on branched seed stems. Flowering and seed setting continue throughout the summer. Cinquefoil is apt to become a serious pest on sandy soils, where fertility is low. It may develop into a dense mat that cannot be killed by close clipping. It is essential that turf be fertilized liberally to increase its density following chemical treatment; otherwise a new crop will develop from seeds in the soil.

CRABGRASSES (*Digitaria* spp.). The two most common types of crabgrasses are the hairy crabgrass (*D. sanguinalis*) and smooth crabgrass (*D. ischaemum*) sometimes called large and small, respectively. Both are summer annuals. The seed germinates through a 6- to 8-week period during the late spring and early summer. Plants mature before frost in the fall of the same season. Seed heads are borne on semi-creeping stems which will root at the joints. Crabgrasses are widely distributed throughout the Northern and Southern Humid regions; but they are most serious in the belt consisting of the southern part of the Northern region and the northern part of the Southern region. This belt extends from Baltimore and Washington on the east to the Kansas City–St. Louis area on the west.

Control is a matter of good cultural practices and chemical herbicides used at the proper time. These methods are described in Chap. 8.

DAISY (*Chrysanthemum leucanthemum*) is a perennial that reproduces entirely from seeds. The characteristic flowers are borne on upright stems that grow from a single crown. When close clipped it will flatten down into a dense mat that completely smothers the grass. Clipping will reduce seed production but will not completely suppress it because many flowers are borne so low that they are not cut off.

The daisy is a hard-to-kill weed and is resistant to treatment with herbicides at standard strength. Individual plants can be killed by spot treatments with concentrated solutions of arsenicals, 2,4-D, and Ammate (see page 205). These materials will kill grass in the concentrations necessary to control the daisy. Care must be used in applying them not to permit them to come in contact with the grass.

DALLISGRASS (*Paspalum dilatatum*) is a perennial bunch grass that thrives throughout the southern states and in the irrigated sections of the milder portions of the Southwest. It is classed as a weed in closely clipped turf on the golf course because of the heavy clumps which it produces. These create an uneven bunchy sod that is not suitable for play. Dallisgrass reproduces only from seed and can be prevented from spreading into fairways and other turf areas by mowing roughs and nonuse areas before seeds mature.

DANDELION (*Taraxacum officinale*) is a perennial rosette-type weed and propagates entirely from seeds. It has a deep taproot that makes it highly drought tolerant. Dandelions seed most profusely in the spring, but they will blossom and produce seed in any month of the year when freezing temperatures do not occur. Seeds mature within 18 to 21 days after flowering. The weed is so widely distributed and has such an excellent means of distributing the seed, through the parachutelike appendage, that close clipping to cut off the blossoms is of no great assistance in control. Where herbicides are used for dandelion control, at least one treatment will be required every season. Large quantities of seed are blown into the turf each year and will cause heavy reinfestations unless the seedlings are eradicated promptly.

DICHONDRA (*Dichondra repens*) is a low-growing creeping perennial that spreads by underground runners. It is related to the morning glories and somewhat resembles white clover, although the leaves are kidney shaped and may be much larger than white clover leaves. The heavier soils that are well supplied with moisture are preferred. Dichondra will grow at low fertility levels. It is native in the Southern Warm Humid region and in Southern California.

GOOSEGRASS (*Eleusine indica*) is sometimes called silver crabgrass because the crown of the plant is silvery white in color. It is a summer annual like crabgrass. Under close clipping it forms a dense rosette of short heavy stems that seed close to the ground. Seed germinates in the spring and early summer. The plant matures and ripens seed before frost in the fall.

Cultural practices that are effective in discouraging crabgrass also will reduce the vigor and aggressiveness of goosegrass. Eradication with chemicals is difficult unless treatments are applied when the plants are very young (2- to 3-leaf stage). Retreatments usually are required after plants develop the rosette stage.

GROUND IVY (*Nepeta hederacea*), also called gill-over-the-ground, is a creeping perennial. The prostrate stems (stolons) root at the joints and send out numerous branches that form a dense mat over occupied areas. The leaves are kidney shaped and scalloped like those of a geranium plant. They grow in pairs at each joint. Ground ivy blooms from May to August. The flowers are purple and are borne in small solid clusters.

HAWKWEED (*Hieracium* spp.). Two types of hawkweeds (devils'-paintbrush) are common weeds of turf. The one type bears a cluster of brilliant orange flowers at the top of a wiry upright stalk. The second type has light lemon-yellow flowers. The plant is a rosette-type perennial which spreads by fleshy underground runners. It has a long blooming period starting in midsummer. Seed production can be reduced materially by clipping the seed heads when they are in bloom. Hawkweed is highly tolerant of dry soils and low fertility and frequently develops heavy infestations in roughs. It will not compete with grass that is dense and vigorous.

KIKUYUGRASS (*Pennisetum clandestinum*) is a native of Africa and was introduced into the United States by way of New Zealand in 1927. It is a long-lived perennial, spreading by heavy rootstocks. It is classed as a warm-season species and is extremely aggressive and hard to eradicate in areas where climatic conditions favor it. Trial plantings made on fairways of several golf courses in California have developed into problem areas. It develops a deep thatch which is highly undesirable from a playing standpoint, and once established, will persist under even the most unfavorable growing conditions. The only herbicides that have controlled it effectively remain toxic in the soil for long periods after application (a minimum of one full season). Consequently, new seedings on areas where an eradication program has been used must be delayed until the chemical has lost its toxicity.

KNOTWEED (*Polygonum aviculare*) is an annual that produces a large number of heavily branched stems that spread out flat from a single crown. Seed germinates in the spring, and the plant matures and sets a new crop of seed before frost. Its habit of growth is so flat that it cannot be destroyed by close clipping. It will thrive on heavily compacted soil that bakes hard in the summer but will not compete with grass that is growing vigorously. It is easily killed by standard rates of treatment with 2,4-D and sodium arsenite when in the seedling stage. New plants will reappear the following season from seed in the soil unless a good turf cover has been established on infested areas by a fall program of aeration, fertilization, and reseeding.

MONEYWORT (*Lysimachia numularia*), or *creeping Charley*, is a vining perennial that roots at each joint of the creeping stems. It bears small yellow flowers in the axils of the round waxy leaves that are arranged opposite to each other on the stems. Moneywort grows so close to the ground that it cannot be discouraged by close cutting. It thrives in shade and prefers moist soil. Raising the stems by raking or brushing followed by close clipping will check it. Eradication is difficult because each jointed piece of stem that is not removed will continue to grow.

NIMBLEWILL OR MUHLENBERGIA (*Muhlenbergia* spp.). Several closely related types of this grass occur in various sections of the country. The most troublesome are perennials. They form a stemmy loose type of sod that is slow to start growth in the spring and is very undesirable for turf on golf courses. The plants propagate by seed and spread by underground runners. Aboveground stems root at the lower joints forming a tough sod that is difficult to eradicate. Solid patches of muhlenbergia can be killed by spot spraying with a solution of ammonium thiocyanate made by dissolving 1 lb. of the chemical in 1 to 2 gal. of water. Ammonium thiocyanate at this strength will kill desirable grasses with which it comes in contact. If spot treatments are made, care must be used not to spray surrounding grasses with the solution.

NUTGRASS (*Cyperus rotundus*) is a sedge although it is grasslike in appearance. It is a perennial and spreads chiefly by underground stems that bear tubers or nuts which develop new plants. The plants have a somewhat yellowish-green color. The leaves are harsh and coarse. Where an area that is to be planted is infested with nutgrass, it should be cultivated for a full season to remove the rootstalks and kill developing plants before it is seeded.

PEARLWORT (*Sagina procumbens*) is a viny perennial that spreads by creeping stems which root at the joints. It tolerates close clipping and forms solid patches on greens that closely resemble a fine-textured grass. Infestations occur first on areas where turf has been killed or seriously injured by disease or insect attacks and also on greens where the turf consists of weak types of grasses not adapted to the location. Strong grasses that are capable of vigorous growth will check its spread. It is highly tolerant to selective treatments with herbicides. The best methods of control are to plug it out and replace with good sod or to spot treat with concentrated herbicide solutions. It can be severely burned with fertilizing materials containing soluble nitrogen, such as sulfate of ammonia, nitrate of soda, or Cyanamid. Arsenate of lead rubbed into the patches with a rubber glove will kill it.

PENNYWORT (*Hydrocotyle rotundifolia*) is a creeping perennial that spreads by numerous creeping stems both above and below ground. Roots and leaves develop at each joint of the stems. It forms a solid mat over the ground that crowds out grass almost completely. The leaves are round to kidney shaped with crinkled margins. It resembles ground ivy in size of leaves and general habit of growth but bears small white flowers in contrast with the purple blossoms of ground ivy. It is easily killed by single applications of 2,4-D at standard rates. Retreatments usually are necessary to kill new plants that develop from the large quantities of seed that are always present in soils because of its heavy seed production.

PLANTAIN (*Plantago major*), or broad-leaved plantain, is a rosette-type perennial with a fibrous root system. Its leaves are broad and oval in shape. It develops a short upright seedstalk that bears a long narrow seed head. Like buckhorn, seed production of broad-leaved plantain can be reduced materially by timely clipping to destroy the seeds before they mature sufficiently to grow. The seed heads develop from July to September and should be clipped before blossoming.

PUNCTUREVINE (*Tribulus terrestris*) is an annual with a prostrate habit of growth. It produces long branching stems that form a dense mat. The yellow flowers are borne in the axils of the leaves, and seeds are enclosed in clusters of burs, each of which has two sharp spines. It is highly tolerant to drought because of its deep taproot and is readily controlled by 2,4-D at standard strength.

PURSLANE (*Portulaca oleracea*) is an annual that germinates as soon as the soil warms up in the spring. It blooms and sets seed from early in July until killed by frost. It develops numerous fleshy stems that grow out from a central crown and lie flat on the ground. The stems

TABLE 13

HERBICIDAL MATERIALS AND RATES FOR CONTROL OF COMMON TURFGRASS WEEDS

(See discussion of individual chemicals in Chapter 8 on use and limitations of materials)

Weed	*Herbicide*	*Rate per 1,000 sq. ft. (actual toxicant)*	*When to apply*	*Remarks*
Black Medic	2,4-D 2,4,5-T	0.4 to 0.5 oz. 0.4 to 0.5 oz.	Nov. and Mar. Nov. and Mar.	2 appl. 2 appl.
Buttercup	2,4-D	0.5 to 0.7 oz.	Spring	Repeat appl.
Carpet Weed	Pot. cyan. + 2,4-D, *or* Disod. methyl arson. + 2,4-D	3.5 oz. + 0.3 oz. 3.0 oz. + 0.3 oz.	When active When active	Repeat appl. Repeat appl.
Catsear (False dandelion)	2,4-D	0.4 oz.	When active	1 appl.
Chickweed (All species)	2,4,5-TP Sodium arsenite	0.6 oz. 0.4 to 0.6 oz.	Late fall and early spring Early fall	Apply at both times 3 to 4 appl.
Cinquefoil (False strawberry)	2,4-D	0.4 to 0.5 oz.	When active	1 appl.
Clovers	2,4-D *or* 2,4,5-TP	0.4 to 0.5 oz.	Fall and early spring	Repeat appl.
Crabgrasses (Hairy and smooth)	Disod. meth. arson. *or* Amm. methyl arson. PMA *or* Sod. arsenite	1.5 to 3.0 oz. 0.6 to 0.7 oz. 0.2 oz. 0.4 to 0.6 oz.	Before seed heads form Before seed heads form Seedling stage (2 to 3 leaf) Seedlings to maturity	Repeat appl. Repeat appl. Repeat as new seedlings appear Repeat as new seedlings appear
Dallisgrass	Disod. meth. arson. + 2,4-D	3.0 oz. + 0.2 oz.	When growth starts	Repeat if recovery occurs

Dandelion	2,4-D	0.3 to 0.4 oz.	Fall or spring	1 appl.
Dichondra	2,4-D	0.3 to 0.4 oz.	When active	1 appl.
Goosegrass (Silver Crab)	Dacthal *or* Amm. methyl arson.	4.0 to 5.0 oz. 0.8 oz.	Preemergence or immediately after Before seed heads form	Trial basis only Repeat appl.
Ground Ivy	2,4-D	0.3 oz.	Spring	1 appl.
Kikuyugrass	Dalapon (Pre- and postemergence	3.0 to 4.0 oz.	Spring and early summer	Delay reseeding 6 to 8 weeks
Knotweed	2,4-D *or* Sod. arsenite	0.4 to 0.5 oz. 0.4 to 0.6 oz.	Seedling stage Seedling stage	Effective only on young plants (repeat)
Lambs Quarters	2,4-D	0.3 oz.	When active	1 appl.
Mallow	2,4-D	0.3 oz.	When active	1 appl.
Muhlenbergia (Nimble Will)	Amm. thiocyanate	Spot treat with solution of 1.0 lb. in 1 to 2 gal. water		Will kill permanent grasses
Nutgrass (Sedges)	2,4-D + Disod. methyl arson.	0.6 to 0.8 oz. + 3.0 oz.	Summer to early fall	Repeat in successive seasons until eradicated
Pearlwort	2,4-D *or* Endothal	Spot treat with solution of 2.0 oz. (active) per 1 gal. water 0.1 oz.	 When active	Apply with brush 2 appl. (10 day interval)
Pennywort	2,4,5-T *or* 2,4,5-T + 2,4-D	0.3 oz. 0.3 oz. (combined)	When active	Repeat if necessary

TABLE 13 (*Continued*)

Weed	*Herbicide*	*Rate per 1,000 sq. ft. (actual toxicant)*	*When to apply*	*Remarks*
Plantains (Broadleaf and Buckhorn)	2,4-D	0.3 oz.	Spring and fall	1 appl.
Poa annua (Annual Bluegrass)	Calcium arsen. (preemergence) *or*	12 to 14 lbs.	Prior to fall germination	High available phos. affects efficiency
	Endothal *or*	0.1 oz.	Spring	Trial basis only
	Lead arsenate	10 lbs.	Spring or fall	Annually
Purslane	2,4-D	0.4 to 0.5 oz.	Seedling stage	Repeat as new plants appear
Poison Ivy	Amino triozole	Spot spray with solution of 1.5 oz. in 2 gal. water when in full leaf		
Sorrel	2,4-D	0.6 to 0.8 oz.	Early fall	Repeat if plants recover
Spotted Spurge	Disod. methyl arson.	2.0 to 3.0 oz.	When active	2 to 3 appl.
Veronica	Potassium cyanate	3.0 oz.	Spring and fall	Repeat if necessary
Wild Garlic and Wild Onion	2,4-D (ester)	0.4 oz.	Spring and fall	Treat at both periods
Wintercress (Mustards)	2,4-D	0.3 oz.	Spring and fall	1 appl.
Yarrow	2,4-D *or* 2,4,5-TP	0.6 to 0.8 oz. 0.3 to 0.4 oz.	When active	Hard to kill Repeat if plants recover

are reddish in color. The leaves tend to develop in clusters at the ends of branches, and the small yellow flowers occur in the center of these clusters.

Purslane is particularly troublesome in new seedings. It is very tolerant of dry weather and makes very rapid growth at such periods, causing serious competition to young grass. It will not compete seriously with mature grass that is vigorous, but it often takes possession of bare areas where turf has been killed by disease or insects.

Fall seeding of new turf on areas infested with purslane seed will permit the grass to become established before the weed has a chance to develop the following spring. Cultivation of seedbeds for several months before seeding will kill it out effectively.

SANDBUR (*Cenchrus pauciflorus*) is an annual grass with flattened branched stems that often forms a solid mat close to the ground. The seedstalks bear spiny burs that contain the seeds. Plants usually are most abundant in roughs and other areas of low fertility where the desirable grasses will not compete with them. Seed production can be checked by burning over infested areas after the plants have matured. The grass will not compete successfully with Bermuda and other desirable grasses on good soil under close clipping. Sandbur can be readily controlled by repeated applications of arsenicals at standard rates.

SELFHEAL (*Prunella vulgaris*) is a dense-growing perennial that spreads by creeping rootstocks (rhizomes). The leaves are broad at the base and taper to a blunt tip. Under close clipping the plant develops many branches that completely choke the grass. The flowers are purplish to white and occur in groups of three on very short stems. Blooming takes place any time between late May and frost in the fall.

SORREL (*Rumex acetosella*). Sheep sorrel is a creeping perennial that spreads by runners just below the surface of the soil. New plants develop at the joints. It is adapted to dry locations and is very tolerant to high acidity and low fertility. Seeds are produced in abundance in branched heads borne on upright seedstalks. The heads must be cut early to reduce seed formation as the seeds mature in late May and June.

Sorrel will not compete with grass that is dense and vigorous. Good cultural practices that will produce a thick turf effectively suppress it. Where it has developed a dense cover and must be killed preparatory

TABLE 14

EFFECT OF HERBICIDES ON TURFGRASSES

Herbicide	*Kentucky Bluegrass*	*Red Fescue*	*Bent-grasses*	*Bermuda-grass*	*Zoysia*	*St. Augustine*	*Remarks*
Amm. meth. arsonate	Discol.	Discol.	Discol.	Discol.	Discol.	Discol.	Discoloration temporary and recovery rapid
Amino Triozole	Sterilant for seedbed treatment only. Delay seeding or vegetative planting for 6 to 8 weeks after treatment.						
Calcium arsenate	Tol.	Slight	Inj.	Tol.	Tol.	Tol.	Injury severe on close mowed bent
Calcium cyanamid	Sterilant for seedbed treatment only. Delay seeding or vegetative planting for 2 to 4 weeks after treatment.						
Chlordane	Tol.	Tol.	Tol.	Tol.	Tol.	Tol.	Slight temporary discoloration
Dacthal	Tol.	Inj.	Discol.	Tol.	Tol.	?	Information limited
Dalapon	Sterilant for seedbed treatment only. Delay seeding or vegetative planting for 6 to 8 weeks after treatment.						

Disod. meth. arsonate	Discol.	Discol.	Discol.	Discol.	Discol.	Discol.	Discoloration temporary and recovery rapid
Lead arsenate	Tol.	Tol.	Tol.	Tol.	Tol.	Tol.	Slow acting
Methyl bromide	Sterilant for seedbed treatment only. Delay seeding or vegetative planting 24 to 48 hrs. after cover removed.						
Phenyl mer. acetate (PMA)	Tol.	Tol.	Tol.	Tol.	Tol.	Tol.	Merion Kentucky bluegrass injured
Sodium arsenite	Discol.	Discol.	Discol.	Discol.	Discol.	Discol.	All grasses injured when used at renov. rates
Trichlor acetate (TCA)	Sterilant for eradication of vegetation in traps, parking areas, etc. Kills permanent grasses.						
2,4-D	Tol.	Tol.	Inj.	Tol.	Tol.	Tol.	Bents injured most by fall treatment
2,4,5-T	Tol.	Tol.	Inj.	Tol.	Tol.	Tol.	Bents injured most by fall treatment
2,4,5-TP (Silvex)	Tol.	Tol.	Inj.	Tol.	Tol.	Tol.	Bents injured most by fall treatment
VPM (Vapam)	Sterilant for seedbed treatment only. Delay seeding or vegetative planting 48 hrs. after treatment.						

to a renovation and reseeding program, two or three treatments of 2,4-D at standard rates, made in the early fall, usually will kill a large proportion of it.

SPEEDWELL (*Veronica serpyllifolia*) is a creeping perennial with branched prostrate stems that turn upright at their ends. The leaves on the creeping part of the stems are in pairs at the joints, while those on the upright part are alternate. The paired leaves are oblong and broader at the base than at the tip (egg-shaped). The single leaves are long and narrow. They are ovate to narrow and lance shaped, the latter type occur on the erect part of the stem. Small star-shaped blue or white flowers are borne in the axils of the leaves. The plants bloom from May to frost and produce large numbers of seeds. A closely related plant, called veronica, is used as a rock-garden ornamental. It often escapes and becomes a serious pest in surrounding lawns. This type has leaves that are somewhat scalloped and bears larger darker blue flowers. Speedwell is a hard-to-kill weed. Repeat treatments of the recommended chemicals usually are required.

SPURGE OR MILKPURSLANE (*Euphorbia maculata*), also called spotted spurge, is a tap-rooted annual. It is related to the common snow-on-the-mountain, a garden plant. It is low growing, and a single plant often will cover an area of 1 sq. ft. or more. It has a characteristic reddish-brown spot in the center of the leaf. When the stems are broken, they exude a milky juice that may produce a rash on the skin of persons sensitive to it. The small inconspicuous flowers occur in the axils of the leaves, and seed is abundant.

Milk purslane becomes a pest only when turf is weak. It will not compete with healthy vigorous grass. Brushing, combing, raking, and frequent mowing will aid materially in checking it.

WHITE CLOVER (*Trifolium repens*) is a perennial legume with a deep taproot. It spreads by creeping stems which have shallow roots at the joints. Because of this dual root system it can survive severe drought and can grow well on compacted soils that are saturated with water. White clover seeds profusely under close clipping and is difficult to eradicate after it is well established. It is undesirable on all playing areas of the golf course. It makes an uneven, slow-putting surface on greens. Fairways and tees containing clover will not provide a firm stance and will not hold up a ball or supply sufficient resistance to a club head for good shot making.

The growth of white clover is checked by frost and cold weather.

High-nitrogen fertilizers and soil aeration that will keep grass growing vigorously at such periods will help to check its spread.

WILD GARLIC AND WILD ONION (*Allium* spp.) are closely related. The names often are used interchangeably. They are perennial and propagate by both underground and aerial bulblets. The former develop from the main bulb during the spring and summer. Aerial bulblets develop in a flowering head borne on a seedstalk. The leaves are slender and tubular, similar to those of cultivated onions.

Wild garlic and onion can be killed by repeated fall or early spring treatments with 2,4-D. The ester form of this chemical is reported to be the best. It should be applied as a spray at a rate of 1½ lb. of the clear acid per acre. The first treatment will kill the aboveground foliage and soft bulbs from which it arises. It will not kill hard bulblets in the soil. New plants will develop in the fall from these bulbs. A second treatment should be made early the following spring to kill these young plants before they set new bulblets. It is sometimes necessary to make spring treatments in three or four successive years to secure complete eradication.

YARROW (*Achillea millefolium*) is a perennial that spreads by underground rootstocks. Under close clipping the branched plant becomes prostrate and forms a dense mat. The branches root at many of the joints. This distinguishes yarrow from wild carrot. The latter weed develops a flat tuft of branches from a central taproot, but the branches do not root at the joints. The leaves have many lobes from a central stem and are lacy and fernlike in appearance. When unclipped the stems grow to a height of 2 ft. or more. Small white flowers are borne in dense flattened clusters at the ends of the branches. Yarrow has a heavy tough root system. Under close clipping it forms a dense surface mat that is quite wear resistant and drought tolerant. It is sometimes seeded on tees and other areas subject to hard use because of its wearing qualities. It is of only limited value for this purpose owing to the development of coarse heavy crowns and stems which produce an uneven humpy condition after two to three years.

IDENTIFICATION OF SPECIAL-PURPOSE TURF GRASSES BY VEGETATIVE CHARACTERS

Identification keys are built on the basis of pairs of contrasting characters. For example, all of the grasses included in the following key are divided into two main groups (*A* and *AA*) depending upon whether the bud leaf is *rolled* (*A*) or *folded* (*AA*). If a grass to be identified is determined to have a rolled bud leaf, all of the grasses listed in the folded or *AA* group are automatically eliminated from consideration. Similarly, if auricles are absent (*BB* group under *A*) all of the grasses in this group are eliminated and the grass will be found among those listed under the *B* group. Thus, by a process of elimination using each contrasting set of characters (as *C* and *CC*, *D* and *DD*, etc.) in alphabetical order, a correct identification finally is reached. To further illustrate, if a grass to be identified has a rolled bud leaf, it would fall in the *A* group. If auricles are present, it is in the *B* section of the *A* group. If leaf margins are smooth, it falls in the *C* of the *B* group section, and if the ligule is parchmentlike and there are no stolons, it classifies under *D* of the *C* group. The correct identification then is annual (Italian) ryegrass. Similarly, if the grass did not have auricles, it would have been necessary to determine successively in the *BB* group, the *C* or *CC*, *D* or *DD*, *E* or *EE*, *F* or *FF*, *G* or *GG*, and *H* or *HH* characters. If it had the strongly stoloniferous character of the single *C*, it would be necessary to consider the successive character contrasts in this class.

Identification Key

A Leaves rolled in bud
- *B* Auricles present
  - *C* Leaf margins smooth
    - *D* Ligule entire; a parchmentlike curtain. No stolons. Annual (Italian) ryegrass (*Lolium multiflorum*)
    - *DD* Ligule a ring of hairs. Stoloniferous
      - *E* Leaf blades broad and coarse. Japanese lawngrass (*Zoysia japonica*)
      - *EE* Leaf blades narrow and medium fine. Manilagrass (*Zoysia matrella*)
  - *CC* Leaf margins serrated
    - *D* Ligule entire, parchmentlike, sometimes fleshy. No rhizomes. Meadow (tall) Fescue (*Festuca elatior*)
    - *DD* Ligule a ring of hairs. Heavy rhizones. Quackgrass (*Agropyron repens*)
- *BB* Auricles absent
  - *C* Strongly stoloniferous
    - *D* Leaf blades and sheaths hairy. Buffalograss (*Buchloe dactyloides*)

DD Leaf blades and sheaths smooth

E Ligule a ring of hairs. Bermudagrass (*Cynodon dactylon*)

EE Ligule entire and parchmentlike

F Ligule long. Leaves fine textured. Velvet bentgrass (*Agrostis canina*)

FF Ligule short. Leaves medium textured. Creeping bent-grass (*Agrostis palustris*)

CC None to few short stolons

D Blades and sheaths hairy

E Ligule a ring of hairs. Crabgrass (*Digitaria sanguinalis*)

EE Ligule entire and parchmentlike

F Sweet, pungent odor when crushed. Sweet vernalgrass (*Anthoxanthum odoratum*)

FF No characteristic odor. Velvetgrass (*Holcus lanatus*)

DD Blades and sheaths smooth

E Ligule long

F Leaf margins serrated. Tall oatgrass (*Arrhenatherum elatius*)

FF Leaf margins smooth. Redtop (*Agrostis alba*)

EE Ligule short

F Numerous fleshy rhizomes. Smooth bromegrass (*Bromus inermis*)

FF None to few short rhizomes

G Ligule crimped. Crested wheatgrass (*Agropyron cris-tatum*)

GG Ligule smooth (not crimped)

H Leaves coarse. Base of stem bulbous. Timothy (*Phleum pratense*)

HH Leaves medium fine. Stem base not bulbous. Co-lonial bentgrass (*Agrostis tenuis*)

AA Leaves folded in bud

B Auricles present. Perennial ryegrass (*Lolium perenne*)

BB Auricles absent

C Leaf sheath hairy. Long ligule. Dallisgrass (*Paspalum dila-tatum*)

CC Leaf sheath smooth. Short ligule

D Rhizomes present

E Leaf blades narrow, stiff, and bristlelike. Veins on upper leaf surface prominent. Creeping red fescue (*Festuca rubra*)

EE Leaf blades flattened and soft. Veins on upper surface of leaf obscure

F Foliage bluish green. Stems severely flattened. Canada bluegrass (*Poa compressa*)

FF Foliage bright apple green. Stems only slightly flattened. Kentucky bluegrass (*Poa pratensis*)

DD No rhizomes

E Stoloniferous

F Collar normal

G Stolons thick. Short internodes. Bahiagrass (*Paspalum notatum*)

GG Stolons slender. Long internodes

H Leaves long, slender and smooth. Adapted only in Northern Cool Humid region. Rough stalk bluegrass (*Poa trivialis*)

HH Leaves short, broad and sometimes hairy at collar. Adapted only in Southern Warm Humid region. Carpetgrass (*Axonopus affinis*)

FF Collar petiolate

G Internodes of stolons about equal in length. One shoot coming from each node. Centipede grass (*Eremochloa ophiuroides*)

GG Internodes of stolons two or more compressed, followed by one long internode, making two or more shoots appear to come from one location. St. Augustinegrass (*Stenotaphrum secundatum*)

EE No stolons

F Leaf blades narrow, stiff, and bristlelike. Veins on upper leaf surface prominent

G New shoots extravaginal. Chewings fescue (*Festuca rubra commutata*)

GG New shoots intravaginal

H Leaves fine textured. Fine-leaved fescue (*Festuca capillata*)

HH Leaves coarse textured. Sheep fescue (*Festuca ovina*)

FF Leaf blades wide and soft. Veins on upper surfaces obscure

G Leaf blades short and medium fine with tendency to curl at tips. Leaf blades show a light line along each side of midrib when examined with lens against light. Annual bluegrass (*Poa annua*)

GG Leaf blades medium long and medium to coarse. No light lines along midrib

H Leaf blades medium coarse. Plant heads *under close clipping*. Annual goosegrass (*Eleusine indica*)

HH Leaf blades long and coarse. Will not head under close clipping. Perennial. Orchardgrass (*Dactylis glomerata*)

Description of Characters Used in Identification Key

1. *The Grass Leaf.* A grass leaf starts growth from a joint (node) on the stem. Under close clipping the stem is kept short with the joints crowded together, so that many leaves appear to develop at the same location. The leaf consists of two main parts: the sheath and the blade. The leaf sheath encloses the stem or the new bud leaf that arises at the top of the stem. The margins of the sheath may overlap or may sometimes form a solid cylinder to the junction with the blade. The leaf blade is the upper part of the leaf that extends out and away from the stem, from the point where it joins the sheath.

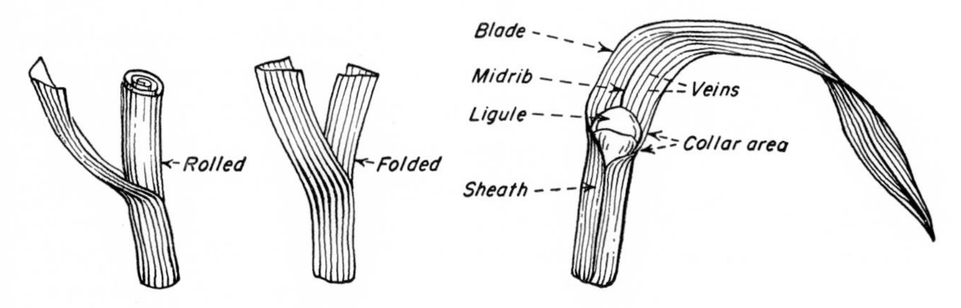

Fig. 41. Types of bud leaves.

Fig. 42. The grass leaf.

2. *Bud Leaf.* The bud leaf is the youngest or topmost leaf on a developing stem. It is clasped by the sheath of the next lower leaf. Grass leaves are either rolled or folded when in the bud stage. They do not open out to their mature form until they have emerged completely from the enveloping sheath.

3. *Auricle.* On some grasses two thickened fingerlike appendages develop on the margins of the leaf, just at the junction of the sheath and the blade. These projections are called auricles. They clasp the stem and assist in preventing the weight of the blade from pulling the sheath away from the bud leaf or young stem.

4. *Leaf Margins.* Margins of leaves may be smooth or serrated (like saw teeth). The serrated character of the margin can be determined by holding the leaf by the tip of the blade with one hand and drawing the thumb and first finger of the other hand along the margin of the leaf from the tip toward the sheath.

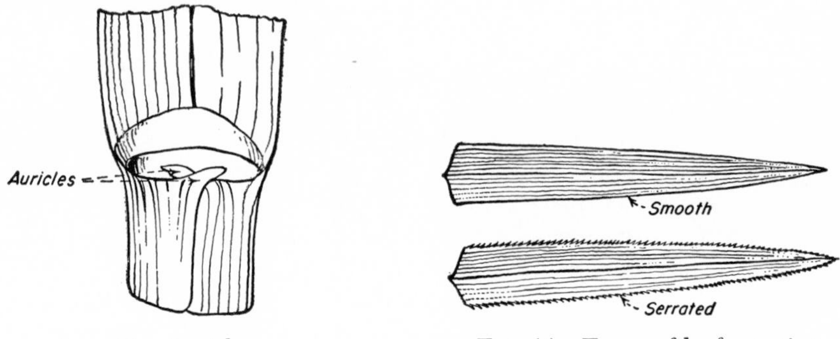

FIG. 43. Auricles.

FIG. 44. Types of leaf margins.

5. *Ligule.* The ligule is a curtainlike appendage on the inner (upper) side of the leaf at the junction of the sheath and blade. Ligules may be entire and parchmentlike, or they may consist entirely of a semicircle of hairs. Parchment-type ligules may be smooth or crimped like a

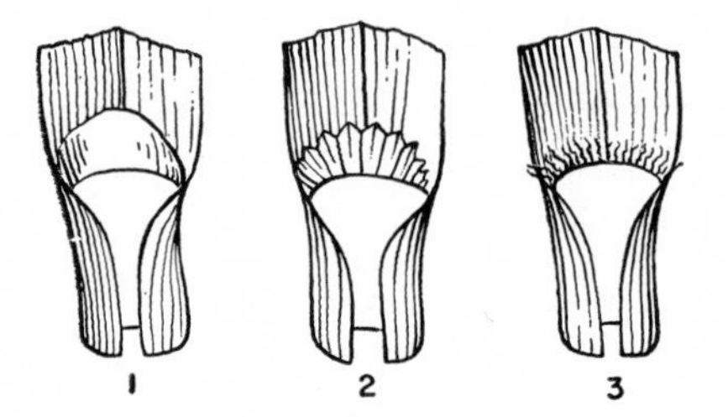

FIG. 45. Types of ligules. (1) Smooth. (2) Crimped. (3) Ring of hairs.

folding fan. Solid ligules vary in length from their tip to the point of attachment. A ligule is considered "long" when its length from tip to base is more than one-half the width of the leaf blade. A short ligule is less than one-half the width of the leaf blade.

6. *Leaf Collar.* The leaf collar is a thickened area on the back (underside) of the leaf at the junction of the sheath and blade. The collar may extend across the entire width of the blade, or it may be divided into

two parts by the mid vein of the leaf. Collars may be smooth or pubescent (covered with fine hairs). They may be normal or petiolate (constricted so that an indentation is produced in the margins of the leaf at the junction of the sheath and blade).

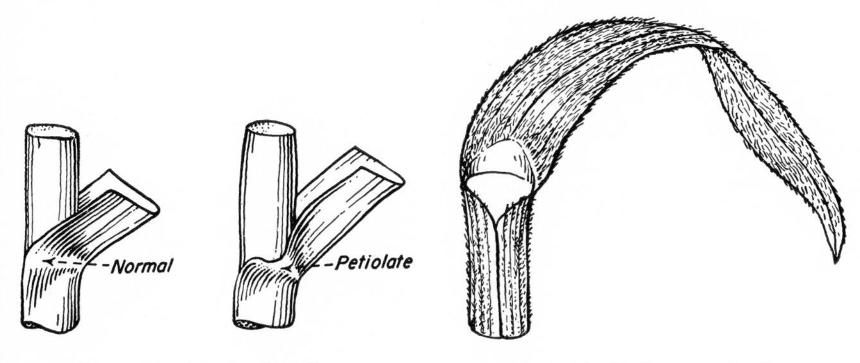

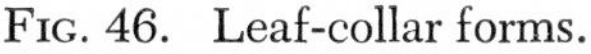

FIG. 46. Leaf-collar forms.

FIG. 47. Pubescent leaf.

7. *Pubescence.* Leaf blades, sheaths, and collars may be pubescent (hairy) or glabrous (smooth). The hairs are very fine and, when present, give the leaf a downy appearance. They may cover the entire leaf or may occur only on the blade, collar, or sheath.

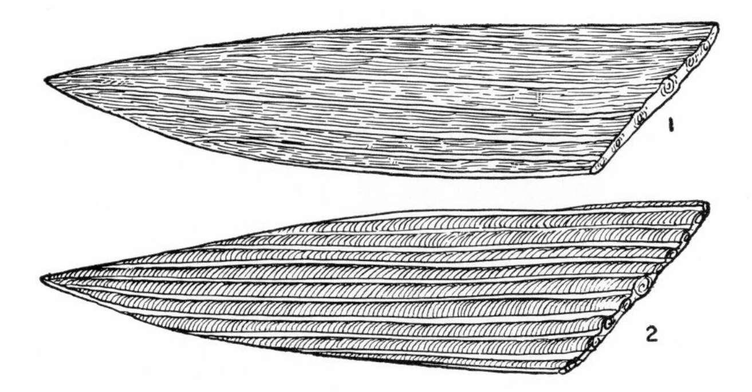

FIG. 48. Semi-diagrammatic sections of grass leaves showing types of veination. (1) Obscure. (2) Prominent.

8. *Leaf Veins.* Grass leaves have a heavy mid vein (the midrib) running through the center of the leaf longitudinally from the base of the sheath to the tip of the blade. A number of secondary veins run through the leaf on each side of the mid vein and parallel to it. In

some grasses the veins are imbedded in the fleshy part of the leaf and are obscure, giving the upper leaf surface a flat smooth appearance. In others, the veins extend above the upper surface of the leaf, giving it a corrugated appearance.

9. *Light Lines.* The leaves of some grasses have a narrow band of very thin tissue on both sides of the midrib and immediately adjacent

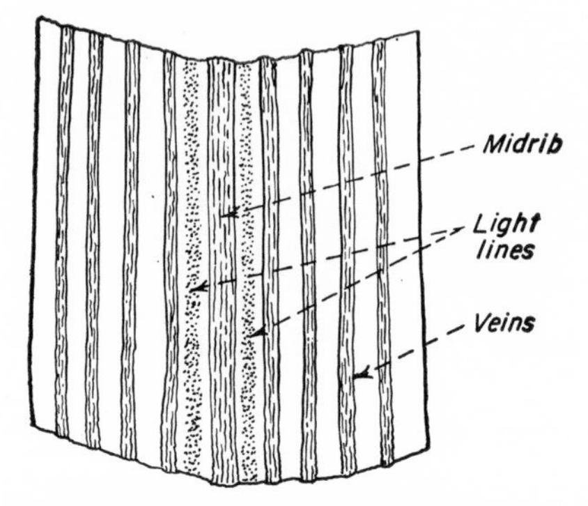

FIG. 49. Diagrammatic section of leaf blade showing location of light lines.

to it. If the leaf is examined with a low-power hand lens against the light, these thin bands of tissue show as whitish, semitransparent lines, running parallel to the midrib for the full length of the blade.

10. *Texture of Blade.* Leaf blades may be stiff and bristlelike or soft and flat. Stiff bristlelike blades usually are fleshy and appear somewhat

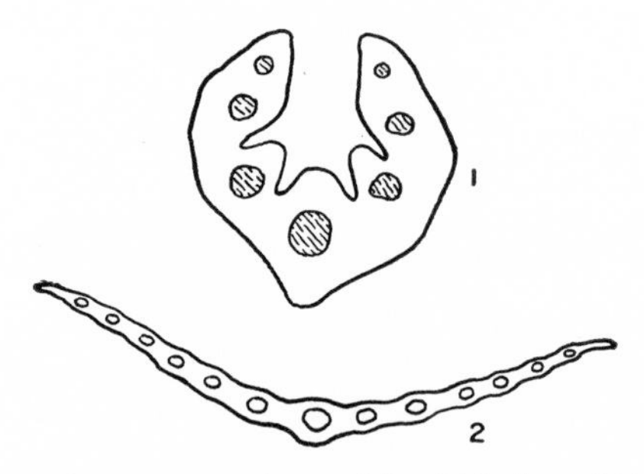

FIG. 50. Diagrammatic cross-sections of leaf blades. (1) Fleshy, bristlelike. (2) Flat, soft.

U-shaped in cross section. In contrast, soft-textured blades are V-shaped in cross section. Leaf-blade texture usually may be determined readily by rubbing the palm of the hand back and forth, gently, over the surface of the grass.

11. *Stem Type.* The stems (culms) of grasses are of three types: severely flattened, moderately flattened (oval), and round. The severely and moderately flattened types usually are associated with folded bud leaves, while the round type normally has rolled bud leaves. The

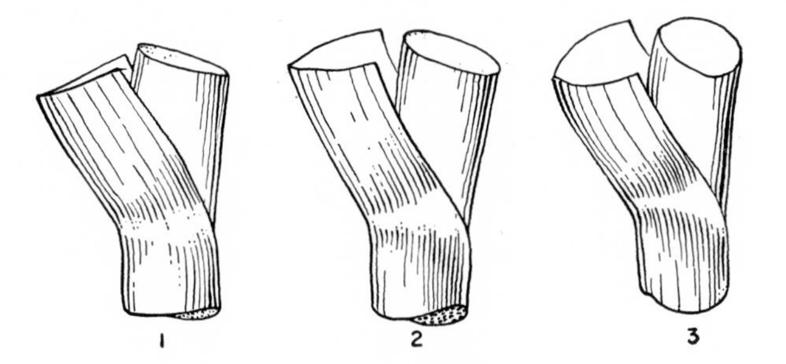

FIG. 51. Stem types. (1) Severely flattened. (2) Moderately flat. (3) Round.

stem type is determined in close-clipped grasses by examining the shortened portion below the lowest leaf. This section of the stem usually is enclosed by the sheath of the bottom leaf.

12. *Bulbous Stem Base.* Some grasses produce bulbous structures (corms) at the base of the stems. New shoots develop from these

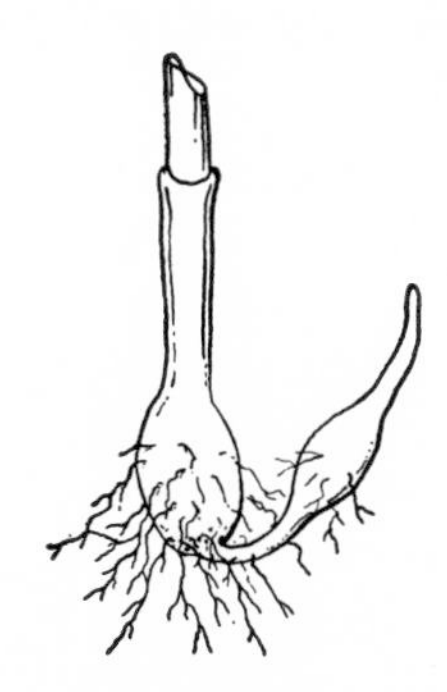

FIG. 52. Bulbous stem base.

structures, so that the base of the stem is swollen and similar in appearance to a young onion. Timothy is the only grass of the special-purpose group that has this characteristic.

13. *Rhizome.* A rhizome (rootstock) is a modified stem that grows underground and can produce roots and shoots at the joints. Ordinarily, they are roughly parallel to the surface of the ground and are

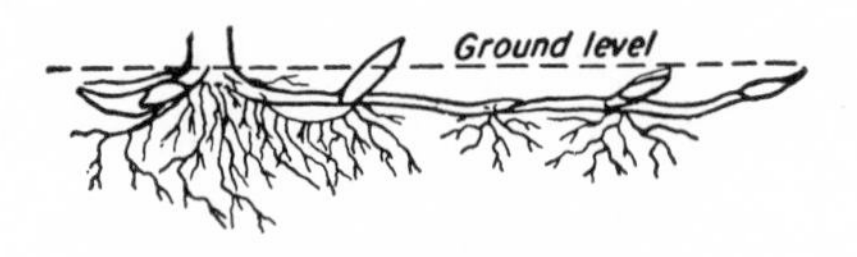

FIG. 53. Rhizome.

heavier and more fleshy than roots. Rudimentary leaves called bracts are present at the joints and indicate that the rhizomes are true stems.

14. *Stolon.* A stolon is a modified stem that grows aboveground and produces roots and new shoots at the joints. The stolons of creeping

FIG. 54. Stolon.

bentgrass, Bermudagrass, and similar creeping grasses are used to propagate new turf vegetatively.

15. *Intravaginal and Extravaginal Growth Habit.* New shoots arise from the base of grass plants in two ways. Buds may form on the crown of the plant inside the sheath of the basal leaf of the stem or outside (independently) of it. When buds form inside the basal leaf sheath, the growth habit is *intravaginal.* Growth habit is *extravaginal* when buds form outside (independently) of the basal leaf sheaths of older stems. Grasses that are intravaginal growers have groups of two or more stems in tight clusters, each stem of the group having the appearance of arising from the same location. Where growth is extravaginal, each stem is independent of all the others. In making growth-habit determinations, only the basal leaf sheath of a stem should be examined. Grass stems are not branched, and new shoots do not occur above the basal joint.

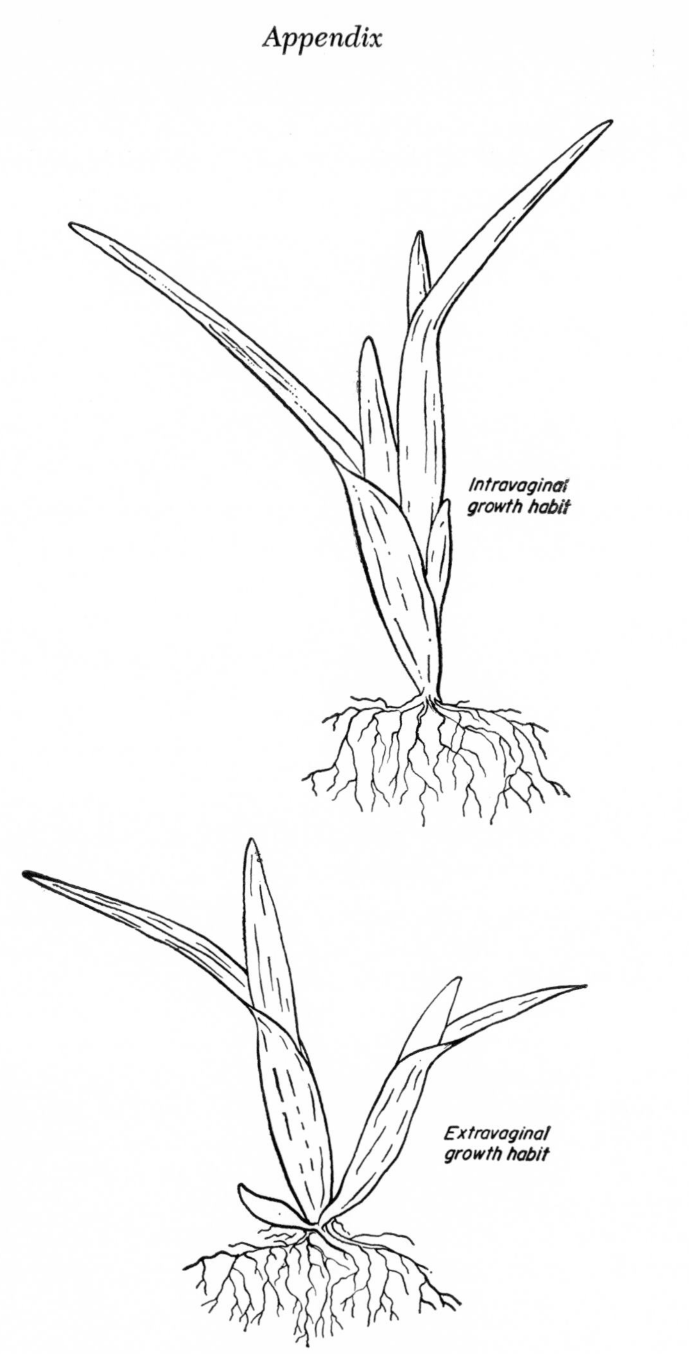

Fig. 55. Intravaginal and extravaginal growth habit.

TABLE 15

Climatic and Use Adaptations of Turf Grasses for the Golf Course

Common name	*Scientific name*	*Regional adaptation (major)*	*Major uses on golf course*	*Relative value for use indicated*
Annual bluegrass	*Poa annua*	Northern humid	Greens, tees, fairways	Questionable
		Southern (Warm Humid and Irrigated)	Winter greens and tees	Excellent
Bahiagrass	*Paspalum notatum*	Southern (Warm Humid and Irrigated)	Tees and fairways	Shows promise
Beachgrasses	*Ammophila* spp.	Northern Humid	Bunkers and dunes	Good
Bermudagrass	*Cynodon dactylon*	Southern (Warm Humid and Irrigated)	Greens, tees, fairways, roughs	Excellent
Broomsedgegrass	*Andropogon virginicus*	Northern and Southern Humid	Bunkers and dunes	Good
Buffalograss	*Buchloe dactyloides*	West Central (nonirrigated)	Fairways, tees, roughs	Excellent
Canada bluegrass	*Poa compressa*	Northern Humid	Fairways, tees, roughs	Good in mixtures
Carpetgrass	*Axonopus affinis*	Southern (Warm Humid)	Fairways, tees, roughs	Very good
Centipedegrass	*Eremochloa ophiuroides*	Southern (Warm Humid and Irrigated)	Fairways, tees, roughs	Very good
Chewings fescue	*Festuca rubra commutata*	Northern Humid, West Central (Irrigated)	Fairways, tees, roughs	Very good
Colonial bentgrass	*Agrostis tenuis*	Northern Humid, West Central (Irrigated)	Greens, tees, fairways, roughs	Excellent
Creeping bentgrass	*Agrostis palustris*	Northern Humid, West Central (Irrigated)	Greens, tees, fairways	Excellent
Creeping red fescue	*Festuca rubra* (*genuina*)	Northern Humid, West Central (Irrigated)	Fairways, tees	Very good
Crested wheatgrass	*Agropyron cristatum*	West Central (nonirrigated)	Fairways, tees, roughs	Excellent
Dallisgrass	*Paspalum dilatatum*	Southern (Warm Humid and Irrigated)	Roughs, nonuse areas	Very good
Grama grasses	*Bouteloua* spp.	West Central (nonirrigated)	Fairways, tees, roughs	Good
Indian ricegrass	*Oryzopsis hymenoides*	Southern (Dry nonirrigated)	Roughs, nonuse areas	Fair
Italian ryegrass	*Lolium multiflorum*	Northern and Southern (Humid and Irrigated)	Temporary and winter turf	Good
Japanese lawngrass	*Zoysia japonica*	Southern (Warm Humid and Irrigated)	Fairways, tees, roughs	Very good

TABLE 15 (Continued)

Common name	Scientific name	Regional adaptation (major)	Major uses on golf course	Relative value for use indicated
Kentucky bluegrass ..	*Poa pratensis*	Northern Humid, West Central (Irrigated)	Fairways, tees, roughs	Fair to good
Little bluestem grass .	*Andropogon scoparius*	West Central (nonirrigated)	Roughs, nonuse areas	Fair
Manilagrass	*Zoysia matrella*	Southern (Warm Humid and Irrigated)	Fairways, tees, roughs	Very good
Orchardgrass	*Dactylis glomerata*	Northern Humid	Roughs, nonuse areas	Fair
Perennial ryegrass ...	*Lolium perenne*	Northern and Southern (Humid and Irrigated)	Temporary and winter turf	Fair
Redtop	*Agrostis alba*	Northern and Southern (Humid and Irrigated)	Temporary cover	Excellent in mixtures
		Southern (Warm Humid and Irrigated)	Winter greens and tees	Excellent
Rhodesgrass	*Chloris gayana*	Southern (Warm Humid)	Roughs, nonuse areas	Fair
Roughstalk bluegrass .	*Poa trivialis*	Northern Humid	Fairways and shade	Fair
Sand dropseed	*Sporobulus cryptandrus*	Southern (Dry nonirrigated)	Roughs, nonuse areas	Good
Sheep fescue	*Festuca ovina*	Northern Humid	Roughs, bunkers	Excellent
Smooth bromegrass ..	*Bromus inermis*	West Central (nonirrigated)	Roughs	Shows promise
St. Augustinegrass ..	*Stenotaphrum secundatum*	Southern (Warm Humid and Irrigated)	Shade	Shows promise
Sudangrass	*Sorghum vulgare sudanese*	West Central (nonirrigated)	Temporary cover	Fair
Tall fescue	*Festuca elatior (arundinacea)*	Northern Humid, West Central (Irrigated)	Fairways, tees, roughs	Very good
Tall oatgrass	*Arrhenatherum elatius*	Northern Humid	Roughs, nonuse areas	Fair
Timothy	*Phleum pratense*	Northern Humid	Roughs, nonuse areas	Good
Velvet bentgrass	*Agrostis canina*	Northern Humid, West Central (Irrigated)	Greens, fairways	Excellent
Weeping lovegrass ..	*Eragrostis curvula*	Southern (Warm Humid)	Roughs, bunkers, sand dunes	Good
Western wheatgrass .	*Agropyron smithii*	West Central (nonirrigated)	Roughs, tee and fairway mixtures	Very good

TABLE 16

Time and Rate of Seeding the Turf Grasses

Grass	Best seeding time	Seeding rate per 1,000 sq. ft., lb.						
		Greens		Tees		Fairways		Other areas
		Winter	Permanent	Winter	Permanent	Winter	Permanent	
Annual bluegrass	Early fall	10	4	10	4			
Bahiagrass	Spring	...	...	...	4–6	...	4–6	1–2
Bermudagrass	Spring	...	3–5		3–5	...	2	½–1
Buffalograss	Spring	...	...	...	1–1½	...	1–1½	½–¾
Canada bluegrass	Fall, early spring	...	...	10–25% of mixtures seeded at 2–4 lb. for permanent turf				
Carpetgrass	Spring, early summer	...	...	...	3–5	...	2	½–1
Chewings and red fescue	Fall, early spring	10–20	...	...	4–6	...	3–5	2
Colonial bentgrass	Fall, early spring	3–6	2–4	...	2–4	...	1–2	...
Creeping bentgrass	Fall, early spring	3–6	1–2	...	1–2	...	1–2	...
Crested wheatgrass	Fall, early spring	...	...	...	1–2	...	½–1	¼–½
Dallisgrass	Spring	...	...	...	...	...	...	2–4
Grama grass	Spring	...	...	...	1–2	...	¾–1½	½–1
Indian ricegrass	Fall	...	...	...	...	...	...	15% of mixtures seeded at rate of ¼–½ lb.
Italian and domestic ryegrass	Fall, spring	20–80	...	10–12	...	10–12		
Kentucky bluegrass	Fall, early spring	8–10	...	8–10	2–4	...	2–4	
Little bluestem grass	Spring	...	...	...	...	...	...	¼–½
Orchardgrass	Early fall, spring	...	...	...	...	...	...	¾–1½
Redtop	Fall, spring	8–10	...	8–10	10–20% of mixtures seeded at rate of 2–4 lb. for permanent turf			

TABLE 16 (*Continued*)

Grass	*Best seeding time*	*Seeding rate per 1,000 sq. ft., lb.*						
		Greens		*Tees*		*Fairways*		*Other areas*
		Winter	*Permanent*	*Winter*	*Permanent*	*Winter*	*Permanent*	
Rhodesgrass	Early spring	...	...	...	...	...	...	¼–½
Roughstalk bluegrass	Fall, spring	...	...	...	...	...	2–4	25% of mixture for shade
Sand dropseed	When moisture good	...	...	...	...	...	...	1–2 oz.
Sheep fescue	Fall, early spring	...	...	...	...	...	...	2
Smooth bromegrass	Spring	...	...	...	2–3	...	1–2	½–1
Sudangrass	Late spring, summer	...	...	...	...	...	...	½–¾
Tall fescue	Fall, spring	...	...	...	4–6	...	2–4	1–2
Tall oatgrass	Fall, spring	...	...	...	...	...	...	½–1
Timothy	Fall, spring	...	...	...	...	...	...	½
Velvet bentgrass	Fall, early spring	...	2–3					
Weeping lovegrass	Spring	...	...	...	...	...	...	¼–½
Western wheatgrass	Spring	...	...	25–40% in mixtures seeded at rate of 1–2 lb. for permanent turf				½–¾

TABLE 17

QUALITY CHARACTERISTICS OF GOOD SEED OF THE TURF GRASSES

Grass	*Minimum purity, %*	*Minimum germination, %*	*Approximate number of seeds per pound*	*Comments*
Annual bluegrass	80	60	2,250,000	Quantity very limited
Bahiagrass	75	80	160,000	Quantity very limited
Beachgrasses	...	...	...	No seed available
Bermudagrass	95	85	1,750,000	Abundant
Broomsedgegrass	...	...	...	No seed available
Buffalograss	85	50	36,500 (burs)	Supplies variable
Canada bluegrass	95	85	2,250,000	Fair quantity available
Carpetgrass	90	90	1,125,000	Fair quantity available
Centipedegrass	...	...	...	No seed available
Chewings and red fescue	95	85	600,000	Abundant
Colonial bentgrass	95	90	7–8,000,000	Abundant
Creeping bentgrass	95	90	6–7,000,000	Abundant
Crested wheatgrass	90	85	325,000	Abundant
Dallisgrass	75	60	160,000	Quantity limited
Grama grasses	40	75	5–800,000	Supplies variable
Indian ricegrass	90	85	140,000	Quantity limited
Japanese lawngrass	...	...	...	No seed available
Kentucky bluegrass	95	75	2,250,000	Abundant
Kikuyugrass	...	...	...	No seed available
Little bluestem grass	40	60	260,000	Supplies variable
Manilagrass	...	...	...	No seed available
Orchardgrass	95	85	750,000	Abundant
Redtop	95	90	5,750,000	Abundant
Rhodesgrass	90	70-80	2,000,000	Supplies variable
Ryegrasses	98	95	275,000	Abundant
Roughstalk bluegrass	95	85	2,500,000	Imported (quantity limited)
Sand dropseed	80	Variable (high % hard seed)	5,000,000	Supplies variable
Sheep fescue	90	80	600,000	Fair quantity available
Smooth bromegrass	85	90	175,000	Abundant
St. Augustinegrass	...	...	...	No seed available
Sudangrass	90	90	150,000	Abundant
Tall fescue	95	90	500,000	Fair quantity available
Tall oatgrass	90	75	150,000	Fair quantity available
Timothy	98	95	150,000	Abundant
Velvet bentgrass	90	90	8,000,000	Supply limited
Weeping lovegrass	95	85	1,500,000	Fair quantity available
Western wheatgrass	85	80	125,000	Supply limited

TABLE 18

VEGETATIVE PROPAGATION OF THE TURF GRASSES

Grass	*Type of material*	*Method of planting*	*Quantity for 1,000 sq. ft.*	*Best planting season*
Beachgrass	Clones (3 to 5 stems)	Hand or machine setting in hills (12–18 in. centers)	450 clones	Pacific coast: Dec. to Mar. Atlantic coast: early spring
Bermudagrass	Shredded sod (sprigs)	In rows by hand or machine. Sprigs 6 in. apart in 12-in. rows Broadcast	5–10 sq. ft. of nursery sod 70–90 sq. ft. nursery sod	Warm Humid: Spring, summer, fall. Southwest Irrigated: fall
Broomsedge-grass	Mature plants	Hand planted in hills on 1½ to 2 ft. centers	250–450 plants	When dormant
Buffalograss	4-in. sod blocks	Blocks set in furrows on 1½–3-ft. centers	25–50 sq. ft.	Spring
Carpetgrass Centipede-grass	Shredded sod (sprigs)	In rows by hand or machine	5–10 sq. ft. of nursery sod	Spring, summer, fall
Creeping bentgrass	Shredded sod (stolons)	Broadcast on prepared seedbed	80–100 sq. ft. of nursery sod	Early fall
Japanese and Manilagrass (zoysia) Kikuyugrass St. Augustine-grass	2-in. sod blocks Shredded sod (sprigs)	2-in. sod blocks set on 12-in. centers. Sprigs 6–12 in. apart in 12-in. rows or sprigs broadcast on prepared seedbed	Sod blocks 30 sq. ft. Sprigs, 3–6 sq. ft. of nursery sod	Early summer
Velvet bent-grass	Shredded sod (stolons)	Broadcast on prepared seedbed	80–100 sq. ft. of nursery sod	Early fall

TABLE 19

Insecticides and Rates of Treatment for Turfgrass Insect Control

(Condensed from information in bulletins and published articles by research workers in the State Agricultural Experiment Stations of Connecticut, Florida, Iowa, New Jersey, New York, Pennsylvania, Rhode Island, and the United States Department of Agriculture)

Insecticide	*Formulation*	* *Treatment rate per 1,000 sq. ft.*	† *Time and number of appls.*	*Insects controlled*
Aldrin	Dust (2.5%) Granul. (2.0%) Wett. powder (25.0%) Emul. (2 lbs./gal.)	2¾ lbs. 3½ lbs. 4½ oz./20 gal. water ⅓ pt./20 gal. water	1 appl. when soil not frozen. Water in	All grubs, ants, sod webworms, mole crickets
Arsenate of lead	Concentrate	10 lbs.	When soil not frozen. Water in. Repeat annually at 2 to 3 lbs./1,000 sq. ft.	All grubs, common earthworms
Chlordane	Dust (5.0%) Granul. (5.0%) Wett. powder (40.0%) Emul. (8 lbs./gal.)	5 lbs. 5 lbs. 10 oz./20 gal. water ½ pt./20 gal. water	Apply as needed when soil not frozen. Double and apply in spring and fall for tropical earthworms	All grubs, ants, chinchbugs, sod webworms, army worms, cutworms, mole crickets, mites, leaf hoppers, common and tropical earthworms
DBCP (Nemagon EC-2 and Fumazone 70-E)	Emul. (70%)	1–2 qts. in 10–20 gals. water	Drench turf after appl. with 1 in. of water	Nematodes only
DDT	Dust (5.0%) Wett. powder (50.0%) Emul. (25.0%)	10 lbs. ½–1 lb. 1–2 pts./20 gal. water.	Apply as needed when soil not frozen. Water in	Japanese beetle, ants, sod webworms, army worms, cutworms, chinchbugs, leaf hoppers, frit fly

Dieldrin	Dust (1.5%) Granul. (1⅓ lbs.) Wett. powder (25.0%) Emul. (1½ lbs./gal.)	4½ lbs. 1⅓ lbs. 4½ oz./20 gal. water ⅜ pt./20 gal. water	Apply as needed when soil not frozen. Water in	All grubs, ants, chinchbugs, army worms, cutworms, sod webworms, mole crickets, chiggers, ticks
Heptachlor	Dust (2.5%) Granul. (2.5%) Wett. powder (25.0%) Emul. (5 lbs./gal.)	2¾ lbs. 2¾ lbs. 4½ oz./20 gal. water ⅓ pt./20 gal. water	Apply as needed when soil not frozen. Water in	All grubs, ants, sod webworms, army worms, cutworms, mole crickets
Malathion	Dust (5.0%) Wett. powder (25.0%) Emul. (5 lbs./gal.)	½ lb. 2½ oz./20 gal. water 1/32 pt. (½ fl. oz.)/ 20 gal. water	Apply as needed. Do not water in. (3 appls. at 3-week intervals)	Leafhoppers and mites For scale insects
Milky disease	Spore powder	2–8 lbs. per acre	1 appl. Spot the treatments. Very slow. Best for parks and large areas	Japanese beetle only
Parathion	Emul. (4 lbs./gal.) + Summer oil emul.	1/10 pt. + ½ pt. in 10 gal. water	2 appls. at 3-week intervals. 3rd appl. 3 weeks later using Parathion only	Scale insects

* Rates given in table are maximum. Should not be increased over quantities shown.

† Treatments for army worms, cutworms, and sod webworms should be made in late afternoon.

TABLE 20

Effective Fungicides and Rate of Treatment for Control of Turf Diseases

Disease	*Grasses commonly attacked*	*Material*	*Rate per 1,000 sq. ft.*	*Treatment interval*
Brown Patch (*Rhizoctonia solani*)	Bentgrasses, Bermuda, Bluegrasses, Carpetgrass, Centipede, Fescues, Ryegrasses, St. Augustine, Zoysias	Mercury chlorides Thiram Kromad	2–3 oz. 4–5 oz. 2–4 oz.	7–14 days
Copper Spot (*Gleocerospora sorghi*)	Bentgrasses	Cadminate Inorg. cadmium PMA Kromad	½ oz. 1–2 oz. 1 oz. 2–4 oz.	7–10 days
Damping Off (Many species of fungi)	All grasses	Treated seed and cultural practices		
Dollar Spot (*Sclerotinia homeocarpa*)	Bahiagrass, Bentgrasses, Bermuda, Bluegrasses, Centipede, Fescues, Ryegrasses, St. Augustine, Zoysias	Mercury chlorides Cadminate Inorg. cadmium	2–3 oz. ½ oz. 1–2 oz.	7–10 days
Fairy Ring (Toadstool, puffball, and mushroom fungi)	All grasses	Mercury chlorides PMA Cadmium compounds	1 oz./100 gal. water ½ oz./100 gal. water 1 oz./100 gal. water	Apply 40 gals. sol. per 100 sq. ft. at monthly intervals
Gray Leaf Spot (*Piricularia grisea*)	St. Augustine	Thiram Mercury chlorides PMA Kromad Thiram	3–4 oz. 1½ oz. 1 oz. 2–3 oz. 3–4 oz	7–10 days

Helminthosporium Blight (*H. erythrospilum*)	Bentgrasses	Acti-dione	60 p.p.m. (2 gal. water)	7–14 days
(*H. sativum*)	Bentgrasses and Kentucky Bluegrass	Kromad Captan	2–4 oz. 4 oz.	
(*H. dictyoides*)	Fescues	Zineb	2–4 oz.	
Leaf Spot of Kentucky Bluegrass (*Helminthosporium vagans*)	Kentucky Bluegrass varieties except Merion	Acti-dione Captan Zineb Kromad PMA	60 p.p.m.(2 gal. water) 4 oz. 2–4 oz. 2–4 oz. 1½ oz.	Before infection and every 7–14 days after
Mildew (*Erysiphe spp.*)	Bluegrasses and Fescues	Sulfur Acti-dione	dust 60 p.p.m.(2 gal. water)	When appears
Pink Patch or Red Thread (*Corticium fuciforme*)	Bents, Fescues Bluegrasses	Cadminate Mercury chlorides PMA Kromad	½ oz. 2–3 oz. 1 oz. 2–4 oz.	10–14 days
Pythium or Grease Spot (*Pythium* spp.)	Bents, Bluegrasses, Ryegrasses, Tall Fescues	Captan + Acti-dione Zineb + Acti-dione	1 lb. + 0.6 gm. 1 lb. + 0.6 gm.	5–10 days
Slime Molds (Species of *Myxomycetes*)	All turfgrasses	Any of above listed fungicides at minimum rate		
Snow Molds (*Fusarium nivale* and *Typhula itoana*)	Bentgrasses, Bermuda, Bluegrasses, Fescues, Ryegrasses, Zoysia	Mercury chlorides	3–4 oz.	Late fall
Algae	All turfgrasses	Hydrated lime	2–5 lbs.	When appears

Laboratory Methods for Evaluation of Putting Green Soil Mixtures

BY MARVIN H. FERGUSON, LEON HOWARD, AND MORRIS E. BLOODWORTH

Mid-Continent Director, USGA Green Section; Former Graduate Assistant and Associate Professor, respectively, at Texas A. & M. College

Reproduced by permission from the United States Golf Association *Journal and Turf Management,* Vol. XIII, No. 5, September, 1960 (pp. 30–33)

The suitability of soil mixtures for putting green use may be evaluated by the determination of certain physical characteristics. These characteristics may be determined by laboratory procedures.

Inasmuch as some of the physical measurements will be affected by the degree of compaction to which the mixtures are subjected, it becomes necessary to outline standard methods of procedure in order that laboratory data may be interpreted properly.

The most useful information in evaluation of putting green soil mixtures comes from determinations of permeability (hydraulic conductivity) and pore space relationships. Information with respect to mechanical analysis, mineral derivation, aggregation, bulk density, and moisture retention characteristics is helpful but is most useful in its relation to the permeability and pore space considerations.

Methods of procedure have been worked out by Kunze (4) and Howard (3) in connection with investigations they carried out while pursuing graduate studies at Texas A. & M. College. For the most part these procedures are modifications of methods in standard use and which are fully described in the literature.

Permeability (*Hydraulic conductivity*). The hydraulic conductivity of a soil is determined by the amount of non-capillary porosity of that soil and it is further affected by the size and continuity of the macropores. Because hydraulic conductivity is dependent upon the pore space relations within the soil, and because the noncapillary pore space is reduced by compaction, it becomes one of the most important measurements in the evaluation of a soil.

In preparing the sample, a copper cylinder three inches in length and two inches in diameter, open at both ends, is used. To the top of this cylinder is fixed a retaining ring of the same diameter and one inch in width. This ring is held on top of the cylinder by a broad rubber band such as may be cut from a bicycle inner tube. The other end of the cylinder is covered by a double thickness of cheese cloth and this is also held in place by a rubber band.

An air dry sample of a soil mixture is placed in the cylinder and settled by gentle tapping. Samples so prepared are placed in water and soaked for two hours to assure saturation. They are then transferred to a tension table. A tension of 40 cm. of water is imposed and samples remain on this table until they reach equilibrium.

It is assumed that samples which have reached equilibrium under this tension are at field capacity and that this is the stage at which compaction is capable of reaching its maximum. Samples are compacted with the impact type compactor shown in Figure 55. A compactor of this type is fully described by Bruce (2). Fifteen drops of the weight (45 foot pounds of energy) have been found to produce a degree of compaction in laboratory samples comparable to that found in undisturbed cores taken from a compacted putting green.

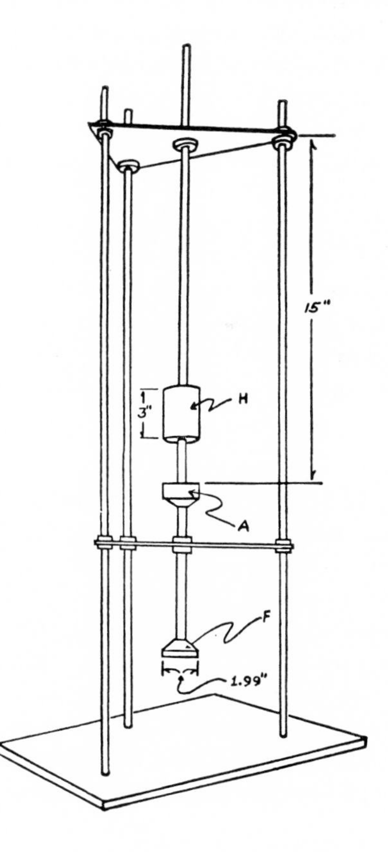

FIG. 56. An impact-type compactor. The soil sample is placed under the foot (F) of a plunger. The hammer (H) which weighs 3 lbs. is dropped 15 times over a distance of one foot. Thus 3 foot lbs. of energy is applied to the anvil (A) and thence to the soil sample at each drop. It has been found that 15 drops of the hammer will produce a degree of compaction comparable to that found in a severely compacted putting green, provided the soil contains moisture approximating field capacity.

After compaction, the one inch retainer ring is removed and the top of the compacted sample is trimmed smoothly to the level of the top of the cylinder. The compacted samples are replaced in water and soaked for 4 hours to insure saturation, weighed, and placed in the permeameter. The infiltration rate is measured with a ¼″ hydraulic head. The permeameter must be so constructed that it will permit very accurate control of the hydraulic head for each sample. Figure 2 shows the type permeameter used.

The sample is kept under a constant hydraulic head of ¼″ for 24 hours. The amount of water passing through the sample is measured at certain intervals of time and the conductivity is calculated and reported in inches per hour.

Porosity Determinations. When the sample is removed from the permeameter, it is again placed on the tension table at 40 cm. of water tension and allowed to come to equilibrium. The equilibrium or field capacity weight of the sample is recorded and the sample transferred to a pressure plate apparatus.

In the pressure plate apparatus, as described by Richards, et al (6) pressures of ½, 2/3 and one atmosphere are maintained and the equilibrium weight of the sample is recorded for each of these pressures. After making the one atmosphere measurement, the sample is trans-

FIG. 57. Cross-section view of the type of permeameter unit used to determine the hydraulic conductivity of soil cores in the laboratory.

ferred to a pressure membrane apparatus where 3, 6, and 15 atmosphere levels are measured and recorded. The pressure membrane apparatus is described in detail by Richards (5).

The sample is now oven-dried and weighed. Bulk density may be calculated by dividing the oven dry weight by the apparent volume of the sample.

Moisture Retention Characteristics. Capillary and noncapillary porosity measurements are made on a gravimetric basis. A tension or suction of 40 cm. of water is applied to saturated core samples. Water removed by this tension is considered to be that which occupies noncapillary pore space and that which is retained is considered to occupy capillary pore space. Baver (1) states that a tension of 40 cm. gives the best agreement between percolation and porosity.

The calculation of pore space is as follows:

$$\frac{S - w}{V} = \text{per cent noncapillary porosity,}$$

and

$$\frac{w - d}{V} = \text{per cent capillary porosity}$$

When S = weight of sample when saturated with water,
w = weight of sample at equilibrium with 40 cm. of water tension,
d = weight of sample oven dry
and V = apparent volume of the sample.

Mechanical analysis, bulk density, degree of aggregation, and mineralogical information are derived through standard procedures which are described in the literature.

References

1. Baver, L. D., *Soil Physics*, Third Edition, John Wiley and Sons, Inc., New York, 1956.
2. Bruce, R. R., An Impact Type Compactor, *Soil Sci. Soc. Am. Proc.* 19:253–257, 1955.
3. Howard, H. L., The Response of Some Putting Green Soils to Compaction. Master's thesis, unpublished, Texas A. & M. College, 1959.
4. Kunze, R. J., The Effects of Compaction of Different Golf Green Soil Mixtures on Plant Growth. Master's thesis, unpublished, Texas A. & M. College, 1956.
5. Richards, L. A., A pressure membrane extraction apparatus for soil solution. *Soil Sci.* 5:377–386, 1941.

6. Richards, L. A., and Fireman, M., Pressure plate apparatus for measuring moisture sorption and transmission by soils. *Soil Sci.* 56:395–404, 1943.

NOTE. An article in the same publication (reference above), titled "Specifications for a Method of Putting Green Construction," gives the following requirements for a putting green soil mixture, based on the above laboratory method:

> *Permeability.* After compaction at a moisture content of approximately field capacity as described by Ferguson, Howard, and Bloodworth [above article], a core of the soil mixture should permit the passage of not less than one-half inch of water per hour, nor more than one and one-half inches per hour, when subjected to a hydraulic head of 0.25 inches.
>
> *Porosity.* After compaction, a sample of the soil mixture should have a minimum total pore space of 33%. Of this pore space, the large (non-capillary) pores should comprise from 12% to 18%, and the capillary pores from 15% to 21%.
>
> Information with respect to bulk density, moisture retention capacity, mechanical analysis, and the degree of aggregation, in the hands of a soil physicist may be helpful in further evaluating the potential behavior of a putting green soil.

TABLE 21

SIZES OF STEEL AND CAST-IRON PIPE RECOMMENDED FOR TRANSPORTING GIVEN QUANTITIES OF WATER

Size of pipe, in.	*Quantity of water transported per min. gals.*		*Size of pipe, in.*	*Quantity of water transported per min. gals.*		*Size of pipe, in.*	*Quantity of water transported per min. gals.*	
	Steel pipe	*Cast-iron pipe*		*Steel pipe*	*Cast-iron pipe*		*Steel pipe*	*Cast-iron pipe*
¾	3–4	...	2½	39–65	43–75	5	230–420	250–460
1	5–7	...	3	66–110	75–120	6	420–720	460–790
1¼	8–14	...	3½	110–170	120–190	7	720–1000	790–1100
1½	15–22	...	4	170–230	190–250	8	720–1000	790–1100
2	23–38	25–42						

From F. E. Staebner, Supplemental Irrigation, *U. S. Dept. Agri. Farmers' Bull.* 1847, October, 1940.

TABLE 22

FRICTION LOSSES IN FITTINGS
(Reduced to equivalent feet of straight pipe)

	Size of fitting, in.									
	1	*1¼*	*1½*	*2*	*2½*	*3*	*4*	*5*	*6*	*8*
Elbow (90°)	3	4	5	6	7	8	11	14	16	21
Elbow (45°)	1	2	2	3	3	4	5	7	8	10
Tees	6	8	9	12	14	17	22	27	33	45
Valve (gate)	1	1	1	1	2	2	3	3	4	5
Valve (globe)	25	35	45	57	68	80	106	146	175	210
Valve (check)	7	10	11	14	16	20	26	33	40	51
Valve (angle)	15	18	22	27	33	40	56	70	85	110

TABLE 23

IRRIGATION DATA
FRICTION LOSS IN RUBBER HOSE
(Pounds per 100 ft.)

Gal. per min.	*Inside hose diameter, in.*				
	¾	1	1¼	1½	2
5	4.0	1.1	0.4	0.2	......
10	14.0	4.0	1.2	0.5	0.2
15	30.0	8.9	2.5	1.1	0.4
20	53.0	14.0	4.3	1.8	0.7
25	79.0	22.0	6.5	2.9	1.0
30	...	31.0	9.2	4.0	1.4
35	...	41.0	12.0	5.3	1.8
40	...	53.0	15.0	6.7	2.4
45	...	66.0	19.0	8.4	3.0
50	...	80.0	24.0	10.0	3.6
60	...	...	35.0	14.0	5.1
70	...	...	45.0	19.0	6.6
80	...	...	58.0	24.0	8.6
90	...	...	71.0	30.0	11.1
100	...	...	88.0	37.0	12.5
125	...	...	...	55.0	20.0
150	...	...	...	78.0	27.0
175	...	...	...	...	37.0
200	...	...	...	...	46.0

TABLE 24

FRICTION LOSSES IN ORDINARY IRON PIPE
(Loss of head in feet per 100 feet of pipe)

Gal. per min.	*Diameter of pipe, in.*										
	¾	*1*	*1¼*	*1½*	*2*	*2½*	*3*	*4*	*5*	*6*	*8*
10	38.00	11.70	3.05	1.43	0.50	0.17	0.07				
20	136.00	42.00	16.50	5.20	1.82	0.61	0.25				
30	...	89.00	21.10	11.00	3.84	1.29	0.54				
40	...	152.00	40.00	18.80	6.60	2.20	0.91	0.22			
50	...	...	60.00	28.40	9.90	3.32	1.38	0.34			
70	...	...	113.00	53.00	18.40	6.20	2.57	0.63	0.21		
90	...	...	...	84.00	29.40	9.80	4.08	1.06	0.29		
100	...	...	...	102.00	35.80	12.00	4.96	1.28	0.41		
120	...	...	...	143.00	50.00	16.80	7.00	1.71	0.57	0.25	
140	...	...	...	190.00	67.00	22.30	9.20	2.26	0.75	0.30	
160	...	...	...	...	86.00	29.00	11.80	2.90	0.96	0.40	
180	...	...	...	...	107.00	35.70	14.80	3.66	1.20	0.54	
200	...	...	...	...	129.00	43.10	17.80	4.40	1.48	0.62	
300	...	...	...	...	...	92.00	38.00	9.30	3.15	1.29	0.36
400	...	...	...	...	...	...	...	16.60	5.40	2.21	0.56
500	...	...	...	...	...	...	...	24.08	8.12	3.36	0.81
600	...	...	...	...	...	...	...	...	11.34	4.70	1.16
700	...	...	...	...	...	...	...	...	15.12	6.28	1.54
800	...	...	...	...	...	...	...	...	...	7.96	1.97
900	...	...	...	...	...	...	...	...	...	10.11	2.46
1,000	...	...	...	...	...	...	...	...	...	12.04	3.02
1,200	...	...	...	...	...	...	...	...	...	16.69	4.16
1,500	...	...	...	...	...	...	...	...	...	...	6.27
2,000	...	...	...	...	...	...	...	...	...	...	10.71

Note: To convert feet to pounds pressure per square inch divide by 2.31.

TABLE 25

RELATION BETWEEN VOLUME CAPACITY AND TIME REQUIRED TO DELIVER VARIOUS QUANTITIES OF WATER

Volume capacity, gal. per min.	*Time required to deliver water to a depth of*									
	½ in.		*1 in.*		*1½ in.*		*2 in.*		*2½ in.*	
	1,000 sq. ft. min.	*1 acre min.*	*1,000 sq. ft. min.*	*1 acre min.*	*1,000 sq. ft. min.*	*1 acre min.*	*1,000 sq. ft. min.*	*1 acre min.*	*1,000 sq. ft. min.*	*1 acre min.*
10	31.0	...	62.0	...	93.0	...	124.0	...	155.0	
15	20.7	...	41.4	...	62.1	...	82.8	...	103.5	
20	15.5	...	31.0	...	46.5	...	62.0	...	77.5	
25	12.4	...	24.8	...	37.2	...	49.6	...	62.0	
30	10.3	...	20.6	...	30.9	...	41.2	...	51.5	
35	8.9	...	17.8	...	26.7	...	35.6	...	44.5	
40	7.8	...	15.6	...	23.4	...	31.2	...	39.0	
45	6.9	...	13.8	...	20.7	...	27.6	...	34.5	
50	6.2	272	12.4	544	18.6	816	24.8	1,088	31.0	1,360
60	5.2	227	10.4	454	15.6	681	20.8	908	26.0	1,135
70	4.4	194	8.8	388	13.2	582	17.6	776	22.0	970
80	3.9	170	7.8	340	11.7	510	15.6	680	19.5	850
90	3.5	151	7.0	302	10.5	453	14.0	604	17.5	755
100	3.1	136	6.2	272	9.3	408	12.4	544	15.5	680
125	...	109	5.0	218	7.4	327	9.9	436	12.4	545
150	...	91	4.1	182	6.2	273	8.3	364	10.4	455
175	...	78	3.5	156	5.3	234	7.2	312	8.9	390
200	...	68	3.1	136	4.7	204	6.3	272	7.8	340
300	...	45	...	90	3.1	135	4.2	180	5.2	225
400	...	34	...	68	...	102	3.1	136	3.9	170
500	...	27	...	54	...	81	...	108	3.1	135
600	...	23	...	46	...	69	...	92	...	115
700	...	19	...	38	...	57	...	76	...	95
800	...	17	...	34	...	51	...	68	...	85
900	...	15	...	30	...	45	...	60	...	75
1,000	...	14	...	28	...	42	...	56	...	70

TABLE 26

CAPACITIES OF CENTRIFUGAL PUMPS IN GALLONS PER MINUTE

Size of pump	*Minimum*	*Maximum*	*Usual*
2	75	200	125
3	150	400	250
4	300	700	450
5	400	1,000	700
6	600	1,200	900
8	800	2,000	1,600

TABLE 27

CAPACITIES OF DEEP-WELL TURBINE PUMPS IN GALLONS PER MINUTE

Diameter of well, in.	*Usual minimum*	*Usual maximum*
4	20	70
6	50	200
7	100	300
8	150	500
10	250	800
12	400	1,200
14	500	1,500
16	700	1,800
18	1,000	3,000

TABLE 28

CAPACITIES OF TYPICAL POWER PLUNGER PUMPS

Diameter of water cylinder, in.	*Length of stroke, in.*	*Revolutions or strokes per min.*	*Discharge, U. S. gals. per min.*
Double-acting single-cylinder pumps			
6	8	35	69
8	8	35	122
Single-acting triplex pumps			
4	6	40	39
5	8	35	71
6	10	35	129
7	10	35	175
8	10	35	228
Double-acting duplex pumps			
4	6	40	52
6	8	35	138
8	10	35	304
9	10	35	385

Etcheverry and Harding, *Irrigation Practice and Engineering*, Vol. 1, McGraw-Hill Book Company, Inc., New York, 1933.

TABLE 29

APPROXIMATE HORSEPOWER REQUIREMENTS FOR IRRIGATION
(Efficiency of pumping plant, 50 per cent of theoretical. Use for estimating purposes only.)

Gal. per min.	*Horsepower required for elevations of*											
	10 ft.	*20 ft.*	*30 ft.*	*40 ft.*	*50 ft.*	*60 ft.*	*80 ft.*	*100 ft.*	*125 ft.*	*150 ft.*	*200 ft.*	*300 ft.*
10	0.05	0.10	0.15	0.20	0.25	0.30	0.40	0.50	0.62	0.75	1.00	1.50
20	0.10	0.20	0.30	0.40	0.50	0.60	0.80	1.00	1.25	1.50	2.00	3.00
30	0.15	0.30	0.45	0.60	0.75	0.90	1.20	1.50	1.87	2.25	3.00	4.50
40	0.20	0.40	0.60	0.80	1.00	1.20	1.60	2.00	2.50	3.00	4.00	6.00
50	0.25	0.50	0.75	1.00	1.25	1.50	2.00	2.50	3.12	3.75	5.00	7.50
60	0.30	0.60	0.90	1.20	1.50	1.80	2.40	3.00	3.75	4.50	6.00	9.00
80	0.40	0.80	1.20	1.60	2.00	2.40	3.20	4.00	5.00	6.00	8.00	12.00
100	0.50	1.00	1.50	2.00	2.50	3.00	4.00	5.00	6.25	7.50	10.00	15.00
125	0.62	1.25	1.87	2.50	3.12	3.75	5.00	6.25	7.81	9.37	12.50	18.75
150	0.75	1.50	2.25	3.00	3.75	4.50	6.00	7.50	9.37	11.25	15.00	22.50
175	0.87	1.75	2.62	3.50	4.37	5.25	7.00	8.75	10.94	13.12	17.50	26.75
200	1.00	2.00	3.00	4.00	5.00	6.00	8.00	10.00	12.50	15.00	20.00	30.00
300	1.50	3.00	4.50	6.00	7.50	9.00	12.00	15.00	18.75	22.50	30.00	45.00
400	2.00	4.00	6.10	8.00	10.00	12.00	16.00	20.00	25.00	30.00	40.00	60.00
500	2.50	5.00	7.50	10.00	12.50	15.00	20.00	25.00	31.25	37.50	50.00	75.00
600	3.00	6.00	9.00	12.00	15.00	18.00	24.00	30.00	37.50	45.00	60.00	90.00
700	3.50	7.00	10.50	14.00	17.50	21.00	28.00	35.00	43.75	52.50	70.00	105.00
800	4.00	8.00	12.00	16.00	20.00	24.00	32.00	40.00	50.00	60.00	80.00	120.00
900	4.50	9.00	13.50	18.00	22.50	27.00	36.00	45.00	56.25	67.50	90.00	135.00
1,000	5.00	10.00	15.00	20.00	25.00	30.00	40.00	50.00	62.50	75.00	100.00	150.00
2,000	10.00	20.00										

F. E. Staebner, Supplemental Irrigation, *U. S. Dept. Agr. Farmers' Bull.* 1846, October, 1940.

TABLE 30

VOLUME OF TOP-DRESSING MATERIAL REQUIRED FOR APPLICATIONS TO VARIOUS DEPTHS ON GREENS AREAS OF DIFFERENT SIZE

Depth of top-dressing desired, in.	*Approximate volume of material needed for*									
	1,000 sq. ft.		*3,000 sq. ft.*		*5,000 sq. ft.*		*7,000 sq. ft.*		*10,000 sq. ft.*	
	Cu. ft.	*Cu. yd.*	*Cu. ft.*	*Cu. yd.*	*Cu. ft.*	*Cu. yd.*	*Cu. ft.*	*Cu. yd.*	*Cu. ft.*	*Cu. yd.*
1/8	10.4	0.4	31.2	1.2	52.0	1.9	72.8	2.7	104.0	3.9
1/4	20.8	0.8	62.4	2.3	104.0	3.9	145.6	5.4	208.0	7.7
3/8	31.2	1.2	93.6	3.5	156.0	5.8	218.4	8.1	312.0	11.6
1/2	41.7	1.5	125.1	4.6	208.5	7.7	291.9	10.8	417.0	15.4
5/8	52.1	1.9	156.3	5.8	260.5	9.6	364.7	13.5	521.0	19.3
3/4	62.5	2.3	187.5	6.9	312.5	11.6	437.5	16.2	625.0	23.1

TABLE 31

SPACING OF DEPTH OF TILE LINES IN DIFFERENT SOILS

Soil	*Depth of tile, ft.*	*Spacing, ft.*
Sandy	3–6	100–150
Light loam	2¾–5	50–100
Heavy loam	2½–3	25–50
Clay	2½	10–25

TABLE 32

MAXIMUM LENGTH OF TILE LINES FOR MINIMUM GRADE

Tile Size, in	*Length, ft.*
4	2,000
6	3,000
8	3,500
10	4,500

Index